A Review of Science and Technology During the 1974 School Year

Science Year
The World Book Science Annual

1975

Field Enterprises Educational Corporation
Chicago   Frankfurt   London   Paris   Rome   Sydney   Tokyo   Toronto

The publishers of *Science Year* gratefully
acknowledge the following for permission to use
copyrighted illustrations. A full listing of illustration
acknowledgments appears on pages 440 and 441.

31   Map courtesy of *Natural History* magazine
112   "The Rapid Intermixing of Cell Surface Antigens
       After Formation of Mouse-Human Heterokaryons"
       by L. D. Frye and M. Edidin
       © 1970 *Journal of Cell Science*
241   Thony B. Jones and Alan C. Kamil, University of
       Massachusetts from *Science.* Copyright 1973 by The
       American Association for the Advancement of Science.
286   Drawing by Alan Dunn © 1972
       The New Yorker Magazine, Inc.
289   Schmidt-Thomsen, Landesdenkmalant from *Science*
       Copyright 1973 by The American Association
       for the Advancement of Science
290   Drawing by Ed Fisher © 1973
       The New Yorker Magazine, Inc.
325   Drawing by Koren © 1974
       The New Yorker Magazine, Inc.
346   Drawing by Lorenz © 1974
       The New Yorker Magazine, Inc.

The Cover: Portraits of four planets taken from spacecraft pose
the question: Which, if any, contain life?

Preface

With this edition, *Science Year* celebrates its 10th anniversary. Such an event tempts an editor to wax historic and philosophic, taking note of the highlights in his field over the years and making sage observations about them. Science reporting is no exception, and indeed, there have been many exciting successes, and failures as well, in science and technology during the past decade.

Some fields have made encouraging advances. Since Isaac Asimov described what was known about the "code of life" in 1965, *Science Year* has reported on a wealth of research in the life sciences: The increased understanding of the genetic code; viruses, and their role in cancer; the immune response; fusing cells from different species; and this year, the activity at the cell's surface. All of this work is leading to a better understanding of life processes and holds out hope that many human health problems may soon be solved.

In other fields scientists have known frustration. In 1965, *Science Year* reported on the quark, envisioned as the ultimate, indivisible piece of matter. Ten years, several high-powered accelerators, and numerous revised theories later, the quark is still missing. In this edition, three leading theoretical physicists, including the quark's "inventor," muse over the reasons why.

Still other fields of science have experienced a change in emphasis. When *Science Year* was launched in 1965, NASA's Gemini program was in full swing, with men and machines being tested for that great adventure—landing men on the moon. Less attention was paid to the unmanned space vehicles that were providing world-wide communications, or taking the first close-up look at Mars. Today, the moon shots are a memory and the Skylab program has also been completed; the only remaining manned flight planned by the United States is a joint venture with the Russians in 1975. Meanwhile, the unmanned space probes have been generating increasing interest. The Mariners and Pioneers are teaching us many new things about our neighboring planets and providing evidence that some of them may harbor life.

On a broader scale, during the decade *Science Year* has watched the interest in and attitude toward science and technology appreciably change. Much of the excitement and promise of the 1960s has been tempered by sober reflections on what man is doing to nature. Scientists are warning that we are misusing our technology. Some people have turned away from science as the solver of problems, dismissing it with cynicism, or replacing it with mysticism. At the same time, the lavish financial support that science had come to enjoy diminished, with many programs having been cut back or even eliminated. There is recent evidence, however, that this support is returning—the 1974 federal budget included increased funds for basic research.

Throughout all these ups and downs, *Science Year* readers have remained loyal. Perhaps they know that success is cyclical and that science will survive and continue to provide excitement and surprises. They realize that some fields will continue to know success, others to know failure, and still others to change their direction. And they know they can count on *Science Year* to report it all.   [Arthur G. Tressler]

Contents

Staff

Contributors

Adelman, George, M.S.
Managing Editor
Neurosciences Research Program
Massachusetts Institute of Technology
Neurology

Alderman, Michael H., M.D.
Assistant Professor of Public Health
Cornell University Medical College
Medicine, Internal

Araujo, Paul E., Ph.D.
Assistant Professor
Department of Food Science
University of Florida
Nutrition

Auerbach, Stanley I., Ph.D.
Director, Environmental Sciences Division
Oak Ridge National Laboratory
Ecology

Becker, Robert O., M.D.
Medical Investigator
Veterans Administration Hospital
Syracuse, N.Y.
Boosting Our Healing Potential

Bell, William J., Ph.D.
Associate Professor of Entomology
University of Kansas
Zoology

Belton, Michael J. S., Ph.D.
Astronomer, Kitt Peak
National Observatory
Astronomy, Planetary

Bromley, D. Allan, Ph.D.
Henry Ford II Professor and Chairman
Department of Physics
Yale University
Physics, Nuclear

Buchsbaum, S. J., Ph.D.
Executive Director
Research, Communications Sciences
Division, Bell Telephone Laboratories
Communications

Bylinsky, Gene, B.A.
Associate Editor
Fortune Magazine
Carl Djerassi

Chedd, Graham, B.A.
Science Editor
WGBH-TV
Dixy Lee Ray
Closing in on the Flu

Chesher, Richard H., Ph.D.
Vice-President
Marine Research Foundation
Oceanography

Chiller, Jacques M., Ph.D.
Associate, Scripps Clinic
and Research Foundation
Immunology

Cromie, William J., B.S.
Director of Research and Development
Field Enterprises Educational Corporation
Research in Orbit

Davies, Julian, Ph.D.
Professor of Biochemistry
University of Wisconsin
Biochemistry

Deffeyes, Kenneth S., Ph.D.
Associate Professor of Geology
Princeton University
Geoscience, Geology

Drake, Charles L., Ph.D.
Professor of Earth Sciences
Dartmouth College
Geoscience, Geophysics

Ensign, Jerald C., Ph.D.
Professor of Bacteriology
University of Wisconsin
Microbiology

Gerhardt, John R., M.S.
Technical Editor
American Meteorological Society
Meteorology

Gingerich, Owen, Ph.D.
Professor of Astronomy and of
History of Science
Harvard University
Close-Up, Astronomy, Planetary

Goldhaber, Paul, D.D.S.
Professor of Periodontology and
Dean, Harvard School
of Dental Medicine
Medicine, Dentistry

Gray, Ernest P., Ph.D.
Principal Staff Member
Applied Physics Laboratory
Johns Hopkins University
Physics, Plasma

Griffin, James B., Ph.D.
Director, Museum of Anthropology
University of Michigan
Archaeology, New World

Gwynne, Peter, M.A.
Associate Editor
Newsweek
Science on the Ice

Hartl, Daniel L., Ph.D.
Associate Professor
Purdue University
Genetics

Hasler, Arthur D., Ph.D.
Professor of Zoology, and Director
of the Laboratory of Limnology
University of Wisconsin
How the Salmon Comes Home

Hawthorne, M. Frederick, Ph.D.
Professor of Chemistry
University of California, Los Angeles
Chemistry, Synthesis

Hayes, Arthur H., Jr., M.D.
Chief, Division of Clinical Pharmacology
Milton S. Hershey Medical Center
Drugs

Henahan, John F., B.S.
Free-Lance Science Writer
The Biologists Bite Back

Herschbach, Dudley R., Ph.D.
Professor of Chemistry
Harvard University
Chemistry, Dynamics

Hines, William
Science Correspondent
Chicago Sun-Times
Space Exploration

Ibers, James A., Ph.D.
Professor of Chemistry
Northwestern University
Chemistry, Structural

Isaacson, Robert L., Ph.D.
Professor of Psychology
University of Florida
Psychology

Johnson, Richard T., M.D.
Professor of Neurology
The Johns Hopkins University
School of Medicine
Close-Up, Microbiology

Kendall, Henry W., Ph.D.
Professor of High-Energy Physics
Massachusetts Institute of Technology
Nuclear Power: How Great Is the Risk?

Kessler, Karl G., Ph.D.
Chief, Optical Physics Division
National Bureau of Standards
Physics, Atomic and Molecular

Kristian, Jerome, Ph.D.
Staff Member, Hale Observatories
Astronomy, Cosmology

Lapp, Ralph E., Ph.D.
Secretary, Quadri-Science Incorporated
Can Coal Make a Comeback?

Lawson, Louis J., B.S.
Chief, Technology Programs
Lockheed Missiles and Space Company
Close-Up, Transportation

Leach, Gerald, B.A.
Science Writer, and Visiting Fellow
Science Policy Research Unit
Sussex University
England
Technology Tunes to Nature

Maglio, Vincent J., Ph.D.
Research Associate
Princeton University
Geoscience, Paleontology

Maran, Stephen P., Ph.D.
Head, Advanced Systems and
Ground Observations Branch
Goddard Space Flight Center
A Cosmic Laboratory
Astronomy, Stellar

March, Robert H., Ph.D.
Professor of Physics
University of Wisconsin
The Quandary Over Quarks
Physics, Elementary Particles

McBride, Gail, M.S.
Associate Editor
JAMA Medical News
Close-Up, Immunology

McCarthy, John, Ph.D.
Professor of Computer Science and
Director, Artificial Intelligence Laboratory
Stanford University
Modeling Our Minds

McCrone, Lucy B., B.A.
Research Microscopist
Walter C. McCrone Associates, Inc.
Close-Up, Chemical Technology

Melzack, Ronald, Ph.D.
Professor of Psychology
McGill University
Shutting the Gate on Pain

Merbs, Charles F., Ph.D.
Chairman, Department of Anthropology
Arizona State University
Anthropology

Miller, Richard T., B.S.
Contributing Science Editor
IBM Corporation
Close-Up, Electronics

Nickerson, Norton H., Ph.D.
Associate Professor of Biology
Tufts University
Botany

Nicolson, Garth L., Ph.D.
Head, Cancer Council Laboratory and
Director, Electron Microscopy Laboratory
The Salk Institute for Biological Studies
Cancer Clues at the Cell's Surface

Novick, Sheldon
Publisher, *Environment*
Environment

Price, Frederick C., B.S.
Managing Editor
Chemical Engineering
Chemical Technology

Rassmussen, Norman C., Ph.D.
Professor of Nuclear Engineering
Massachusetts Institute of Technology
Nuclear Power: How Great Is the Risk?

Revelle, Roger, Ph.D.
Richard Saltonstall Professor of
Population Policy and Director,
Center for Population Studies
Harvard University
Close-Up, Science Support

Rodden, Judith, M.Litt.
Research Archaeologist
Archaeology, Old World

Romualdi, James P., Ph.D.
Professor of Civil Engineering
Carnegie-Mellon University
Transportation

Sagan, Carl, Ph.D.
Director, Laboratory for Planetary Studies
Cornell University
The Climates of Planets

Shank, Russell, D.L.S.
Director of Libraries
Smithsonian Institution
Books of Science

Shapley, Deborah, B.A.
Staff Writer, News & Comment
Science Magazine
Science Support

Taylor, C. Richard, Ph.D.
Alexander Agassiz Professor of Zoology
Harvard University
Muscles and Motion

Tilton, George R., Ph.D.
Professor of Geochemistry
University of California, Santa Barbara
Geoscience, Geochemistry

Weber, Samuel, B.S.E.E.
Executive Editor
Electronics Magazine
Close-Up, Neurology
Electronics

Wittwer, Sylvan H., Ph.D.
Director, Agricultural Experiment Station
Michigan State University
Agriculture

Woltjer, Lodewyk, Ph.D.
Rutherfurd Professor of Astronomy
Columbia University
Astronomy, High Energy

Wood, Fergus J., A.B.
Research Associate
National Oceanic and
Atmospheric Administration
Close-Up, Oceanography

Zikria, Bashir A., M.D.
Associate Professor
College of Physicians and Surgeons
Columbia University
Medicine, Surgery

Contributors not listed on
these pages are members of
the *Science Year* editorial staff.

Special Reports

The Special Reports and the exclusive *Science Year* Trans-Vision® give in-depth treatment to the major advances in science. The subjects were chosen for their current importance and lasting interest.

A Cosmic Laboratory

By Stephen P. Maran

Comet Kohoutek was a fizzle for thousands of hopeful viewers, but a bonanza for scientists seeking the nature of comets and their role in the solar system

On a cold winter day in mid-December, 1973, the *Queen Elizabeth II* steamed out of New York Harbor. The ship carried 1,693 passengers on a special three-day ocean cruise to view Comet Kohoutek, the "comet of the century." But heavy clouds and rain prevented even a fleeting glimpse of the comet, and Lubos Kohoutek, the Czech astronomer who had discovered it nine months earlier, was sick and spent much of the cruise below deck. Thousands more persons around the world looked, most of them in vain, for a glimpse of the heavenly visitor. But Kohoutek failed to brighten as originally predicted, leaving the public disappointed and some of us astronomers embarrassed.

To scientists, however, Comet Kohoutek was a triumphant success. One reason was that the scientific community had had time to mount a massive investigation. Usually, only a short time is available to plan observations when a new comet is discovered. But Kohoutek was discovered almost 10 months before it reached its perihelion, or closest approach to the sun, on December 28.

The early discovery of Comet Kohoutek gave astronomers ample time to prepare equipment, schedule telescope time, and coordinate

Kohoutek may have been born from an icy wisp of gas and dust and deserted in outer space by the huge cloud that condensed into the sun and planets.

13

their plans with colleagues throughout the world. The National Aeronautics and Space Administration (NASA) organized Operation Kohoutek to coordinate the effective use of space apparatus with ground-based observations. Important observations were planned for Skylab, which would be in orbit and manned when Kohoutek came to perihelion, and for Mariner 10, which would be en route to Venus and Mercury. On the ground, improvements in electronic image tubes for optical telescopes and in radio telescope equipment would permit astronomers to obtain much more sensitive measurements than were possible for previous comets.

Among the experiments planned were observations at infrared and ultraviolet wave lengths that would show phenomena not revealed in visible light, and spectroscopic studies of the emission lines of various elements and molecules. Each chemical element emits at a characteristic set of wave lengths and can be identified by the pattern of its spectrum. Radio astronomers can also identify emission spectra at radio wave lengths.

Lubos Kohoutek, working at the Hamburg Observatory in Germany, discovered the comet on March 7, 1973. Photographs taken in March, April, and early May show the comet as a small spot, fuzzier than the image of a star, and not very impressive. But its properties were rather special. Orbital calculations by Brian G. Marsden of the Smithsonian Astrophysical Observatory in Cambridge, Mass., showed that it would approach to within almost 13 million miles of the sun, well inside the orbit of Mercury. Later, Marsden's further calculations indicated that Kohoutek's course probably had been altered by a star some 2 million years ago, and that it was making its first close approach to the sun. This meant that astronomers would have a chance to study a piece of the original solar system, which had been preserved in the dark deep-freeze of space. As the comet made its approach, the sun would vaporize and then ionize material of its outer layer in a cosmic laboratory experiment, just as a chemist uses heat and electricity to excite a chemical specimen in a test vessel for examination. A comet is most stimulated by solar radiation during the month before and after perihelion, and this is the best time for scientists to perform most of their investigations.

After mid-May, the earth's orbit took it toward the opposite side of the sun from Kohoutek, and the comet could not be seen again until late September. The astronomers settled back to wait.

Comets have been a source of awe and superstition throughout history. Many persons believed that they signified terrible events, and cited a dire happening for every famous comet. Comets supposedly marked the deaths of such rulers as Demetrius of Syria in 146 B.C., Julius Caesar in 44 B.C., and the Roman emperor Vespasian in A.D. 79. Comets were also blamed for the destruction of Jerusalem in A.D. 70, the loss of Constantinople to the Turks in 1453, and the defeat of the English at the Battle of Hastings in 1066.

The author:
Stephen P. Maran, head of the Advanced Systems and Ground Observations Branch, Goddard Space Flight Center, headed Operation Kohoutek for NASA. He contributes the Stellar Astronomy article to *Science Year*.

The comet delusions persisted into the present century. When the earth passed through the tail of Halley's Comet in 1910, people feared poisonous fumes. Lumbermen in Texas refused to cut wood, peasants in Asia Minor prepared barrels of water in which to dunk themselves, and there was a brisk business done in "comet pills." Some persons blamed the Paris floods of 1910 on Halley's Comet. In 1973, Kohoutek inspired a rash of pseudoscientific, astrological, and promotional activities, and revived old rumors of the imminent end of the world.

The English astronomer Edmund Halley in 1705 was the first to classify comets as regular members of the solar system, and not chance visitors. Halley had determined from the historical record that bright comets had been observed several times, at intervals of roughly 75 years. By calculating the orbits, he concluded that they all might belong to one comet. "Hence I think I may venture to foretel, that it will return again in the Year 1758." Halley's prediction, one of the most famous in the history of astronomy, was verified in 1758, 16 years after his death. The return of Halley's Comet also was dramatic proof of the theory of universal gravitation put forth by Halley's mentor, Sir Isaac Newton, and of Newton's idea that comets might follow ellipses —elongated, closed paths.

Most astronomers now believe that the typical comet consists of the nucleus, which may range from a fraction of a mile to 20 or 30 miles in diameter; the coma, a roughly spherical cloud of gas and dust that begins to develop as the comet approaches the sun and may swell to a diameter of more than 300,000 miles; and the tail, or tails, which may stream across space as far as 100 million miles.

Many comets have two tails. One is a plasma tail, composed of atoms and molecules that have been ionized, or stripped of an electron. This tail always points away from the sun, pushed out by the

Czech astronomer Lubos Kohoutek first spotted the comet in March, 1973, while working at Hamburg Observatory. NASA photos, taken 97 minutes apart on April 28, show the comet as a faint smudge that has moved slightly upward.

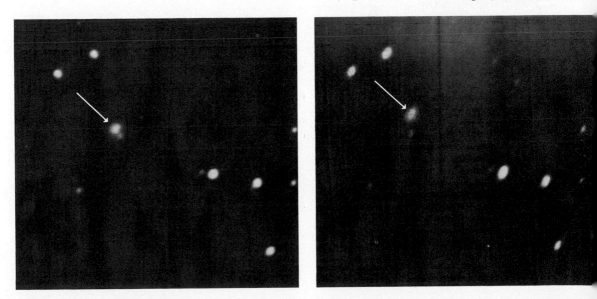

electrons and protons of the solar wind that constantly streams from the sun. The plasma tail appears blue, because of the emissions of carbon monoxide ions (CO^+). The other tail is a curved dust tail. The reflection of sunlight makes it appear yellow in color photographs. It is formed as the photons of solar radiation push dust particles out from the coma. The more massive the particle, the less it is repelled, so the dust particles curve slightly away from the plasma tail.

Each time a comet passes around the sun, its frozen nucleus is heated, causing it to shed the dust and gas, which then form the coma and tail. Eventually this material is lost into space. One estimate suggests that Halley's Comet loses a layer about 10 feet thick every time it goes around the sun. If the nucleus were originally about 30 miles in diameter, much larger than the average comet is estimated to be, the nucleus would be reduced to nothing after fewer than 8,000 passes, or about 600,000 years. The calculation is a crude one, but the implication is clear: The expected lifetime of Halley's Comet in its present orbit is vastly less than the 5-billion-year age of the solar system. At that rate of dissipation, there would be no comets left to visit us today, unless they were constantly being replenished from some distant source.

But what if the comets that appear in the inner solar system were once in much larger orbits that did not bring them so close to the sun? Astronomers now think that perhaps 100 billion comets may be traveling in such huge orbits, with their aphelions, or points farthest from the sun, located in a zone extending from about 30,000 to 100,000 or more astronomical units from the sun. (An astronomical unit is about 93 million miles, the average distance of the earth from the sun.) Some of these huge elliptical orbits may extend halfway to the nearest star,

Art throughout history has pictured comets as mysterious objects to be feared. The Bayeux Tapestry, *below,* shows Halley's Comet as an evil omen for England in 1066. In 1596, some people turned to astrologers for an explanation of a comet. The comet of 1857 was shown devouring the earth. Halley's Comet returned in 1910 to spook men and horses.

and even at perihelion most of these comets never get within the orbit of Jupiter. This great swarm of comets is called the Oort Cloud, after the Dutch astronomer Jan Oort, who first suggested the existence of such a phenomenon in 1950.

The comets in the Oort Cloud spend most of their time so far from the sun that they are easily perturbed by the gravitational influences of other stars. These perturbations send some into new orbits that carry them into the inner solar system. But as the comets approach the sun, they also become subject to the gravitational force of Jupiter, which can drastically change a comet's orbit. Some comets that encounter Jupiter are ejected from the solar system forever, while others are diverted into much smaller orbits. An Oort Cloud comet can have a period—the time it takes to make a complete orbit—measured in millions of years, but the comets captured by Jupiter may have periods as short as Halley's 76 years, or even Comet Encke's 3.3 years. Jupiter has now reduced Comet Kohoutek's period to 75,000 years.

Despite all that astronomers knew about comets in 1973, fundamental questions still existed about their structure, chemical composition, and origin. Is the nucleus a solid, icy core at the center of the coma, as most astronomers believe? Or is there just a loose "sandbank" of solid particles, as a few die-hards continue to maintain? Also, nearly all of the atoms and molecules identified in the coma and tail in past years appear to be "daughter products"—fragmented molecules that could not exist as stable ices in the nucleus. What, then, are the parent molecules in the nucleus that are broken down by solar radiation, or collisions with other particles?

And what of the origin of comets? Are they frozen remnants of the solar nebula, the great cloud of gas and dust that condensed to form

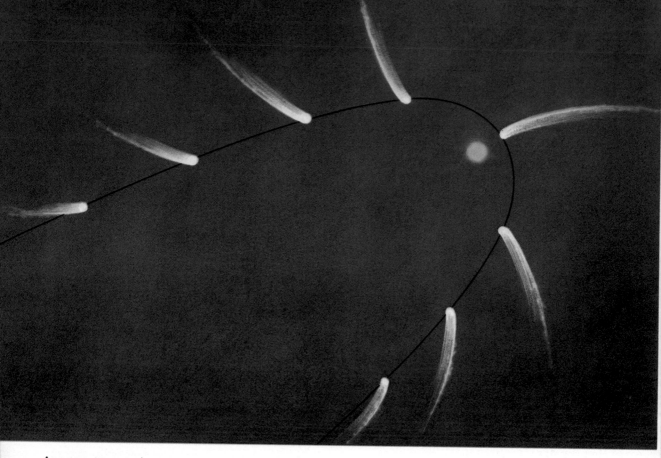

As a comet approaches the sun, solar radiation heats its icy nucleus. Gas and dust are freed and form a streaming tail that always points away from the sun.

the sun and planets? If so, did the comets originate near Jupiter and the other giant planets? And were they only later ejected into their distant orbits in Oort's Cloud? Or did they form originally on the outskirts of the solar nebula, beyond the warming influence of the condensing sun?

Some of the questions may not be answered until a space vehicle flies through a comet and takes data near the nucleus. But Comet Kohoutek offered astronomers a unique opportunity to make a concerted attack on many of them.

The Japanese amateur astronomer and comet-seeker, Tsutomu Seki of Gesei, was the first to find Kohoutek again, on September 23. Shortly after, George Rieke at the University of Arizona's Catalina Observatory made the first infrared measurements of the comet while it was still well beyond the orbit of Mars, the farthest away a comet has ever been detected in the infrared. A photograph taken on September 29 by Elizabeth Roemer, also of the University of Arizona, revealed a short, broad tail on Kohoutek.

Spectrographic observations of Kohoutek by astronomers in Italy and California revealed five strong emissions in the red part of the visible spectrum. The unknown substance that produced the radiation appeared to be streaming into the tail; it was found in the tail and in the half of the coma away from the sun, but not in the nearer half.

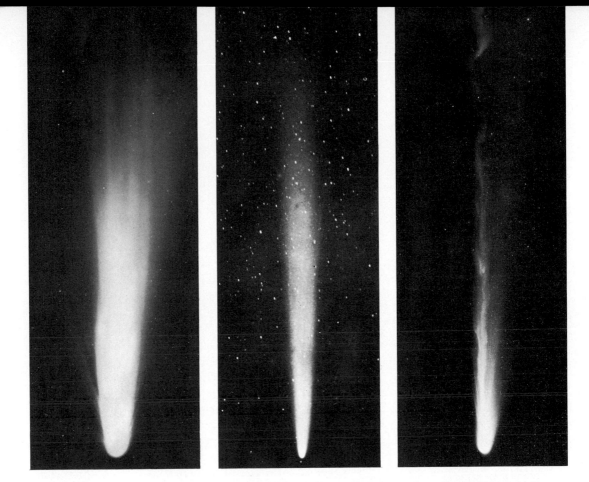

Comet Bennett, *left,*
Halley's Comet, *center,*
and Comet Kohoutek,
right, illustrate that
no two comet tails are
ever quite the same.

Chemists Gerhard Herzberg and Hin Lew of the Canadian National
Research Council in Ottawa noted that these emissions matched wave
lengths for ionized steam that they had measured in their laboratory.
This proved that the tail contained water vapor ions (H_2O^+) that must
have been produced when parent water molecules from the nucleus
sublimed – turned directly from a solid form to gas – and were ionized
by solar radiation. The solar wind then blew the water vapor ions
back into the plasma tail.

The discovery of water vapor in Kohoutek strongly supports the
"dirty snowball" theory of cometary structure published in 1950 by
Fred L. Whipple of the Harvard College Observatory. Whipple suggested that the comet nucleus was a ball of frozen gases in which tiny
solid particles of dirt or dust are imbedded. As the comet approaches
the sun, the ice sublimes and releases the dust particles. The dust and
gas that are released then form the coma and tail. The earlier discovery of an immense hydrogen cloud around Comet Bennett and Comet
Tago-Sato-Kosaka in 1970 had given strong support to Whipple's
concept, but the Kohoutek observations established the dirty snowball
theory as a near certainty.

Another major component of the Kohoutek snowball appears to be
frozen carbon monoxide (CO). A rocket experiment launched on January 4 found strong ultraviolet emission, apparently coming from

Cataloging Kohoutek

Studies of Kohoutek's structure and composition revealed water vapor ions in a comet's tail for the first time, and found two complex molecules, HCN and CH₃CN, in the coma. A photograph taken through an ultraviolet filter, *opposite page,* shows a hydrogen cloud surrounding the coma that extended millions of miles into space.

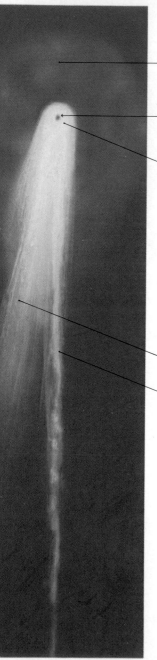

Hydrogen cloud

Nucleus
Frozen parent molecules

Coma
Atoms and radicals:
  Oxygen (O)
  Carbon (C, C₂, C₃)
  Sodium (Na)
  Hydroxyl (OH)
  Cyanogen (CN)
  Methylidyne (CH)
  Amino (NH₂)
Molecules:
  Water (H₂O)
  Methyl cyanide (CH₃CN)
  Hydrogen cyanide (HCN)
Silicate particles
Ice grains

Dust tail
Silicate particles

Ion tail
Water vapor (H₂O⁺)
Carbon monoxide (CO⁺)
Carbon (C⁺)

carbon atoms. Carbon dioxide (CO_2) is another possible parent for the carbon, but CO seems to be a more likely source.

The hydrogen cloud was a principal target of NASA's Operation Kohoutek. This cloud, which is visible only in photos taken with ultraviolet light, is much larger than the visible coma. Photographs taken by Skylab astronauts with a special camera that was sensitive to the far-ultraviolet radiation of the hydrogen atom reveal Kohoutek's hydrogen cloud growing to a diameter of several million miles as the comet approached the sun in December (see RESEARCH IN ORBIT). However, Skylab was inside the earth's geocorona, a zone of hydrogen in the upper atmosphere that extends to at least 40,000 miles above the surface. The geocorona's interfering hydrogen light obscured the dim, outer regions of the comet's hydrogen cloud.

But in mid-January, as Mariner 10 approached Venus, well beyond the geocorona, an ultraviolet spectrometer on board observed the outer layers of the hydrogen cloud. Although the Mariner 10 data do not reveal structure as precisely as the Skylab photos, A. Lyle Broadfoot and his colleagues at Kitt Peak National Observatory in Tucson, Ariz., said the data clearly show that the hydrogen cloud extended from the nucleus tens of millions of miles.

Astronomers also studied the smaller hydroxyl (OH) cloud, whose molecules share the same parent, H_2O, with the hydrogen. Most water molecules in the coma are not ionized; instead, they are dissociated, or broken up, into OH molecules and hydrogen atoms by solar ultraviolet light.

One instrument used to study the OH cloud was a telescope designed by French astronomer Jacques Blamont that registers radiation in the near-ultraviolet portion of the spectrum. Blamont and his associates mounted the equipment on NASA's Galileo II, a research version of the Convair 990 aircraft. Studying the pattern of brightness on one photograph taken with this equipment, Blamont and his colleague Michel Festou found that the OH is produced in a region extending to about 9,000 miles from the nucleus. This must be the zone of the parent water molecules. Beyond it, most of the water vapor is dissociated into OH molecules and hydrogen atoms. More than 28,000 miles from the nucleus, most of the OH is dissociated into oxygen and hydrogen. The hydrogen liberated directly

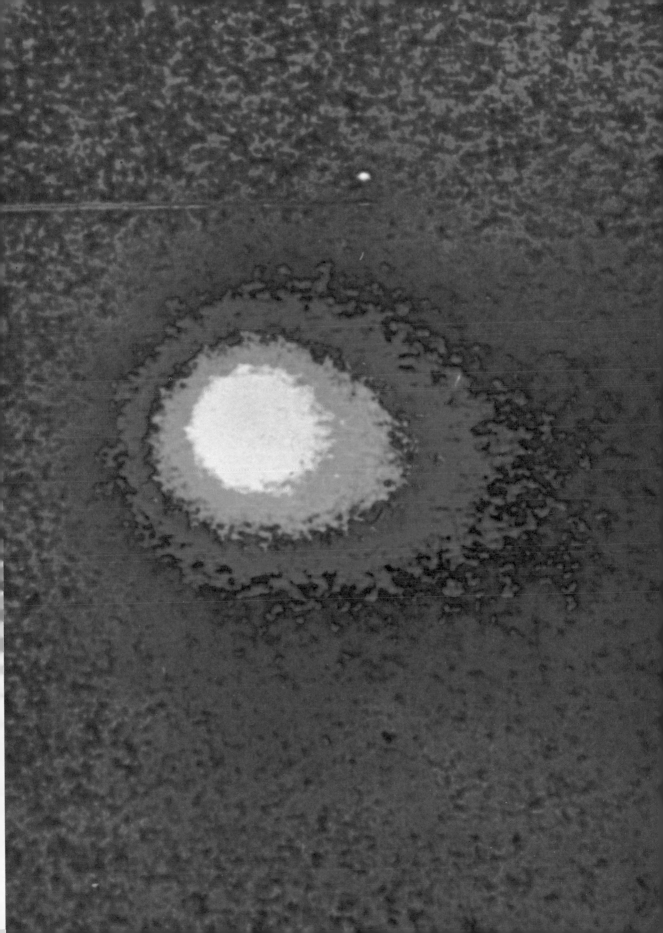

Oort Cloud · Original orbit · Perturbed orbit

from water molecules in the 9,000-mile zone collides with other atoms and molecules in that relatively dense region and therefore expands rather slowly, traveling less than a mile a second. But the hydrogen atoms produced by the dissociation of OH move out at about 5 miles per second. The French astronomers concluded that the large hydrogen cloud came primarily from the breakup of OH.

The radio spectrum, for the first time, also proved to be a rich source of information. Astronomers had tried repeatedly to detect radio emissions from comets, without confirmed success. Observers at Kitt Peak, using the 36-foot, computer-controlled dish antenna of the National Radio Astronomy Observatory (NRAO), detected two emission lines near wave length 2.7 millimeters on December 1. Bobby L. Ulich of NRAO and Edward K. Conklin of the National Astronomy and Ionosphere Center in Arecibo, Puerto Rico, concluded that the emitting molecule was CH_3CN—called methyl cyanide by astronomers and acetonitrile by chemists. This was the first clear evidence of radio signals from a comet, and the first direct detection of a complex parent molecule. Using the same radio telescope, Lewis Snyder, David Buhl, and Walter Huebner found emission from another parent molecule, hydrogen cyanide (HCN), later that month.

The discovery of such complex molecules in Kohoutek verifies predictions made by Harvard astrophysicist Alastair G. W. Cameron in 1973. Cameron believes that comets may have actually originated in the Oort Cloud. If so, he suggested, radio astronomers should find in Comet Kohoutek many of the complex interstellar molecules that have been observed in the dense clouds of the Milky Way where new stars and solar systems are thought to be forming. Such molecules normally are highly unstable, but at the distance of the Oort Cloud, conditions are so cold that they would be able to survive without being broken down by the sun's radiation.

Whipple, on the other hand, had suggested earlier that comets might be similar in composition to the cool atmospheres of the large outer planets. This was in line with the idea that the comets formed originally in the region of the outer planets and were later ejected to the vicinity of the Oort Cloud. If comets had formed in the region of Jupiter to Neptune, any unstable complex molecules would have been rapidly broken down into simpler, more stable molecules, and astron-

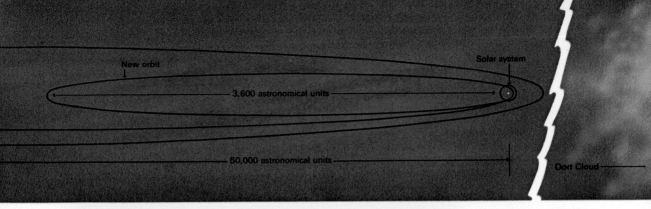

New orbit

Solar system

3,600 astronomical units

50,000 astronomical units

Oort Cloud

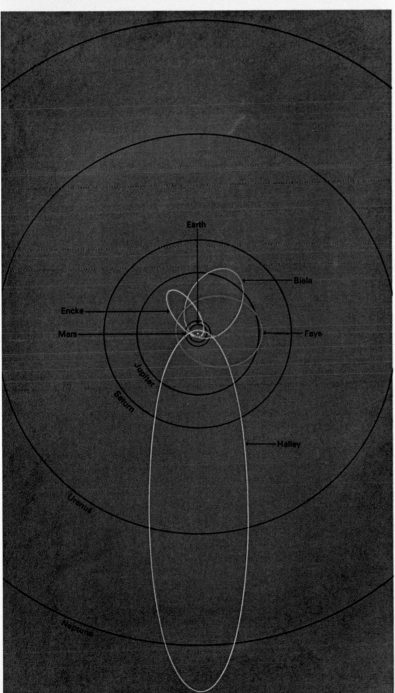

Earth

Biela

Encke

Mars

Faye

Jupiter

Saturn

Halley

Uranus

Neptune

Capturing a Comet

Kohoutek's original orbit, *above,* kept it in a distant swarm of comets known as Oort's Cloud. A passing star may have changed its orbit, bending it toward the solar system, where Jupiter's strong gravity bent it further. Some comets captured by Jupiter have their orbits entirely within the solar system, *left.*

A spiked antitail was drawn by the Skylab astronauts and sent to earth one day after Kohoutek's closest approach to the sun. The antitail included small meteoroids that were drawn away from the regular tail by the sun's gravity.

omers could expect to find parent molecules such as H_2O, CO_2, ammonia (NH_3), and methane (CH_4).

Neither CH_3CN nor HCN had previously been observed in a solar system object, although both have been found in dense interstellar clouds of the Milky Way. Their detection in Kohoutek lent support to Cameron's idea that comets are born between the stars.

In another radio observation on January 10, Robert W. Hobbs, William J. Webster, and I detected radiation from Kohoutek at the 3.7-centimeter wave length. I first thought that this came from the hot dust in the coma. However, analysis of the data convinced us that we had actually observed a halo of icy grains around the nucleus.

Such an icy halo had been suggested in 1968 by the Belgian astronomer-chemist Armand Delsemme. He found that Whipple's dirty snowball theory only partially explained the characteristics of the coma. Extending Whipple's theory, Delsemme suggested that only some of the daughter products in the coma result from the breakup of parent molecules that sublime directly from the surface of the nucleus. Other parent molecules are trapped in icy grains that are blown out from the nucleus by escaping gases and form a halo around the nucleus. As the comet nears the sun, the ice grains gradually sublime, releasing the trapped molecules into the coma. Delsemme concluded that the icy grain halo might extend perhaps 600 miles from the nucleus. The exact size would depend in part on the position of the comet, since the halo shrinks as the comet comes close to the sun.

Delsemme's icy grain halo had never before been detected. However, analysis of our observations, plus theoretical calculations of the properties of icy grains by NASA's John C. Brandt and K. S. Krishna Swamy, convinced us that we had observed the icy grain halo. The key point was that the radio waves we detected came from a region of the comet that was definitely less than 1,000 miles in diameter. Radiation from the microscopic dust particles of the coma would originate from a far larger area.

While Kohoutek was very close to the sun on December 29, the astronauts discovered a bright spike, or antitail, seeming to point toward the sun. The astronauts drew pictures of the antitail and transmitted them to the ground. Zdenek Sekanina of the Smithsonian Astrophysical Observatory analyzed the astronauts' drawings of the spike. Sekanina considered how various sizes of dust particles would act when they were repelled by solar radiation and attracted by the sun's gravity. He concluded that in order to reach the area of the spike, antitail particles must be up to $1/25$ of an inch in diameter. This is much larger than the microscopic dust in the coma and dust tail of Kohoutek. Sekanina's findings were supported by Edward P. Ney of the University of Minnesota, who analyzed Kohoutek's infrared radiation and confirmed that the antitail particles were much larger than the silicate dust particles in the coma and tail.

One question still unanswered is why Kohoutek failed to brighten as expected. Normally, a comet's brightness at great distances from the sun is due mostly to reflection from the nucleus. On the other hand, when a comet is close to the sun, its light is due largely to reflection of sunlight by dust in the coma. When first seen, Kohoutek may have been surrounded by an icy grain halo that led us to overestimate the diameter of its nucleus. Early observations suggested it had a diameter of about 25 miles, but later measurements indicated that 6 to 10 miles may be more accurate. This possibility, combined with the failure to release enough dust at the right time, may explain the comet's disappointing performance.

Despite the unanswered questions, Kohoutek has amply rewarded the astronomers' work and expectations. It provided a wealth of new data about the structure, behavior, and origin of comets that astronomers will be analyzing for months to come. Perhaps one of the more important long-range effects will be an increase in the number of scientists interested in studying comets. This, in turn, may lead to new studies that will surpass the Kohoutek findings. The next major step in comet research will be the direct probe of a comet by an automated interplanetary spacecraft, possibly in the 1980s when Comet Encke makes one of its periodic visits.

Closing in
On the Flu

By Graham Chedd

By studying the ever-changing influenza virus, scientists are fashioning unique vaccines that may one day put an end to the last of the great plagues

The news arrived at the U.S. Bureau of Biologics (BOB) the day after Thanksgiving, 1973. A few weeks earlier, an influenza outbreak had occurred in Australia and New Zealand. As part of the routine worldwide flu watch, coordinated by the World Health Organization, swabs from the noses and throats of the flu patients had been sent to virologists Geoffrey C. Schild at the National Institute for Medical Research in London and Walter R. Dowdle of the Center for Disease Control in Atlanta, Ga. Schild and Dowdle independently checked out the virus responsible for the Australasian influenza epidemic and passed their findings on to the BOB, which regulates vaccines used in the United States.

Schild and Dowdle discovered that while 20 million Americans were receiving their flu shots, the influenza virus had been taking

evasive action on the other side of the world. It had adopted a new disguise that would lessen the protective effect of the vaccine prepared to combat it. A new strain of the so-called influenza A virus had emerged, the Australasian strain.

Although such diseases as measles and poliomyelitis have been brought to the brink of extinction through vaccination, 30 years after the development of the first effective influenza vaccine, the flu is still with us. This is because the influenza virus evolves very quickly, every year or so. Thwarted by one vaccine, it simply changes its form slightly, making the vaccine less effective. As soon as scientists discover the change and begin making a new vaccine to counter the newly disguised virus, it changes again. And about once every 10 years, apparently growing impatient with this game of cat and mouse, the influenza virus performs a trick equivalent to changing into a rat. It alters its character so drastically that existing vaccines are rendered powerless against it. When that happens, a global epidemic of influenza results, as in 1957 when the Asian influenza strain emerged and again in 1968 when Hong Kong flu swept around the world.

Years of study, particularly research on the molecular biology of the virus, have yielded some fascinating clues about the influenza virus's unique ability to evolve rapidly. And, having learned the virus's tricks, scientists are now trying to turn these tricks against it. The result may be a new generation of influenza vaccines that will give man the drop on the virus rather than the other way around.

All three types of influenza virus—A, B, and C—attack the respiratory tract, causing such major symptoms as coughing, aching, running nose, and fever. But the B and C viruses are less changeable and cause less widespread and debilitating disease than does influenza A. It is the wily ways of the influenza A virus that have caused influenza to be called "the last of the great plagues."

In 1917 and 1918, a world-wide influenza epidemic killed an estimated 20 million persons, including 548,000 Americans. The influenza virus rarely kills by itself, except in cases where the victim already has chronic heart or lung disease. But it can weaken the patient so that he falls an easy prey to other infections, such as bacterial pneumonia. Today these secondary effects can be controlled with antibiotics. Even so, in 1968, Hong Kong flu killed at least 20,000 of its 51 million victims in the United States alone.

While vaccines have had some effect against influenza, the virus is still the clear winner in its combat with vaccines. Influenza vaccines in the United States are made by isolating strains of influenza virus and growing them in large quantities in a culture medium, usually fertilized hens' eggs. The viruses are harvested, purified, and killed, and the prepared vaccines are packaged in measured doses. Like all vaccines, they act as practice targets for the body's immune system so that if the same virus strains are ever encountered naturally, antibodies are made quickly to neutralize them.

The author:
Graham Chedd, science writer and author of several books, is the science editor for WGBH-TV in Boston. He also wrote "Dixy Lee Ray" for this edition of *Science Year.*

28

During the flu epidemic of 1918, Seattle required its citizens to wear gauze masks on streetcars. San Francisco judges held court sessions outdoors, and soldiers gargled daily with salt water. They did this to "prevent" the spread of influenza.

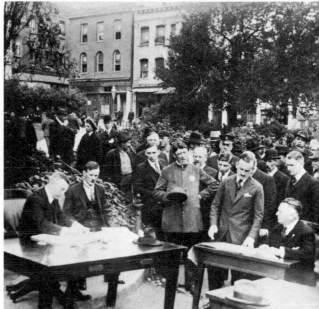

All viruses eke out a precarious existence, but the influenza viruses walk a particularly delicate tightrope. In order to survive, they need continued access to the cells of the human respiratory tract. The viruses must produce disease so that they will be transmitted to a new victim through coughs and sneezes. But, if the disease so weakens the human host that it dies before the viruses can find a new one, the viruses themselves will die. At the same time, even without a vaccine, the human victim is fighting back by producing antibodies to kill off the invading viruses and make the body immune to any further infection by the same form of virus.

So the influenza viruses must always keep on the move. Once they have passed through a human host, they can seldom return because of the antibody defenses the host has built up. As time goes by and more people develop immunity through vaccination or natural infection, the viruses' opportunities are reduced. Their ecological niche grows smaller and smaller. And so, like other forms of life that have evolved throughout the ages, the virus must adapt to its changing environment or perish. Consequently, the virus undergoes genetic changes, or mutations, and a different form emerges. The external structure of these mutant viruses is changed slightly so that some of them have a chance of slipping unrecognized past the body's defenses. The Australasian strain, which evolved from the London flu strain, is a product of this talent as a quick-change artist.

Eventually, however, these small changes are no longer enough. The numbers of antibodies in the human population build to such a high level that the virus is forced to resort to a more drastic solution. So it undergoes major "plastic surgery." The resulting new virus escapes all control and causes such massive epidemics as the Asian flu of 1957 and the Hong Kong flu of 1968.

These constant changes in the virus make life very difficult for the vaccine manufacturers and have also resulted in the rather disappointing record of influenza vaccines. With conventional methods, it takes several months from the time a new strain of influenza A is isolated until a vaccine effective against it can be produced and distributed. The vaccine is often out of date by the time it is ready, conferring useless protection against an influenza strain that has already been replaced by a new mutant virus.

Attempting to overcome this problem, scientists developed purer, more concentrated vaccines that could be given in higher doses. The dosage could stimulate extremely high levels of antibody production to knock out the changed influenza virus simply by brute force. Because this has a chance of working against the new viral strains that differ only slightly from their ancestors, existing vaccines worked fairly well against London flu in the winter of 1972-1973. But to really cope with the disease, particularly with the major leaps of the influenza A virus, scientists need a new approach to creating influenza vaccines. And several new approaches are emerging, because scientists now

The 1968–69 Itinerary of the Hong Kong Flu

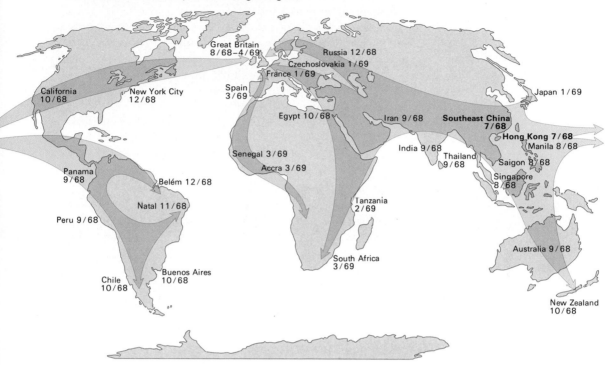

know more about how the influenza A virus's molecular structure allows it to evolve so rapidly and effectively.

The influenza virus itself consists of nucleoprotein, genetic material encased in a protein coat, and two kinds of protein spikes that bristle out from the coat. These spikes, called hemagglutinin (HA) and neuraminidase (NA), play a major role in the survival of the virus.

The virus uses the HA spike to attach itself to a host cell so that it can enter, take over the cell, and make it produce more viruses. The new viruses use their NA spikes to break out of the cell and spread the infection. But each of these spikes is also an antigen, a kind of dog tag by which the host's immune system recognizes the foreign invader and blocks the spikes. So, in order to evade the body's defenses, the influenza virus must disguise itself through major or minor changes in the makeup of its spikes.

These changes can occur in two ways. First, like all protein, the spikes are made up of amino acids arranged in a particular order. To fool the immune system, the virus can simply change one of these amino acids as a result of a minute change in the gene that produces the spike. This is known as a point mutation and is responsible for the minor changes in the virus's structure.

The second way in which the virus can make changes on its spikes is through a process known as recombination. Two different strains of virus come together in a cell and exchange genes. The result can be an entirely new strain of influenza A virus. And so, many scientists believe that recombination causes the major changes.

Always on the alert for major changes, influenza watchers identify each new influenza virus by testing for the antibodies with which it will react. If a newly isolated virus fails to react with any existing antibodies, then the alarm bells ring. They rang very loudly, for instance, in 1957, when the Asian flu strain emerged. At that time, researchers did not have enough knowledge about the microbiology of influenza to realize it, but both the HA and NA antigens had changed drastically. The bells rang again in 1968, when the HA changed drastically once more, to produce Hong Kong flu. Since 1968, the new variants, such as London and Australasian, have been produced by minor changes in the basic Hong Kong HA and NA antigens. But between 1957 and 1968, scientists, by piecing together knowledge about the molecular structure of the virus, had been catching up in the race to produce vaccines.

The influenza A virus's uncanny ability for recombination was first noted by Nobel prizewinning virologist Sir Macfarlane Burnet of Australia during the 1940s. It seemed to him that the virus's genes were rather loosely stuck together. In 1963, virologist George K. Hirst of the Public Health Research Institute in New York City concluded that the influenza genes were not stuck together at all but were individually packaged. In most living organisms, genes are strung together on chromosomes. Each of influenza A's seven or eight genes constitutes a separate minichromosome.

Two years later, virologist Edwin D. Kilbourne of Mount Sinai School of Medicine in New York City developed the key concept that the virus uses separate surface molecules—the HA and NA spikes—to enter and exit a host's cells. Kilbourne expanded this idea into a persuasive theory to account for influenza's trickery. Because the genes that determine the structures of the HA and NA spikes are separately packaged, two influenza viruses infecting the same cell can exchange either their HA genes or their NA genes, or both. If the two influenza viruses are genetically identical, the new viruses produced after this recombination are also identical.

But suppose two different types of influenza virus infect a cell at the same time? For example, there are influenza viruses that mainly infect domestic animals, such as pigs and horses. If a human virus and, for example, a pig virus entered the same cell, they might swap HA genes. The new viruses would have a new HA spike, and if one of them could infect humans, there would be no antibodies in the population to stop it. A world-wide epidemic would result.

Kilbourne believes that most animal influenza viruses were once human viruses that "escaped" into animal hosts before they could be wiped out by the antibodies in the human population. There they underwent their own independent evolution and built up a reservoir of HA and NA genes. Some of these genes mutated to produce spikes

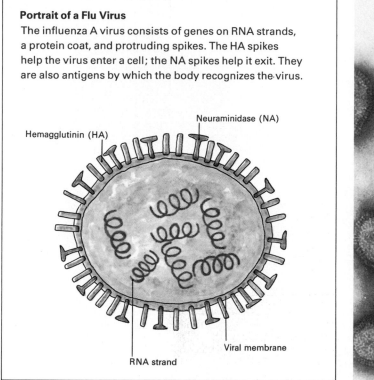

Portrait of a Flu Virus
The influenza A virus consists of genes on RNA strands, a protein coat, and protruding spikes. The HA spikes help the virus enter a cell; the NA spikes help it exit. They are also antigens by which the body recognizes the virus.

Hemagglutinin (HA)

Neuraminidase (NA)

RNA strand

Viral membrane

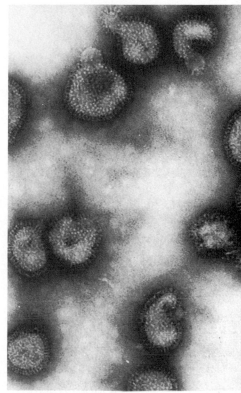

Magnified 115,000 times, the tiny viruses of the London flu reveal their shadowy forms.

that were very different from those of their human-virus ancestors. These genes are ready to make the trip back into humans when the rare opportunity arises through recombination. This hypothesis fits in with the fact that the major influenza epidemics invariably begin in Asia, where man and his domestic animals often live cheek by jowl.

This understanding of the influenza A virus's ability to shuffle its genes is now being turned to its victims' advantage. Scientists have learned to carry out the recombination process in the laboratory and produce new viruses with new properties to aid in the manufacture of vaccines. For example, they have learned how to manipulate the properties of a newly discovered wild virus, a variant that occurs naturally, so that it will grow vigorously in fertilized hens' eggs. In the early 1960s, Kilbourne came up with the idea of "mating" new, wild viruses with a "master strain," a strain of viruses that already grew rapidly in hens' eggs. By recombining the genes of these viruses, he could produce a new virus that would grow as fast as the master strain, but would carry the spikes of the new strain. This allowed manufacturers to produce new vaccines more quickly.

By 1968, Kilbourne had perfected this recombination method. But when the Hong Kong virus emerged, he received his stock of the new strain too late to help vaccine manufacturers. Since then, however, Kilbourne's hybrids of a fast-growing virus and the Hong Kong vari-

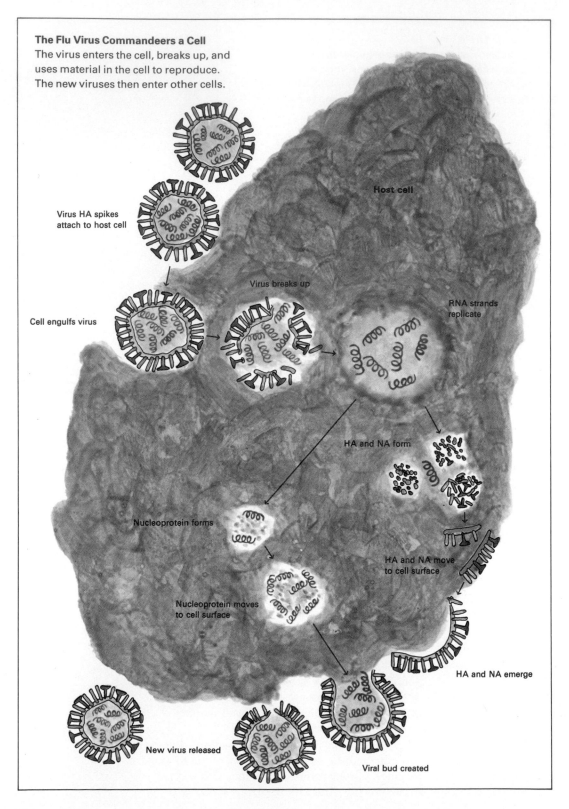

The Flu Virus Commandeers a Cell
The virus enters the cell, breaks up, and
uses material in the cell to reproduce.
The new viruses then enter other cells.

Host cell

Virus HA spikes
attach to host cell

Virus breaks up

RNA strands
replicate

Cell engulfs virus

HA and NA form

Nucleoprotein forms

HA and NA move
to cell surface

Nucleoprotein moves
to cell surface

HA and NA emerge

New virus released

Viral bud created

ants have been used extensively for commercial vaccine production. His recombination technique has reduced the time it takes to get a new vaccine into production from 6 months to about 8 to 12 weeks, and it has increased the yield of vaccine per hen's egg up to 10 times.

Recombination is also at the heart of what many researchers believe will be the next big step forward in influenza vaccines: the use of live viruses rather than dead ones. Because live viruses can actually grow and replicate in the host, a small dose will produce longer-lasting, more effective immunity against the disease. Of course, the virus in a live vaccine must be weakened so that it cannot cause disease. But producing a weakened live-virus vaccine that is safe is a time-consuming business. And in dealing with the fast-changing influenza A virus, scientists do not have much time.

Again, making custom-tailored hybrids by recombination may provide the answer. Researchers must first find a suitably weak master strain of influenza virus with properties such as the ability to grow quickly. Then, as soon as a new influenza strain emerges, they can make a recombinant virus that has the properties of the master strain and the antigens of the newly emerged strain.

At least in principle, such a master strain is not difficult to find. Schild and his colleagues found that several of the recombinants he made between a fast-growing strain and Hong Kong flu viruses were naturally weak. One of these recombinants has already undergone some preliminary clinical testing in Great Britain.

Robert M. Chanock and his colleagues at the National Institute for Allergy and Infectious Diseases in Bethesda, Md., began searching for a suitable master strain for a live-virus vaccine in 1965. They based their approach on the fact that the human respiratory tract is warmer at the bottom than it is at the top. The temperature in the lungs is about 37°C. (98.6°F.), while in the nose it is usually between 32°C. (89.6°F.) and 34°C. (93.2°F.). Normal influenza viruses grow well at either temperature. But, Chanock reasoned, what if he could find a virus that would grow only at the lower temperatures? Such a virus would infect the nose, perhaps cause mild sniffles, and stimulate antibody production. But it would not be able to grow in the warmer temperature in the lungs and cause more serious disease.

So Chanock treated the current variant of the Asian influenza strain with chemicals known to cause or speed up mutations. By 1968, he had isolated a master strain that was sensitive to the higher temperatures. When Hong Kong flu emerged that year, he experimented to see if the temperature-sensitive properties of his Asian virus could be recombined with the antigens of the Hong Kong variety. He produced several recombinant viruses and tested them on human volunteers. The best of the recombinants, tested on 17 men, produced only mild symptoms in 5, yet it protected all of the men against Hong Kong flu.

Kilbourne has been pursuing a very different approach to the vaccine problem. His approach relies on recombination, but it also draws

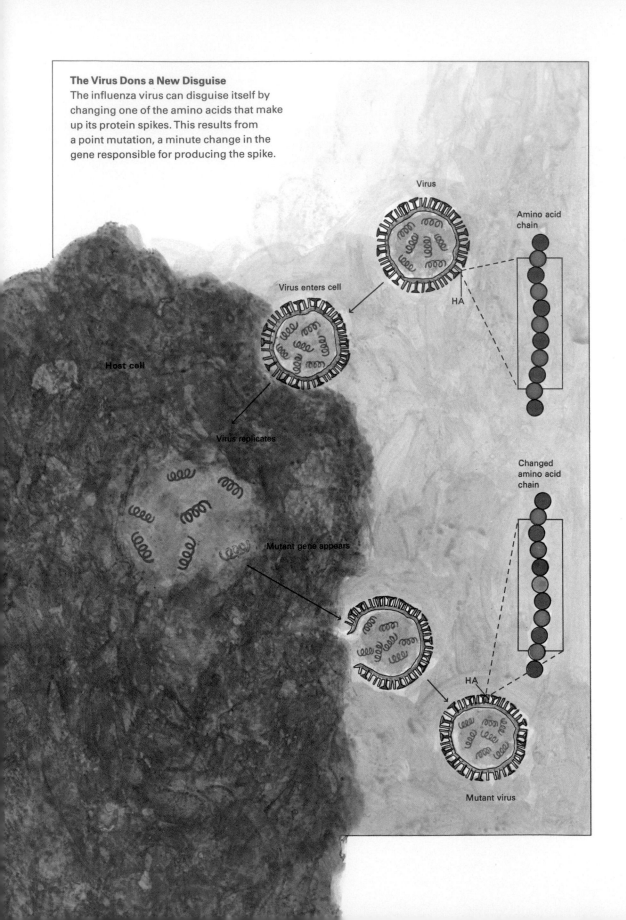

The Virus Dons a New Disguise
The influenza virus can disguise itself by
changing one of the amino acids that make
up its protein spikes. This results from
a point mutation, a minute change in the
gene responsible for producing the spike.

Virus

Amino acid
chain

Virus enters cell

HA

Host cell

Virus replicates

Changed
amino acid
chain

Mutant gene appears

HA

Mutant virus

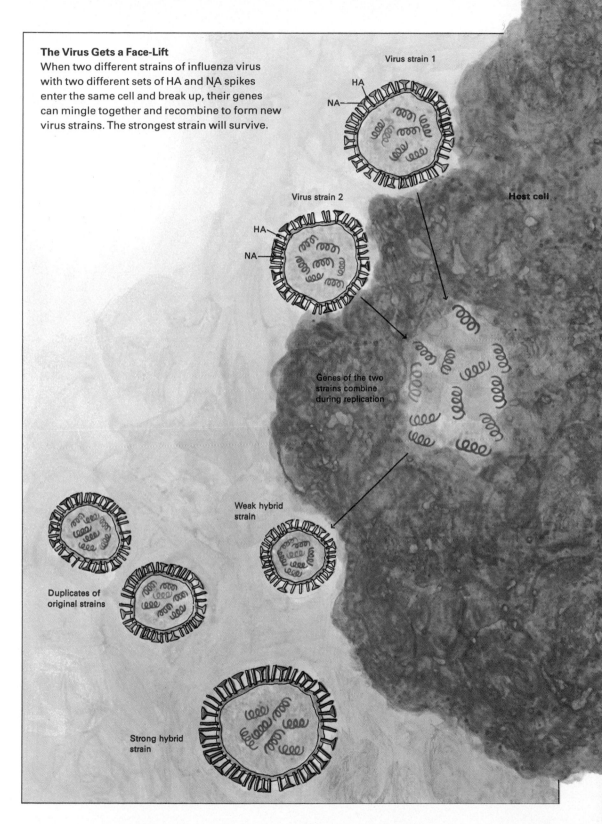

The Virus Gets a Face-Lift
When two different strains of influenza virus with two different sets of HA and NA spikes enter the same cell and break up, their genes can mingle together and recombine to form new virus strains. The strongest strain will survive.

Virus strain 1

HA

NA

Host cell

Virus strain 2

HA

NA

Genes of the two strains combine during replication

Weak hybrid strain

Duplicates of original strains

Strong hybrid strain

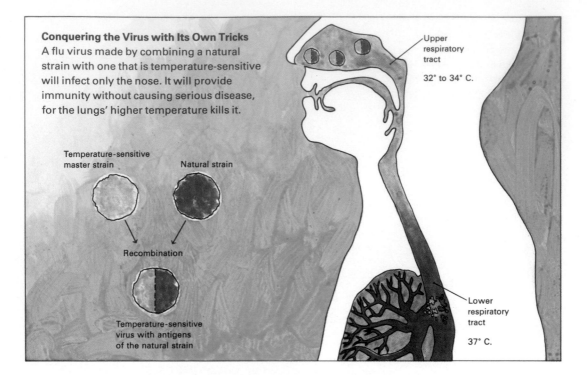

Conquering the Virus with Its Own Tricks
A flu virus made by combining a natural strain with one that is temperature-sensitive will infect only the nose. It will provide immunity without causing serious disease, for the lungs' higher temperature kills it.

Temperature-sensitive master strain

Natural strain

Recombination

Temperature-sensitive virus with antigens of the natural strain

Upper respiratory tract
32° to 34° C.

Lower respiratory tract
37° C.

on his ideas about the roles of HA and NA and the ability of human influenza A viruses to recombine with animal viruses in cell culture. Kilbourne reasons that, while antibodies formed against HA prevent the virus from infecting a cell, antibodies against NA prevent its spread from cell to cell. So a vaccine specifically directed against the NA would not prevent initial infection but would greatly limit its spread. Meanwhile, that infection should provide extremely effective immunity against reinfection. Kilbourne calls his technique infection-permissive immunization.

Probably the most direct way of providing antibodies solely against NA would be to isolate and purify the NA molecule itself for use as the basis of a vaccine. But the approach is fraught with difficulties. Isolating the antigens is one problem. A more serious one is administering them in a form that provokes a strong antibody response. For some reason, once they are separated from the rest of the virus, the antigens stimulate the body's immune system only weakly. So, while research into the general possibilities of using isolated antigens in influenza vaccines continues, Kilbourne has turned to recombination for implementing his infection-permissive idea.

In 1970, Kilbourne created a hybrid strain that is a cross between the Hong Kong flu virus and a horse influenza virus. The hybrid possessed the human NA and the horse HA. The virus was then used to produce a killed-virus vaccine. Researchers at Baylor University in Waco, Tex., then tested this vaccine on human volunteers. The killed viruses raised antibodies against both the horse HA and the human NA antigens. But, with Kilbourne's infection-permissive technique, the real immunization comes from a natural case of the flu caught after vaccination. So next the volunteers were exposed to the natural Hong Kong variant. The immune systems of the volunteers, having previously encountered only horse virus HA, ignored the human virus HA molecules, thereby allowing infection to take place. And so the Hong Kong variant caused an infection, but one severely limited by the antibodies that attacked the NA which was common to both the vaccine and the natural·virus. The infection was mild, but provided immunity to reinfection. Kilbourne's vaccine has already undergone limited clinical testing, and the National Institutes of Health has arranged for more intensive testing during the winter of 1974-1975.

Kilbourne hopes that his technique, using killed virus, will provide the advantages of live vaccination—a vigorous challenge to the immune system—with none of the live virus's disadvantages. He also hopes that the next big change in the antigens of the influenza virus will involve only the HA antigen and not the NA. The protection afforded by an NA specific vaccine, allowing only mild disease with subsequent full protection no matter how the HA molecule changes, might then be effective against the next big shift in the virus, expected in the late 1970s. The odds are with him. While HA has gone through major changes at least four times this century, the NA antigen has had only one drastic change.

The most speculative research on influenza vaccines is being done by Claude Hannoun and his colleagues at ·the Pasteur Institute in Paris. The Pasteur researchers are trying to create a vaccine that will prove effective against all the minor variants of the Hong Kong strain. To do this, they are putting the virus through forced evolution. First, Hannoun and his colleagues grew the London influenza strain in the presence of antibodies effective against it. A mutant slightly resistant to the antibodies soon emerged. They injected the mutant virus into animals, collected the antibodies it stimulated, and grew the virus in the presence of these antibodies. The researchers repeated this cycle until they produced a virus that could no longer mutate. Hannoun suggests that this virus is the evolutionary dead end for Hong Kong flu and represents the strain that will be prevalent later in the 1970s, immediately before the virus makes its next big leap. He hopes that a vaccine based upon this end-point virus will be effective against all the minor variants that emerge between now and then.

While the exciting advances that have come from a greater understanding of the influenza A virus's talents for disguise and deception are certain to lessen the effects of future influenza outbreaks, it is not likely that the new techniques will be perfected in time to prevent the next big epidemic, predicted for the late 1970s. But the flu scientists are watching, learning, and preparing, and that next world-wide epidemic could very well be influenza's last fling.

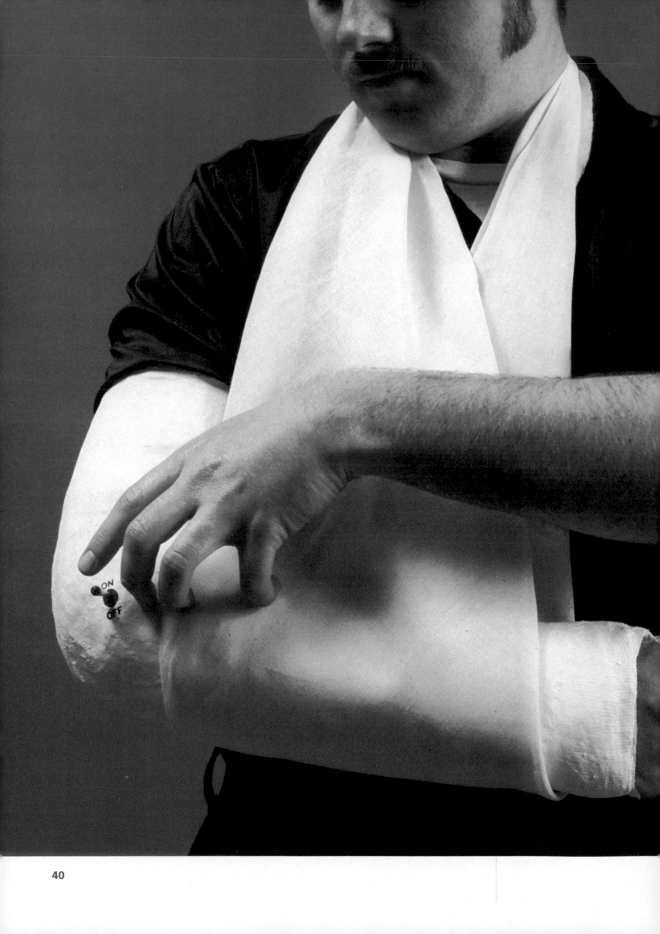

Boosting Our Healing Potential

By Robert O. Becker

The discovery of a basic electrical control system in mammals may lead to more efficient injury repair and eventually to regeneration of limbs and organs

A 45-year-old man came to the Veterans Administration Hospital in Syracuse, N.Y., in February, 1973, with a fractured right ankle. Broken more than two years earlier, the ankle had failed to mend, even after two operations. X rays showed that the bone on both sides of the break had deteriorated. A mild diabetic condition apparently was interfering with the patient's ability to heal. Normally, we would have had to amputate his leg. But this man was lucky.

As an orthopedic surgeon at the Veterans Hospital, I had been investigating a system in animals that seemed to govern healing by electrical control. After 16 years of research on animals, my colleagues and I were ready to apply what we had learned to a human being.

We inserted a single silver wire electrode into the patient's ankle. A battery-powered device delivered a constant, tiny electrical current, from 300 to 400 nanoamperes (billionths of an ampere) at 0.2 to 0.8 volt. After two months, we removed the electrode. X rays showed that the bone had begun to heal. After another month, the patient could walk without pain, and X rays showed that the fracture had healed completely. Four months after the start of treatment, we removed a piece of the anklebone and found it to be normal.

The ability of living organisms to heal themselves is one of their most important and basic characteristics. Without it, life could not

The Contrast in Amphibian Healing

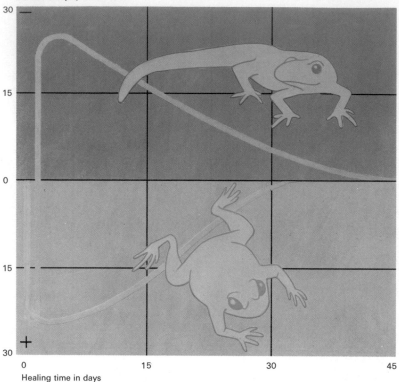

Current of injury in millivolts

Healing time in days

The current of injury after amputation of a limb differs markedly in the frog, which heals by scarring, and the salamander, which is able to regenerate the missing limb.

The author:
Dr. Robert O. Becker, an orthopedic surgeon and medical researcher at the VA Hospital in Syracuse, N.Y., has studied the DC control system since 1958.

have evolved. The surgeon relies on this capability, over which he has essentially no control, when he repairs an injury or sutures an incision. But much remains unknown about this self-repair process. What starts healing? What tells it when to stop? Can it be stimulated artificially?

I became interested in these problems in the late 1950s when I found that many of my patients had broken bones that failed to heal properly. In some cases, where the ends of the fractured bones did not touch, the ends had healed over without rejoining. Normal treatment in such cases includes an operation in which we freshen, or scrape, the bone ends. Then we insert bone grafts and perhaps metal pins to hold the bone ends together. However, the procedure does not always work. In addition, several disorders, including certain types of diabetes, interfere with the healing process.

When I started my research in 1957, we knew that healing, like all other biological processes, is a function of the cells. In some way, injury immediately triggers the cells' healing activity, which gradually turns off as healing is completed. Some type of feedback system seems to constantly measure the damaged tissue remaining and adjusts cell activity to produce the exact amount of healing needed.

There are three types of healing, determined by how the cells react to injury. The simplest type is scarring, in which the cells produce scar tissue that binds together the edges of the injured tissue. In the higher animals, including man, the heart, skeletal muscle, and nerve tissue, including the brain, heal by scarring.

A second healing process is tissue replacement, in which the cells of some tissues produce more of their own kind to replace missing portions. In man, this process heals skin and parts of the gastrointestinal tract. These tissues are made up of cells that normally "wear out" rapidly and continuously replace themselves throughout life. But there appears to be a limit to the amount of replacement healing possible. Beyond that point, scarring takes over.

The best and most complex healing process is regeneration. In this process, cells revert to a primitive, unspecialized form when triggered by an injury. These cells concentrate at the site of injury, then respecialize into the different types of cells needed for complete healing. This process can completely restore a single tissue or a complex, multi-tissue portion of the body.

Apparently, the control system that regulates healing becomes less efficient as animals proceed up the evolutionary scale. The most specialized animal with the greatest capability of regeneration is the salamander. It has the same general anatomy as man, yet it can completely regenerate a leg that has been amputated. In man, only bone heals by regeneration. Obviously, it would be beneficial if human beings could regenerate other damaged tissues.

Measuring a DC Field
Electrodes connected to a large salamander, *left,* measure the electrical potentials at several sites to plot its DC field, *below.*

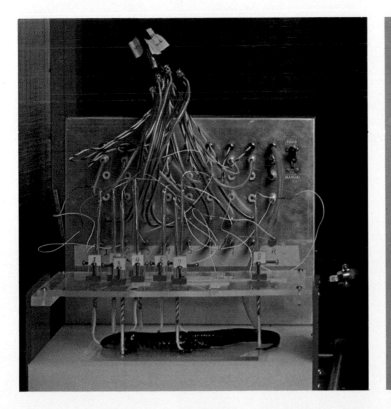

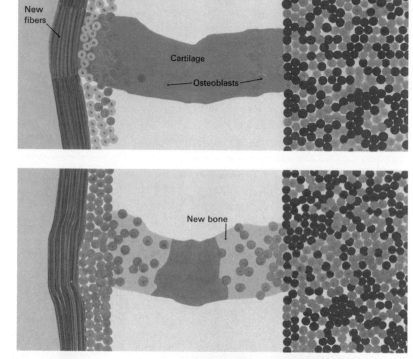

How Fractures Heal
A fracture triggers electrical changes that cause bone membrane cells to divide and produce osteoblasts (bone-forming cells), (left). Marrow cells become primitive cells that also produce osteoblasts, (right).

Cell division

Bone

Fibrous layer

Marrow cells

Primitive cells

New fibers

Cartilage

Osteoblasts

New bone

After X rays showed an unhealed thigh fracture in a 22-year-old man, *left,* a battery unit taped to his skin sent a steady current of about 300 nanoamperes to an electrode implanted at the site of the break, *center.* The thigh then began to heal, *right.*

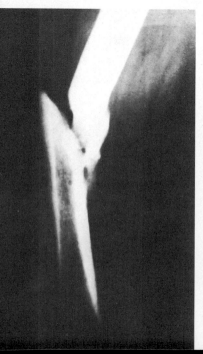
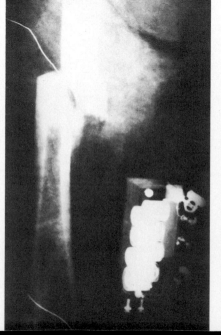
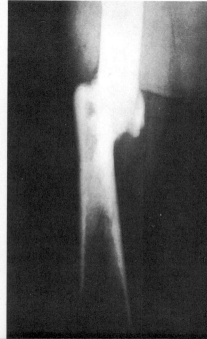

In 1945, S. Meryl Rose, now professor of anatomy at Tulane University College of Medicine in New Orleans, produced the first partial limb regeneration in the adult frog, an animal not normally capable of regeneration. Rose amputated frog forelegs between the elbow and wrist. He then bathed each amputation stump in a strong salt solution every day to retard the scarring and skin regrowth that would normally occur. As a result, about half of each amputated limb, including new bone and muscle tissue, regrew. In some instances, a single digit grew at the end of the limb.

Lev Vladimirovich Polezhaev, a Russian scientist now at the Institute of Developmental Biology, Academy of Sciences, in Moscow, obtained similar results in 1946 by repeatedly puncturing the amputation stumps with a needle. Polezhaev's experiments indicated that Rose's daily salt bathing had produced regeneration by stimulating the cells, rather than by preventing the scar from growing. In the 1950s, Marcus Singer, now professor of anatomy at Case Western Reserve University in Cleveland, produced the same amount of limb regeneration in frog forelegs by transplanting additional nerves from the hind legs into the stumps. His experiments indicated that regeneration would occur if at least 30 per cent of the tissue at the amputation site consisted of nerve.

At this point, we knew that both the amount of injury and the amount of nerve tissue were somehow related to regeneration. But we did not know how they acted. Then, in 1958, a little-known Russian scientist, A. V. Zhirmunskii, began investigating an electrical phenomenon. Measurements on the unbroken skin of any organism show a slight difference in electrical potential, or voltage, between any two points. When an injury occurs, the potential difference between the site of the injury and the surrounding undamaged tissue changes sharply. This is called the current of injury. Scientists have been aware of it since the late 1700s, but modern biologists tend to dismiss it as a simple by-product of the injured cell membranes. However, it was known that the magnitude of the current of injury was proportional to the amount of injury. Zhirmunskii showed that the current of injury also was related to the amount of nerve tissue in the injured area.

When I considered all this, it occurred to me that the current of injury might trigger regeneration. But probably the necessary amount was furnished only when a certain proportion of nerve tissue was present. To explore this possibility, my colleagues and I began studies on salamanders and frogs in 1957. Although these two amphibians are closely related, only the salamander can regenerate its limbs. We amputated a foreleg between the elbow and wrist in each of a group of frogs and a group of salamanders. Then we measured the current of injury with a microvoltmeter daily until healing—skin regrowth and scarring in the frog, regeneration of the forearm and hand in the salamander—was complete. We reported our results in 1960. The first day, the currents of injury were the same in both animals. But then the salamanders showed a marked electrical difference compared with the frogs. Both animals initially generated a positive voltage of about 20 millivolts (thousandths of a volt). This gradually declined to zero in the frog. In the salamander, between the third and fifth days, the voltage switched to a negative polarity and then gradually declined, reaching zero when regeneration was complete.

Next, we began searching for the source of the current of injury. Most scientists think that it is generated when damaged cells allow electrons to "leak" through the cell membranes. We knew, however, that this was not the complete explanation. We had found measurable currents of injury in both frogs and salamanders many days after injury. Damaged cells either die or repair themselves within a day or two; they could not produce such long-lasting electrical factors.

We began our search for the source of the current of injury by following up Zhirmunskii's theory of a connection with the nervous system. We knew that the nerves transmit the information that allows us to see, feel, hear, smell, and taste by means of nerve impulses. But there were indications that there might be other ways of transmitting more basic data, such as pain, or the control of healing and growth. The nerve impulse system is a high-speed, sophisticated communications system that transmits very complex data. The first primitive living organisms could not have had such a system, yet they must have had some means of communicating information within themselves—of sensing injury and repairing it, for example.

We suspected that the current of injury might be related to this more basic transmission system. We began our investigations in 1960 by measuring the electrical potentials between many different points on the skin of human beings and many other animals. We found that the potentials are organized into an electrical field, represented by lines of force, that roughly parallels the pattern of the nervous system. Changes in the field must permit information to be transmitted to and from the living cells throughout the body. An injury produces a local disturbance in the field pattern, stimulating the cells to regrow and heal the injury. We thus concluded that the field was the primitive data transmission system that took care of more basic functions than the nerve impulse system.

We also found that the field appeared to be directly associated with some element of the nervous system that generated and distributed the potentials. Electrical potentials in a conducting medium such as the nerve cell implies there also is a steady direct current (DC) flow.

To discover how the nerves generated and transmitted the current, we isolated living nerves within several animals, leaving the nerves still connected to the animals. We then studied the effects that anesthesia, injury, temperature changes, and cutting the nerve had on the potentials. Our results, reported in 1963, seemed to indicate that the nerves not only transmitted impulses, but also that electrons actually flowed within some element of the nerves. Furthermore, the way they flowed

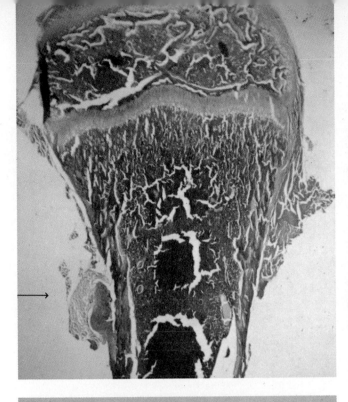

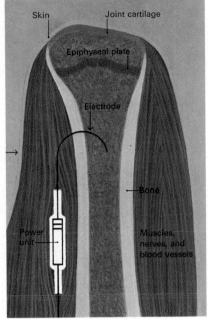

Some Regrowth of a Rat's Leg

A rat foreleg, *top left,* was amputated between the shoulder and elbow joint (arrow). A small device, *above,* in the stump supplied a tiny electrical current that produced partial regeneration of the leg, including bone, muscle, nerves, blood vessels, and joint cartilage, *center.* Without treatment, an amputated limb will simply scar over, *bottom left.*

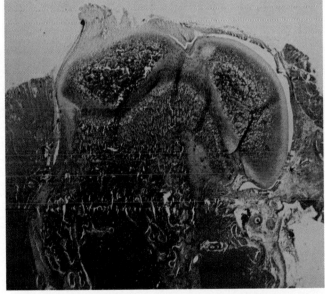

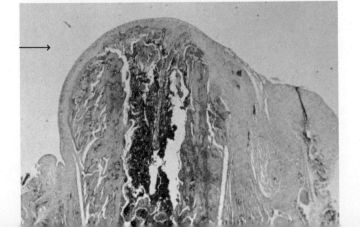

Regenerating a Rabbit's Cartilage

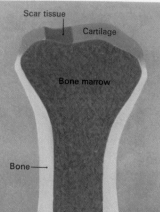

Scar tissue

Cartilage

Bone marrow

Bone

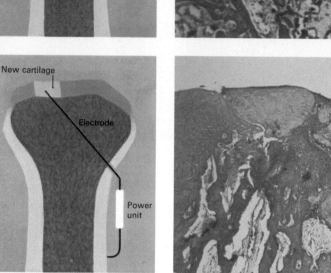

New cartilage

Electrode

Power unit

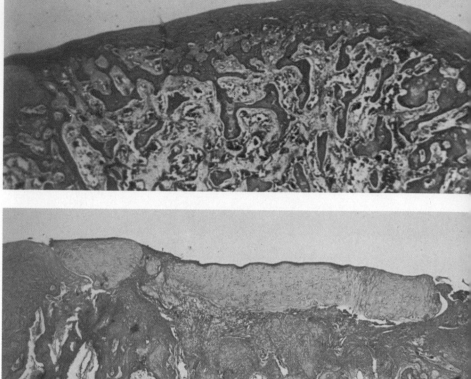

Damaged joint cartilage in a rabbit normally heals with scar tissue, *top.* With the help of an electric current, the cartilage regenerates almost wholly, *above.*

implied that a very ordered crystallinelike arrangement of atoms existed somewhere in the nerve tissue. But experiments aimed at finding these atoms were very difficult because the nerve is composed mostly of water. As a result, we could not identify the portion of the nerve that carried the electron flow.

So we turned our attention to bone. Bone can regenerate even though it has far less nerve tissue than is needed for this process. This indicates that bone might contain its own electronic healing control system to make up for the deficient nerve supply. If we could discover how this system works, we would probably get important clues to how the overall healing control system operates. In addition, bone is easier to study than nerves. It is mostly solid, and has a well-organized structure that has been studied in submicroscopic detail.

We began by studying a bone-growth process that, although simpler than the growth involved in healing, appears to be equally well controlled. This is the growth of bone in response to mechanical stress. Bone constantly alters itself to produce the shape that best resists stress.

This is as if a bridge could sense the loads applied to it by traffic, wind, and tides, and constantly adjust its structure and strength to accommodate them. For example, when a bone is bent, one side is compressed and the other side is stretched. The bone grows on its compressed side and dissolves on its stretched side. We wondered whether bone responds to such mechanical stresses by generating electrical potentials proportional to the stress and whether these potentials then stimulate bone cell growth.

To find out, we removed bones from frogs and other animals and placed them in insulated clamping devices that left one end free. We attached electrodes at various places along the bone shaft and then recorded the electrical potentials that were generated as we bent each bone. We found that the compressed side becomes electrically negative and the stretched side becomes positive. If these differences in electrical potential regulate bone growth under stress, we reasoned that inserting electrodes into the bone and running the appropriate current through them should cause bone to grow at the negative electrode and to dissolve at the positive electrode.

In 1964, we tested this concept on adult dogs in conjunction with C. Andrew L. Bassett, research professor in the Department of Orthopedic Surgery at Columbia University College of Physicians and Surgeons in New York City. Into the bone of one hind leg, we inserted a small battery-powered unit with two platinum electrodes penetrating the bone, one centimeter (0.4 inch) apart. As a control, we inserted a similar unit, without the battery, into another leg. After two weeks, microscopic examination of the leg with the battery unit showed considerable new bone growth around the negative electrode. There was no bone growth around the positive electrode, although some would have been expected simply to repair the injury caused by the electrode insertion. This indicated that the positive electrode had prevented new growth, or else had dissolved any new growth as fast as it occurred. In the control leg, without the battery, bone growth was identical around both electrodes. We tested currents ranging from 1 to 10 microamperes (millionths of an ampere) and found that currents between 2 and 5 microamperes produced the most growth.

Next, we studied the regenerative process of bone healing by applying electrodes to frogs' broken leg bones to measure the electrical potentials. Experiments with several hundred animals revealed that the potentials lasted much longer than those found with simple bending stress and produced a more complex electrical field centered at the break. We also found that the difference in the potentials in the broken leg promptly dropped to almost zero when we cut the nerves to the site of the break. This indicated that the electrical field depended partly on the nerves.

We viewed the healing process through a microscope and noted the cell changes in the blood clot surrounding the fractures that led to the formation of a mass of primitive cells which then became new bone.

A New Leg for a Frog

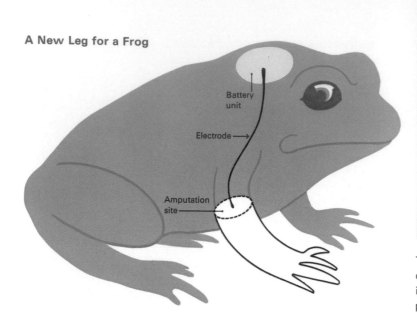

Battery unit

Electrode →

Amputation site —

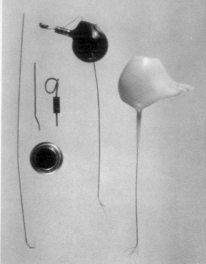

The implanted healing device is embedded in silicon rubber to prevent rejection.

An amputated frog leg was completely regenerated for the first time in 1973. A battery unit was implanted in the frog's back and a lead wire was run down to an electrode at the amputation site, *above.* The stump, *below left,* grew into a new leg and foot in about one year, *below right.*

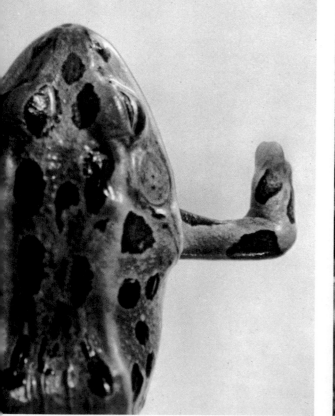

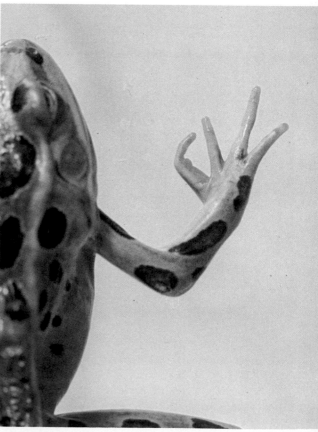

Next, we attempted to produce the same changes in normal cells. We placed blood cells from the frog in plastic chambers and exposed them to the same electrical field we had found around the broken bone. The cells responded exactly as had those at the site of the break. This proved that the electrical field found at the fracture site controlled the cellular changes that led to regeneration. Most important, we were able to determine very precise ranges of voltage and current that most effectively produce the desired changes. For cells in a chamber 1 centimeter in diameter, we achieved the best results with currents of about 0.5 nanoampere. Currents below 0.1 nanoampere and above 0.9 nanoampere were much less effective in producing the changes that lead to regeneration.

By 1970, we could trace in detail a control system for the bone-healing process. A fracture produces local changes in the DC field in two ways. Like all injuries, it stimulates the neural system, which produces a DC electrical signal at the fracture site. In addition, the bone produces its own electrical signal in response to stress. The combined changes stimulate two types of cells. The cells of the membrane covering the surface of the bone begin dividing rapidly to produce osteogenic, or bone-forming, cells. At the same time, the red blood cells of the bone marrow revert to primitive cells, which then respecialize into osteogenic cells. As these cells produce new bone and the fracture heals, the electrical field gradually returns to normal.

Learning what we have about the bone healing control system has had two important results. We found that the control system can be reactivated in human patients whose fractures fail to heal, by supplying the proper currents at the appropriate site. This technique is now being evaluated at several medical research centers, both in the United States and other countries.

Also, our knowledge of the control system for healing broken bones suggested a control system that regulates regeneration in other tissues. According to our concept, organisms lose regenerative ability as they increase in complexity because more and more of their nerve tissue is concentrated in the brain, leaving less available for the rest of the body. With less nerve tissue, the body cannot provide the voltages needed to trigger regeneration. We still cannot explain why the adult human brain heals by scarring instead of regeneration, although some studies indicate that infants can regenerate brain tissue to some extent.

We reasoned that if we could induce the missing voltages in the stump of an animal's severed limb, its cells might return to a primitive type and respecialize into all the cell types necessary to regrow the missing part. The first attempt at this had come in 1967, when Stephen Smith, a graduate student working with Rose, produced partial regeneration of an amputated leg in the frog. He duplicated the salamander's current of injury in the frog by implanting in its leg a short piece of silver wire soldered to a short piece of platinum wire with the negative end in the stump. The solder joint and adjacent parts of both wires were covered with insulation. Such a device, when placed in any conducting solution, such as tissue fluid, generates a small amount of electricity. In effect, Smith's device was a crude battery that generated 300 nanoamperes at 0.1 millivolt. It produced the same amount of regeneration in a frog's amputated leg as did the experiments of Rose, Polezhaev, and Singer.

By 1972, we were ready to try a similar experiment on mammals. We amputated one foreleg between the shoulder and the elbow in each of a group of laboratory rats. We modified the bimetallic device Smith had used in earlier experiments by inserting an electrical resistor in place of the solder joint. We inserted one electrode into the marrow cavity of the bone at the amputated end, and sewed the other end in the shoulder muscle. By varying the size of the resistor, we were able to test the rate of healing using devices with high, medium, and low currents. As a control, we studied the rate of healing in animals that were not fitted with devices.

In the controls, as expected, the bone grew closed at the end and the amputation stump scarred over. The animals with low-current devices (0.1 nanoampere at 350 millivolts) had a small amount of regeneration. The high-current devices (15 nanoamperes at an immeasurably low voltage) seemed to destroy, rather than regenerate, tissue. Animals with medium-current devices (5 nanoamperes at 75 millivolts) showed varying degrees of regeneration. The best results occurred in one rat with a device that produced 8 nanoamperes at 100 millivolts with a 10 megohm (million ohms) resistor. This regenerated the missing portion of the upper limb down to the elbow joint, including regrowth of muscle, nerve, bone, and blood vessels.

While we had not restored a complete limb in the rat, we had succeeded in growing normally organized complex structures composed of many different types of cells and tissues in a mammal, the first step toward similar work in humans. And, we had achieved such growth through an electrical stimulus. Further evidence that regeneration could be electrically induced came in late 1973 when Smith, now associate professor of anatomy at the University of Kentucky in Lexington, reported that he had regenerated the entire foreleg in a frog, using implanted battery-operated devices.

In 1973, we used rabbits to investigate a regenerative process that could affect the treatment of arthritis. All types of arthritis occur because injured cartilage heals only by scarring. Scar tissue cannot withstand much pressure and the pain of arthritis develops rapidly. Because cartilage is a single tissue, we reasoned that stimulating it to regenerate would be easier than working with an entire multitissue limb. We removed a piece of cartilage from the knee joint of each rabbit, then inserted a medium-current, bimetallic device. After three weeks, all of the animals with devices had regenerated some cartilage and a few had regenerated almost all of it. With Bruce Baker, assistant professor of orthopedics at Upstate Medical Center in Syracuse, we

Discovering the Signal Path

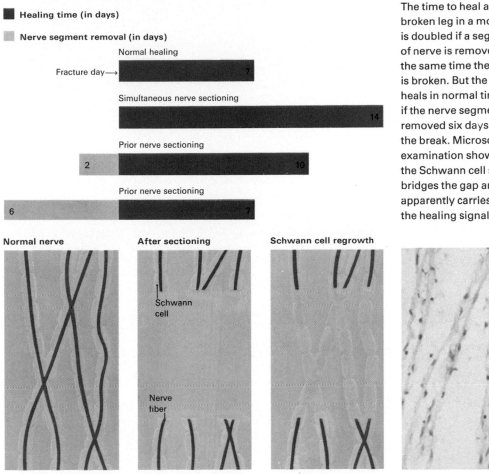

■ Healing time (in days)

■ Nerve segment removal (in days)

Normal healing

Fracture day→ | 7

Simultaneous nerve sectioning

| 14

Prior nerve sectioning

2 | 10

Prior nerve sectioning

6 | 7

Normal nerve

Schwann cell

Nerve fiber

After sectioning

Schwann cell regrowth

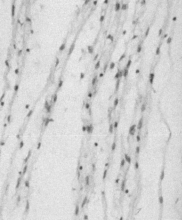

The time to heal a broken leg in a mouse is doubled if a segment of nerve is removed at the same time the leg is broken. But the leg heals in normal time if the nerve segment is removed six days before the break. Microscopic examination shows that the Schwann cell sheath bridges the gap and apparently carries the healing signal.

are testing battery-operated devices to try to get complete healing in all cases, and to search for side effects.

But there was still a missing link. We had not identified the part of the nerve that transmits the control signal for healing.

We knew that the nerves' role in fracture healing was rather mysterious. For example, the patient who is paralyzed by an injury to the spinal cord can neither feel nor control muscle movement below the point of his spinal cord injury. But broken bones in this part of his body heal about twice as fast as normal. This is because the nerves to this part of the body are still intact and functioning, but the spinal injury has separated them from the regulating influence of the brain, which normally keeps healing under stricter control. However, in patients with damage to the peripheral nerves (those serving the extremities), broken bones heal very slowly or not at all.

We used laboratory mice to explore the subtle relationship between nerves and the healing of broken bones. First, we broke a small bone in

Electrical Needlepoint

Scientists have not yet been able to explain how acupuncture works. Practitioners of this ancient Chinese technique relieve pain and treat disease by inserting long, fine needles into the body at various points and rapidly twirling them. While the value of acupuncture in treating disease is hotly debated, its effectiveness as an analgesic, or pain reliever, for some people is generally accepted.

According to legend, acupuncture originated more than 3,600 years ago when Chinese Emperor Shih Huang-ti noticed that the soldiers who received arrow wounds in battle sometimes had ailments cured in other parts of the body. The first published reports appeared about 500 B.C. In succeeding years, Chinese doctors worked out an elaborate theory to explain acupuncture based on the flow of energy along 12 pathways, or meridians, in the body. They believed that an imbalance in the flow caused disease and pain. But needles inserted at specific points along the meridians would change the flow, correct the imbalance, and restore health. Acupuncture charts show at least 350 points where needles can be inserted into the body.

Instead of twirling the needles, acupuncture practitioners sometimes apply either continuous or pulsed direct current (DC) electricity to the needles, as another form of stimulation (see Shutting the Gate on Pain). There are also reports that the acupuncture points may be precisely located by measuring the skin's electrical resistance. The points appear to have much lower resistance than the surrounding skin. These electrical effects cannot be explained on the basis of the known functions of the nervous system, but they seem to fit the concept of the DC communications system that my colleagues and I have developed.

In fact, the existence of the acupuncture points can be predicted by any electrical engineer who understands our studies. An engineer designing a system to transmit direct current must allow for factors called cable constants. Examples of cable constants are resistance and capacitance, which cause a current to lose strength progressively as it travels along the wire. Engineers overcome this loss by inserting amplifiers, or boosters, at strategic points along the transmission line, so that the original signal is delivered at full strength at its destination.

If our theory of a DC control system is correct, such amplifiers must exist along the course of the Schwann cell transmission lines in order to carry the control signal for healing. The sites of these amplifiers would also be sources of DC. To find the sites, we measured electrical resistance at various points on the skin because it is much easier to measure resistance than to find evidence of DC emission. The sites appear as points of diminished resistance. We measured resistance at 22 listed acupuncture points on the forearm and found significantly decreased resistance at 11.

We are now looking for evidence of DC emission from those points in the forearm that register decreased resistance. We use a device called the high resistance electrometer to measure the electrical potential. So far, we have found DC current emitted at enough points to indicate that we are probably correct in describing these "low resistance" points as DC sources.

Next, we plan to search for evidence that the DC system can transmit messages in two directions within the body. We plan first to measure the potentials at, say, six points along an acupuncture meridian. Then we will attach electrodes to the five points nearest the body and insert a needle into the sixth, or farthest, point. If our theory is correct, we should see a change in potential move progressively from point to point. We can measure the change and also how much time it takes to move. This would be evidence that a message is being transmitted and would firmly substantiate our thesis of a DC control system for healing.

It would also indicate that inserting needles into the body may not be the most efficient way to administer acupuncture analgesia. If the system is as we envision it, applying carefully measured electrical current alone may give the best results. Small battery-operated devices could deliver the necessary electrical pulses through skin surface electrodes to provide safe, easy, and effective analgesia. [R.O.B.]

A multielectrode probe measures the electrical field surrounding an acupuncture point on the human forearm. Emissions from some points seem to support the theory of the DC communications system.

the hind leg, leaving the nerves intact, and examined the break microscopically each day until it healed. This showed us how the cells changed and how long it took to heal the break.

Then, we broke the same bone in another group of mice and also removed a quarter-inch segment of the main nerve to the hind leg. We wanted to produce a major defect that would interfere with healing as peripheral nerve damage does in human beings. But all the bones did heal, although healing took twice as long as normal.

Next, since we were trying to produce a condition that would prevent the bones from knitting, we removed segments of the nerve two and three days before we broke the bones. We thought that this would produce partial degeneration in the part of the nerve that we had separated from the rest of the nervous system. But the result was just the opposite of what we had hoped for. The fractures healed faster than when we broke the bone and cut the nerve at the same time, though not quite as fast as normal.

Still hoping to prevent the bones from joining, we removed the nerve segments five and six days before breaking the leg bone. To our surprise, the mice responded as if the nerve had not been cut at all. The bones healed in a normal amount of time.

It was highly unlikely that the nerve itself had regrown, and microscopic examination of the interrupted nerves showed that this was the case. Obviously, the nerve was not the tissue that transmitted the healing control signal after all. However, we discovered that another thin tissue had bridged the gap in the nerve. In late 1973, we identified this tissue as the Schwann cell sheath, which surrounds each peripheral nerve. We now believe that the Schwann cell sheaths transmit the healing signal, at least in the limbs.

More important, our experiments provided a clue to the source of the entire primitive data transmission system. The Schwann cells are part of a group of cells known as the perineural cells. These are derived from the same tissue that forms the nerve, and they form a complete network that pervades the entire central nervous system, extending from the Schwann cells, which surround even the smallest peripheral nerve, to the glial cells, which form a complex mass in which the brain cells are imbedded. It was known that the glial cells have different electrical properties than the nerve cells, such as slow waves and steady potentials, yet their function was largely unknown. Our work indicates that all the perineural cells link together to form the primitive data transmission system we sought.

As we learn more about how the healing system works, we will begin to use it medically—from controlling pain to regenerating complex tissues. We have already helped to repair broken bones that refused to mend by themselves. Soon we may be restoring the damaged joint cartilage that leads to arthritis. And I believe that, in time, we can induce total regeneration in man, not only in his limbs, but also in his heart and other vital organs.

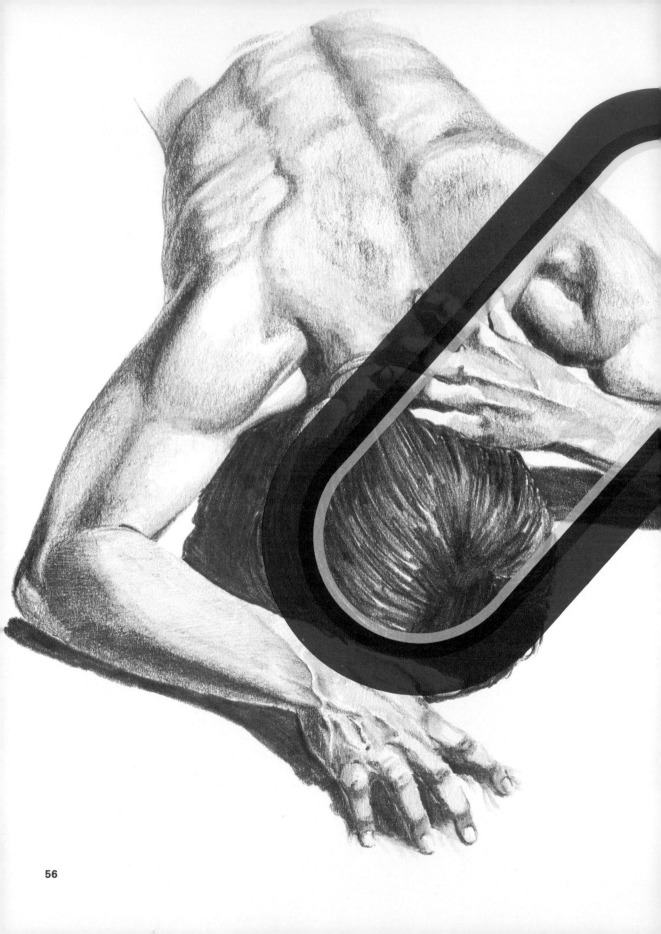

Shutting the Gate on Pain

By Ronald Melzack

A controversial theory explains part of the puzzle of how pain is transmitted, and sheds light on why acupuncture works

The age-old practice of using pain to kill pain has never been readily accepted by the medical profession. The various methods seem not only unscientific, but downright barbaric. However, the use of acupuncture to induce analgesia (insensitivity to pain), first in Chinese and later in Western hospitals, is changing medical opinion about this folk practice. Moreover, research on the chemical basis of acupuncture is producing surprising insights into the nature of pain itself.

When the first reports and films of acupuncture being used during surgery reached the West in 1971, they seemed to support what doctors in

China claimed. They could perform painless surgery after inserting long, fine needles into specific points in the skin. Most Western doctors were skeptical at first. They attributed the analgesia to hypnosis, or even propaganda and fakery. Then, firsthand observations by visiting Western doctors began to show that the analgesia, for many people, is a genuine experience.

For example, Dr. E. Grey Dimond of Kansas City, Mo., observed an operation in Canton in 1971 in which the patient had part of his stomach removed under acupuncture analgesia. Four acupuncture needles were attached to a direct-current (DC) battery that sent electrical pulses through them. The man reported that all he felt was a pulling sensation in his internal organs. In 1972, British physician Peter E. Brown witnessed a lung removal in Shanghai. This time, only one acupuncture needle was used. It was rotated manually by the anesthetist, and the patient said that he was able to feel only an occasional pulling sensation.

The first writings on acupuncture were compiled about 500 B.C., though scholars think they originated as traditional treatment passed on by word of mouth as long ago as 2700 B.C. By A.D. 400, a complex system of medicine had developed around the writings that included elaborate charts tracing the circulation of the blood and guidelines to treat virtually every kind of pain or major disease. It is interesting to note that the charts were in use long before the English physician William Harvey published his research on blood circulation in 1628.

The traditional Chinese explanation of acupuncture is that the body contains two universal forces, the spirits (Yin) and the blood (Yang), which circulate through a series of 12 invisible channels called meridians. When Yin and Yang fall out of harmony, pain and disease occur. By inserting needles at one or more of 365 specific points designated on the meridians, the acupuncturist somehow brings the Yin and Yang into harmony again.

While the use of acupuncture during surgery is highly dramatic, the most common use is to relieve headache, backache, and other forms of pain. In fact, acupuncture is related to other forms of intense surface stimulation generally described as "counterirritation" in Western medical texts. Among the oldest techniques used to control pain are applying mustard plasters, ice packs, or hot-water bottles to various parts of the body. The Druses who live in Syria and Lebanon put hot nails on a patient's arms and legs to control pain, believing that this drives out pain-producing spirits. The ancient Greeks and Romans applied hot cups to a person's back to ease leg and back pains. Cupping is still used in Italy, Greece, Eastern Europe, China, and Africa. A small, heated jar or cup is placed on the back with the open end down. As the air in the cup cools, a partial vacuum develops that sucks the skin into the cup, breaking blood vessels and creating a black-and-blue area. Although this is moderately painful, it seems to relieve far more severe pains in other parts of the body for long periods of time.

The author:
Ronald Melzack, a psychologist at McGill University in Montreal, is co-developer of the gate-control theory of pain. He has been engaged in pain research for nearly 20 years.

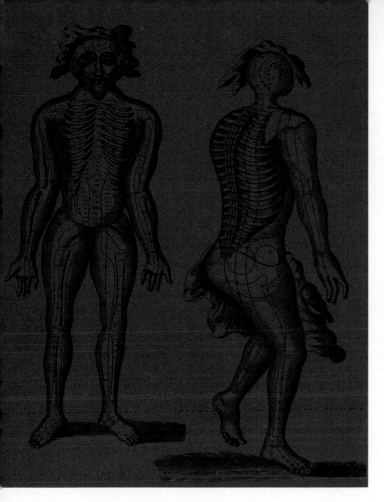

Ancient Pain Remedies
Acupuncture points for pain control were first pictured in a Western text, *left,* by a physician in 1683. Cupping to control pain, *above,* has long been used in parts of Europe and Africa.

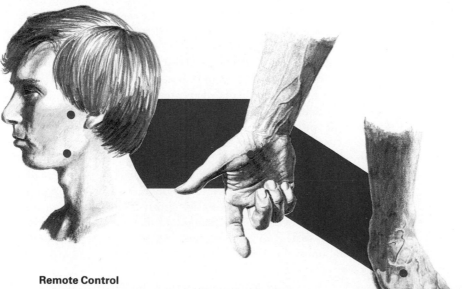

Remote Control
Points in hands and feet that can sometimes start or relieve a toothache have been mapped by doctors.

Other counterirritations include pushing threads through the skin and moving them back and forth, applying substances that blister the skin, and cutting the skin. In many parts of Africa, prolonged, severe headaches are sometimes treated effectively by tribal doctors who make large cuts into the scalp and briefly scrape the skull. This process is known as trepanation.

Interestingly enough, acupuncture has been "rediscovered" by Western doctors many times since it was described in a book by the Dutch physician Willem Ten Rhyne in 1683. However, the technique was discarded each time because so many flamboyant claims were made for its curative powers. Unfortunately, its usefulness against pain also was lost each time. This will happen again, I fear, unless we carefully analyze its properties, determine the neurophysiological mechanisms that explain them, and incorporate these into our knowledge and treatment of pain.

Fortunately, the renewed interest in acupuncture this time has sparked widespread research. Perhaps the most exciting research is being carried out on rats and rabbits by Dr. Hsiang-tung Chang and his colleagues at the Shanghai Institute of Physiology. They have recorded electrical activity in several areas of the central nervous system—the spinal cord and the brain—that are known to transmit pain messages when parts of the body are injured. When they inserted acupuncture needles into areas on an animal's body comparable to acupuncture points on a human body, the pain signals stopped. This confirms the belief that acupuncture works on pain through known pathways in the central nervous system.

Scientists in other parts of China have carried out experiments that lead to the same conclusion. They have also used pressure cuffs that prevent the flow of blood and "spirits" along the so-called meridian channels, but do not stop the normal action of nerve impulses. The pressure cuffs also do not affect the pain-killing aspect of acupuncture. Experimenters have also found that acupuncture points for the relief of pain have no effect on pain when an analgesic drug is injected at acupuncture sites before the sites are stimulated. They also discovered that most acupuncture points lie over or near major sensory nerves, the nerves that receive and carry impressions from the outside world to the central nervous system. These observations, together with data from many other experiments being carried out in China, lead unequivocally to the conclusion that acupuncture's effects on pain must be due to neurological mechanisms. Reports in early 1974 on studies at Peking Medical College have suggested that chemicals are released in the nervous system by acupuncture. These chemicals can be withdrawn from one animal and injected into another, thereby diminishing its response to pain.

However, three aspects of acupuncture still seem to defy current medical knowledge. These are: (1) control of pain by stimulation, (2) interaction between distant sites in the body, and (3) prolonged time of relief after stimulation stops. All three are so unusual that they cause skepticism among physicians trained in Western medical practice. Yet, interestingly, all three are found in Western medical literature.

The first, control of pain by stimulation, involves fairly intense stimulation of tissues by the acupuncture needles. This stimulation is caused either by twirling the needles or applying an electrical current. If the pain is not blocked, herbs are sometimes placed on the acupuncture sites and burned. This procedure, called moxibustion, stimulates the tissues still more.

In Western medical literature there is considerable evidence to show that brief, mildly painful stimulation can substantially relieve more severe pain, and that the relief lasts much longer than the period of stimulation. For example, vigorously massaging the sensory nerve that serves the lower head and jaw may permanently abolish the excruciating pain of *tic douloureux*, which causes convulsive spasms of the face and mouth. In rare cases, similar kinds of pain may be alleviated or abolished for many days by slowly withdrawing the fluid that surrounds the spinal cord with a hypodermic needle and then reinjecting it very rapidly.

The second aspect of acupuncture is that of stimulation at one site that affects pain at a distant site. For example, in one Chinese hospital the needles were inserted in a patient's forearms during a thyroid operation. For a similar operation in another hospital, the needles were placed in the neck and wrists.

Western doctors have actually known about the interaction between pain and stimulation at distant sites in the human body since 1946. Janet Travell, who later became President John F. Kennedy's personal physician, and Seymour H. Rinzler made some interesting discoveries during research on unusual pain patterns. They mapped more than 40 patterns of pain within which pain can be readily started or stopped by pressing on specific trigger zones. Travell and Rinzler found that many of the trigger zones extended outside the area of pain, and some were a considerable distance away from the areas they affected. Travell also noted that virtually every trigger zone is at or near one of the major acupuncture points shown on acupuncture charts.

Travell and Rinzler found that dry needling—simply moving a needle in and out of the trigger zone without injecting any substance— sometimes relieves pain. They relieved a shoulder pain, for example, by dry needling a trigger point at or near the site of the pain. Intense cold may also bring relief. At first, they assumed the cold produced local analgesia, but they now believe that the intense stimulation itself relieves the pain. Remarkably, this intense stimulation has abolished pain for days, weeks, and in some cases permanently.

The fact that pain can be relieved by stimulation at a point some distance from its source is particularly evident in treating patients with severe phantom-limb pain. Phantom-limb pain is the feeling of burning or shooting pains that seems to come from a leg or an arm after it

Site of salt injection

Severe pain in phantom foot

Phantom Limb Pain
A salt solution injected in the lower back can relieve the pain felt in a person's foot that is no longer there.

A Vertebra's Swinging Gate

According to the gate-control theory, the transmission of pain signals from the body to the spinal cord and to the brain is a variable process. The large (blue) and small (red) nerve fibers either act together or against each other to open, partially open, or close the pain gate, according to the type of signals that reach the spinal cord.

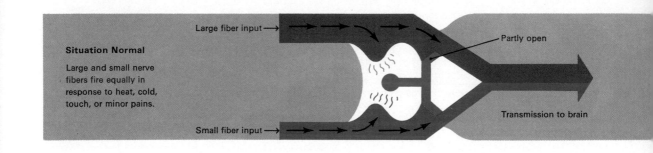

Situation Normal

Large and small nerve fibers fire equally in response to heat, cold, touch, or minor pains.

Large fiber input

Small fiber input

Partly open

Transmission to brain

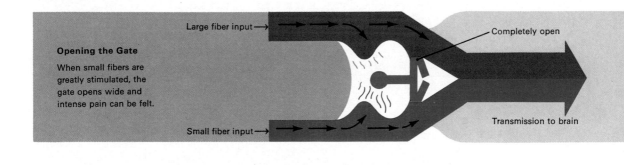

Opening the Gate

When small fibers are greatly stimulated, the gate opens wide and intense pain can be felt.

Large fiber input

Small fiber input

Completely open

Transmission to brain

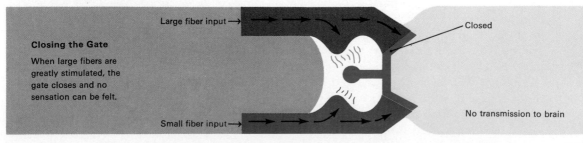

Closing the Gate

When large fibers are greatly stimulated, the gate closes and no sensation can be felt.

Large fiber input

Small fiber input

Closed

No transmission to brain

has been amputated. Doctors in San Francisco found, in 1954, that injecting a saline solution under the skin of an amputee's lower back produces a sharp, localized, burning pain that radiates into his buttocks and thighs, and sometimes into the phantom limb. The pain lasts only about 10 minutes, yet it may partly or completely relieve phantom-limb pain for hours, weeks, or much longer.

The duration of acupuncture stimulation and the analgesia it produces are not related in any simple way. Analgesia tends to develop slowly. Twenty minutes' stimulation is usually needed to produce sufficient analgesia to carry out a surgical operation. Furthermore, acupuncture analgesia may sometimes last for several hours after the stimulation has stopped.

Such prolonged pain relief is particularly puzzling. It suggests that memorylike mechanisms may be involved. In fact, the very existence of phantom-limb pain supports this suggestion. This pain endures long after the injured stump tissues heal. Moreover, the "remembered" pain may include that incurred in the limb before it was severed. In one case, a patient who had a wood sliver jammed under a fingernail shortly before he lost his hand in an accident subsequently reported feeling a painful sliver still under the fingernail of the hand that was no longer there.

There is also experimental evidence of a memorylike mechanism in pain. In 1947, researchers at The Academy of Medical Sciences in Moscow injected turpentine under the skin of a cat's paw. A temporary inflammation caused the cat to flex its paw excessively when it walked. After the inflammation healed, the animal walked normally. The Russian scientists then severed connections between the cat's brain and the rest of its body and found that the animal once again flexed its paw abnormally. This indicated that a memory record of the pain existed for the cat.

Although we do not understand this aspect of pain, we can use certain general theories of memory to speculate on how pain memory works. One theory holds that nerve impulses triggered by the original stimulus activate nerve fibers (neurons) in a reverberating circuit. That is, neuron A activates neuron B, which in turn activates A again, and so on. Theoretically, activity may persist for prolonged periods in such a circuit. It is also conceivable that some sort of change occurs at the connecting junctions between neurons so that a permanent or semipermanent trace of the stimulation remains in the nervous system

Pinning the Gate Closed

According to the gate-control theory, the body's pain gates can be closed through action in the nerves or in the reticular formation of the brain stem. Acupuncture needles inserted at specific points in a patient's arm may trigger nerve impulses that signal these two points to close the pain gate, stopping messages from reaching the patient's brain during any surgical operation on his lungs.

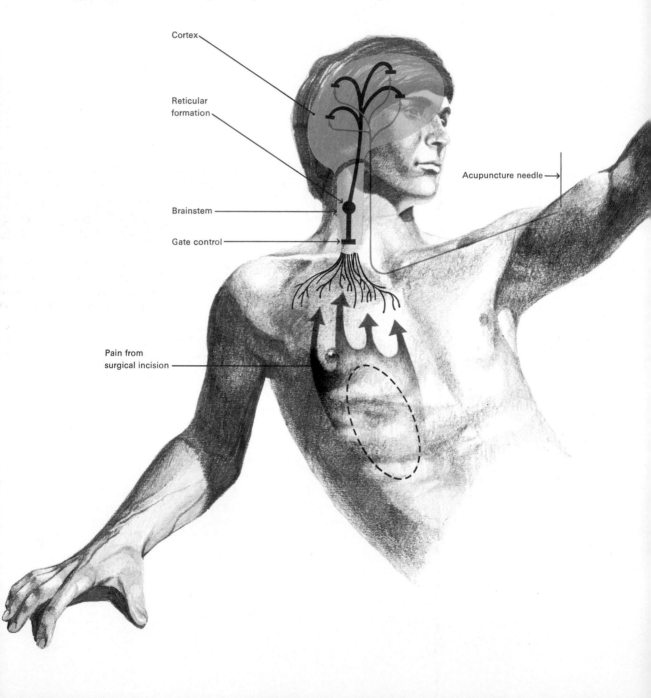

Cortex

Reticular formation

Brainstem

Gate control

Acupuncture needle →

Pain from surgical incision

long after the event occurred. Still another theory is that neuron A activates an inhibitory neuron B, which briefly prevents further activity in neuron A. When neuron B returns to its normal state, release of its inhibitory effect causes neuron A to fire spontaneously and recreate the sequence of events. Presumably, such activity in the nervous system could persist indefinitely.

If some pains result from such memorylike mechanisms, it is conceivable that acupuncture needles could act by disrupting these processes and that the effects would last after the needle is withdrawn. Such mechanisms should also be turned off by analgesics and, indeed, some doctors have injected such drugs into trigger points to stop pains in many parts of the body.

According to the traditional view of pain, known as the specificity theory, specific pain receptors in the body tissues send pain signals directly to a pain center in the brain. The process resembles a simple telephone switchboard—a signal is dialed at one end and a bell rings at the other. This theory assumes that the amount of pain is proportional to the intensity of stimulation, and that the location of the stimulus determines the location of the pain.

However, the specificity theory cannot account for the three properties of acupuncture analgesia—control of pain by stimulation, interaction between distant sites in the body, and prolonged relief after stimulation stops. Scientists have therefore been searching for a more comprehensive theory of pain.

One such alternative is the gate-control theory, which physiologist Patrick D. Wall of University College in London and I proposed in 1965. It provides an explanation for the effects of acupuncture stimulation. Although the gate-control theory is still controversial, recent evidence provides increasing support for it. It is now widely taught in Western medical schools, and is even used by many physiologists and physicians in China to explain acupuncture analgesia.

The theory suggests that the transmission of pain signals from the body to the spinal cord and the brain is a dynamic process capable of variation, not a fixed, unchanging one. The variation stems from a series of gatelike mechanisms in the pain-signaling system. If a gate can be closed, full analgesia follows because pain signals from injured tissues cannot reach the brain.

The gates can be opened or closed to varying degrees by nerve impulses in the large- and small-diameter fibers in each sensory nerve running from the body's surface to the spine and the brain. Activity in large fibers tends to close gates and lessen the pain, while small-fiber activity tends to open gates and increase pain. Activity in the fibers that descend from the brain stem reticular formation, which coordinates information from the sense organs and various parts of the brain, can also open or close gates. This part of the nervous system receives impulses from all the sensory systems as well as other brain areas. It normally keeps the gates partly closed, but it can close them entirely

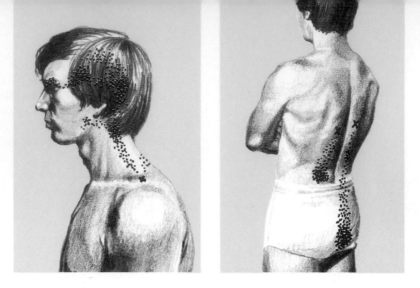

Many trigger points and the general areas of the body they affect have been mapped by scientists. The trigger point on the neck affects a wide area of the head, and the two points on the back affect pain in the lower back and buttocks area.

or open them wide. Fibers from the cortex of the brain – the center of the memory, attention, anxiety, and interpretative functions – also can either open or close gates.

The gate-control theory suggests that acupuncture stimulation might alter pain signals in several ways. For example, gently stimulating the skin and underlying tissues with an electric current usually activates more large fibers than small fibers. This tends to close gates and block the pain signals that result from an injury. This can explain "local" analgesia when the acupuncture needles are inserted near the site of surgery.

The modulating system in the brain stem, which I call the "central biasing mechanism," shows how analgesia may also be produced by stimulating distant sites. Neurons in the brain stem reticular formation are known to receive impulses from widespread regions of the body. When particular points in the reticular formation are electrically stimulated, analgesia is produced in a large part of the body. Stimulation at specific sites of a rat's brain stem may produce complete analgesia in from one-fourth to one-half of the rat's body.

In addition, the fibers that descend from the cortex can block pain signals. In this way, psychological processes such as expectation, suggestion, and anxiety can affect pain. Anxiety and fear, for example, are known to heighten the perception of pain. A given intensity of shock or heat is far more painful when a person is anxious than when he is not. Dogs raised in isolation and protected from normal injuries are not as anxious about pain as nonisolated dogs. The isolated ones frequently fail to respond normally to such painful stimuli as a pinprick or a flaming match.

Lowering the level of anxiety also decreases the level of pain. Relaxation, distraction, strong suggestion, and faith in the physician and his techniques have all been demonstrated to diminish pain. For example, many of the soldiers who were severely wounded during the fighting at the Anzio Beachhead in Italy during World War II denied feeling pain from their wounds. The emotions activated by their relief at no longer having to endure the anxiety of battle apparently reduced their pain. An unusually small number of them—only one out of three—had enough pain to require morphine, while among civilians with similar wounds, four out of five demand morphine to kill the pain. So, the mere suggestion that acupuncture is effective may play some sort of role in the easing of pain.

Although acupuncture could activate all of these mechanisms to abolish pain temporarily or permanently, we have yet to prove that this explains how major surgery can be performed with acupuncture analgesia. I believe that the patient's faith in acupuncture, as a result of long cultural experience, and the explicit suggestion that he will feel no pain, greatly eases anxiety from the outset. In addition, the sensory stimulation from the needles activates brain-stem areas that also tend to close the transmission gates and block the pain signals that are produced by an injury.

Support for the gate-control theory has come from electrical stimulating devices, developed in 1971, that have been used to close the pain gates. These small, battery-driven stimulators, about the size of a pack of cigarettes, stimulate nerve endings when their electrodes are placed over the site of the pain. A low-intensity current activates the large nerve fibers, which prevent pain signals from being transmitted from peripheral nerves to cells in the spinal cord. Stimulators are now being used to treat such ailments as back, arthritic, and phantom-limb pains. Most of them produce a tingling sensation that is followed shortly by a sharp decrease in pain. Low-intensity stimulation may be continued for hours at a time, and the relief it brings often outlasts the period of stimulation by several hours.

We have also used electrical stimulators in my laboratory at McGill University in Montreal in a way that closely resembles acupuncture analgesia. The electrodes are placed over trigger zones associated with the particular pain pattern that is to be relieved, or on the acupuncture points that are believed to be related to the painful area. The trigger zones, or acupuncture points, are then stimulated at a high intensity—usually at a mildly painful level. Stimulation for 15 or 20 minutes often relieves pain for several hours, sometimes for several days. The results of these studies so far are extremely promising and point to exciting new methods of pain control.

When I first began to study the effects of pain nearly two decades ago, my laboratory work with animals was done with the dispassionate curiosity of the experimenter. But after visiting the pain clinic operated by William K. Livingston at the University of Oregon Medical School and seeing human beings suffering terribly from many different types of pain, my whole attitude toward my research changed. I have since directed it toward finding the causes of pain and doing something to alleviate it. I hope that my present work on using electrodes at trigger points will provide a method that physicians can use to control pain selectively, particularly for the chronic forms of pain that incapacitate so many people.

Modeling
Our Minds

By John McCarthy

Scientists are trying to understand the thought processes that we use in solving problems in order to make computer programs with these abilities

Along the driveway leading to Stanford University's Artificial Intelligence Laboratory, a sign reads: Caution Robot Vehicle. Inside the laboratory, a mechanical arm, controlled by a computer and guided by TV-camera eyes, stacks colored blocks or assembles a simple water pump from randomly scattered parts. This is one example of the efforts scientists are making toward creating intelligent machines. At the Stanford laboratory and similar centers around the world, computer scientists, mathematicians, engineers, language experts, and psychologists are delving into the science of artificial intelligence (AI), and how to make computers behave intelligently.

The idea of creating an artificial intelligence is not new. According to a Jewish legend, the rabbi of Prague magically created a monster called the Golem in the 1500s. In 1818, Mary Wollstonecraft Shelley wrote a novel about Dr. Frankenstein using "science" to create an intelligent monster. The idea of a humanlike robot built up from metal parts became common in the 1920s. However, serious efforts toward creating intelligent machines began only after the first electronic computers were designed in the late 1940s. Almost all AI work since then has been based on these definitely nonmagical devices.

Nevertheless, the thought of artificial or machine intelligence arouses a number of fears. Most of these fears center on the idea that evil people might use such machines to conquer the world, or the machines themselves might develop a desire to conquer the world. Some fear that, at the least, human beings might have no motivation to do anything once there were machines smarter than they.

The public spotlight was turned on artificial intelligence after a report by British physicist Sir James Lighthill was published in late

1973, questioning the value of some AI research, particularly its application to other areas of science and technology. However, the science of artificial intelligence has important goals of its own. Progress toward them has been slow and only moderately successful—largely due to the difficulty of understanding human intelligence.

Naturally, there are a number of questions to ask about this young and controversial field. How intelligent are the smartest machines today, and how do these machines work? What have scientists discovered about how to make machines behave intelligently? How soon can something practical come of it? Is it possible for machines to be as smart as, or smarter than, people?

The ultimate scientific, or theoretical, goal of AI research is to understand completely the processes of solving intellectual problems. The ultimate practical goal is to make a computer program having all the intellectual abilities of a human being—and more, if possible.

Neither goal is near at hand, but researchers are making progress in two directions. In AI theory, we are identifying and studying mechanisms of intelligence. In practical areas, we are making programs for increasingly difficult intellectual tasks. The theory and practice come together when we put the intellectual mechanisms that we have identified into a computer program and give the program a certain task to perform. If it does not do the task well, we get clues as to what mechanisms we do not yet understand.

Here are some of the intellectual mechanisms that AI researchers have studied:
- The ability to examine possible actions, their results, and further actions that then become possible. For example, chess players use this ability when they think about the various moves they can make and what might happen if they make them.
- The ability to compare two alternatives and determine which is best. Suppose you want to walk to a town a mile away, and it is raining very hard. You can take a short cut over a bridge, but the bridge may be washed out. By not taking the short cut, you will be out in the rain longer, but you will be sure of getting to the town. You must compare and decide which route to take.
- The ability to solve a large problem by recognizing that it is made up of smaller problems that can be solved separately. If you want to travel to Paris, you must recognize that this involves saving money for the trip and getting plane and hotel reservations.
- The ability to recognize patterns. Successful action often depends on recognizing that a piece of information fits into a particular pattern. Pattern recognition is well developed in natural language studies. Grammatical constructions are used over and over again. For example, the pattern "as...as" is used to compare things: "as much as," "as little as," "as few as."

Chess players recognize patterns on the chessboard. For example, looking at a queen under attack by a bishop, a player might recognize

The author:
John McCarthy is professor of computer science and director of the Artificial Intelligence Laboratory at Stanford University.

that by moving certain other pieces he could not only protect his queen, but could capture his opponent's in a future move.

In studying these intellectual mechanisms, AI researchers experiment with programs that play such games as tick-tack-toe, checkers, or chess. A program that plays good chess needs intellectual mechanisms that are also used in other thinking activities. However, this program can do nothing but play chess. So it does not live up to our idea that a truly intelligent program would not have chess built in, but would learn it the same way a human being does. A program with general intelligence could solve many different problems.

Such a program, which does not exist as yet, would have to be general in what it knows and in its ability to use its knowledge to solve problems. It would have to know about events happening in time. We would have to give it the idea of future. If you told it, "I want to have this egg for breakfast in half an hour," it would understand all the circumstances affecting that statement.

For example, it would have to know how people affect events. (If someone knocks the egg onto the floor, the program would know that the egg is not available for breakfast.) It would be able to compare and decide whether it likes one situation better than another. (Should you wipe up the egg or leave it on the floor?)

It would also have to know about material objects, their motions, their positions in space, and that they are made up of smaller objects and can be destroyed. (It would know that eggs are made up of shells, yolks, whites, and are ground to pieces by garbage disposals.)

It would have to understand itself as a material object, how it is affected by its own actions and other events, and how its physical state affects its possibilities for action. So if the program with general intelligence is hooked up to a single mechanical arm, it would know it cannot flip pancakes and pour milk at the same time.

It must know how knowledge can be obtained—by observation, by asking people, and by reading. It would know, for example, that telephone numbers can be obtained from information operators.

These are only samples of what a general intelligence must know. No one has been able to make a complete list because no one knows for certain what it must contain. But, in this puzzlement, AI researchers are not alone. Philosophers have been concerned with the general structure of the world and the nature of knowledge for more than 2,000 years. Unfortunately, they have not come up with anything concrete enough to form the basis of a computer program. Today, we have some hope that AI research can help with the philosophical problems. Instead of worrying about knowledge in general, we can try to put just enough knowledge about knowledge into a computer program so that it can test the various philosophies.

But how do you represent knowledge in the memory of the computer? There are two schools of thought on this. One group of researchers represents knowledge by procedures that tell what will hap-

"A program with general intelligence . . . would have to be general in what it knows and in its ability to use its knowledge to solve problems."

73

pen when certain actions are performed. They would write a program for the behavior of an egg when dropped. It would begin with the egg falling and end with the egg breaking. The other group represents knowledge by declarative sentences. Their program would be a simple expression of fact, "Eggs break when dropped." Procedural programs can do more complex tasks, but simple facts can be easily transferred from one program to another. However, most researchers now recognize a need to find a way of combining the two methods, since there is no one true way of representing knowledge.

Naturally, the study of such a broad field as intelligence moves across the boundaries of other sciences. Psychologists are interested in the intellectual functions of the human and animal brain. What they discover by experimenting with living subjects, we can try to program on a computer. At the same time, computer scientists can observe themselves and make intelligent programs based on how they think they solve problems.

In addition to philosophy and psychology, artificial intelligence has much in common with mathematics and linguistics. Computer "languages" based on mathematical logic are used to express facts about the world in some intelligent programs. These facts are translated into mathematical symbols that the machine can easily recognize, usually combinations of 1 and 0. Both AI researchers and those who study languages are concerned with what sentences mean. Some AI scientists are developing programs that can understand and respond in English rather than computer language.

But AI researchers do not have to know anything about electronics. Whether a computer is made of vacuum tubes, or transistors, or integrated circuits does not influence what kind of tasks it can do. So AI researchers have only to think about the procedure they want the machine to carry out and how to express it as a computer program.

In carrying out AI experiments, researchers see how well they can program a computer to perform a task, and then they study the intellectual mechanisms involved. Making the computer play chess has been a popular task. To make a chess program, researchers list the location of each chess piece in the memory of the computer. Then they list all the moves that can be made from any position on the board.

With just this data, and a way to recognize checkmate, a researcher could write a simple program that would always determine the best move. It would test all sequences of moves that the two players could make during the course of the game. The only trouble with this program is that it would never be completed in the programmer's lifetime because there are so many possible moves. In fact, it would take billions of years. Therefore, computer scientists have had to develop some short cuts, called heuristics, for avoiding having to search through such an explosion of possibilities.

Picture all the possible moves in a chess game as levels of branches on a tree. As each player moves to a new position, we reach another level of possibilities, or branches, for the next move. This continues through levels and levels of branches until the final move of the game.

A programmer can avoid dealing with these endless branches of possibilities by making the program look at only a small part of the so-called move tree. He prevents the program from looking too far ahead. It must stop and evaluate the situation with some goal in sight. Instead of looking all the way to the end of the game, it might only look three moves ahead. For example, to protect a king or queen, the computer will evaluate these limited possibilities for a move that will accomplish this goal and allow for future moves. Once it finds a suitable move within that limitation, the program knows that there is no need for it to evaluate further.

We have learned to program these heuristics, which are certainly used by humans, fairly well. But there are intellectual mechanisms that we have not been able to incorporate into the programs. For example, we have yet to find a good way of making programs that can recognize problems made up of smaller problems. My guess is that the next big improvement in chess programs will be a good scheme for recognizing that the parts of a position indicate general patterns. Recognizing patterns on the chessboard would give the program the ability to plan a strategy.

A I researchers have been criticized for studying chess. "Why don't you work on important problems requiring intelligence—government policy, for instance?" we have been asked. This is like asking a geneticist why he studies fruit flies when elephants are more important. You cannot keep a thousand elephants in a bottle on the laboratory shelf, and you can't get a new generation of offspring in a few days. With chess, it is particularly easy to compare the performance of our programs with the performance of human beings.

Many programs have been written to prove mathematical theorems. In the early 1960s, programs probed some theorems in high school plane geometry. But the programs could not deal with circles. It is very difficult for us to make programs that can recognize the subtleties of circles and curves. And it is still impractical to try proving important mathematical theorems with computer programs.

Some AI researchers have concentrated on natural languages. They have made programs that can translate from one language into another; answer questions in English; respond to psychiatrists as a paranoid would; and move blocks around when commanded to do so.

The first translation programs in the 1950s operated purely on the basis of sentence structure. Although the program knew nothing about the meaning of the sentence, this worked often enough in the beginning to be encouraging. But it eventually became clear that good translation requires some measure of understanding. There is a famous story about this problem. When "The spirit is willing, but the flesh is weak" was translated into Russian and then back to English, it supposedly came out, "The vodka is strong, but the meat is rotten."

"Modifying a program can be compared to educating human beings by brain surgery, if that were possible — reconnecting nerve cells in new arrangements."

Computer programs take things quite literally. When we hear or speak a sentence, we hardly give it a second thought. We can decipher the meaning of a sentence because we know the rules of grammar and can draw on our considerable general knowledge. But a computer program only knows what the programmer specifically tells it. Trying to make a language program leads to basic questions about how language works, how it relates to physical objects, and what intellectual processes people go through when they talk or listen. One great stumbling block in making natural-language programs is getting the program to understand pronouns, such as one and them.

In tackling this natural-language problem, AI researchers have taken very simple situations and tried to bring all the elements of language and knowledge together to make programs understand the meaning of sentences. The BLOCKS program of computer scientist Terry Winograd, developed at the Massachusetts Institute of Technology in 1970, showed the advantages of such limited situations. Winograd programmed into the computer's "imagination" a table covered with blocks of various shapes and colors and an imaginary artificial arm that could move them around. The program obeys commands and answers questions. Here is a typical conversation:

Operator: "Will you please stack up both of the red blocks and either a green cube or a pyramid?"

Computer: "OK."

Operator: "Which cube is sitting on the table?"

Computer: "The large green one, which supports the red pyramid."

Operator: "Is there a large block behind a pyramid?"

Computer: "Yes, three of them—a large red one, a large green cube, and the blue one."

To obey the command and answer the questions, the program has to have and use information about blocks in general—sizes, colors, shapes—and about the particular arrangement of the blocks on the table. This kind of information is necessary in order for the program to connect the meaning of pronouns with nouns.

Besides these purely intellectual tasks, AI researchers have tried to duplicate such human activities and abilities as seeing, speaking, assembling parts to form objects, and driving a vehicle around obstacles. Engineers and computer scientists have designed computer-operated mechanical arms that can perform simple manual tasks, such as the Stanford arm that can assemble a water pump. For vision and speech work, they hook up television cameras and microphones to computers.

Some of the most important research in this area is on vision. The first research on vision in the early 1960s involved classifying pictures into categories. For example, researchers programmed a computer to identify pictures of letters and know that they belonged to the alphabet category. They trained the computer to make these classifications by showing sample pictures to a television camera and then telling the program to which category each picture belonged.

However, when vision is needed to help a mechanical arm pick up a block, the program must do more than merely decide whether a block is present. The vision program must be able to find a block among other objects and determine its exact position so that the program for the arm can decide where to reach and how to pick up the block. Present programs work fairly well for objects with flat surfaces, but we have barely started to work on visual arrangements that contain curved and irregularly shaped objects.

A major task now facing AI researchers is to make computers learn by experience. This step is needed before we can have truly intelligent machines. But before computer programs can learn, that is, can modify themselves, AI researchers have to develop better methods for modifying programs. It is usually much more difficult to modify a present-day computer program than to teach a person a new trick. We can tell a chess player about a new kind of move without knowing much about the player except that he or she knows English and something about chess. But to insert a new chess tactic into a program requires detailed understanding about the program and probably means it will be changed in several places. Modifying a program can be compared to educating human beings by brain surgery, if that were possible—reconnecting nerve cells in new arrangements.

Some research in AI has already been applied in other fields, and soon we expect more applications, such as automatically controlled vehicles and very sophisticated automatic assembling machines. We can hope for a computer-driven car that will take itself wherever it is ordered to go. Artificial intelligence can also be used in developing computer-flown airplanes.

The social consequences of these applications will be similar to other advances in technology, which have largely benefited human beings. But reaching the ultimate goal of artificial intelligence, developing programs as smart as people, would be something quite different.

If we can make machines as intelligent as people, we can make them much smarter just by increasing their speed and memory size. But humans have complicated emotions and motivations. We change our goals often, and we have a sense of our own rights and self-esteem. It would not seem advantageous to put artificial intelligence programs in humanlike bodies and try to give them human motivations. It would seem better to let these AI programs inhabit computers and answer our questions as best they can.

For example, we might ask a very intelligent program what would be the consequences of various ways in which we might use it. Thus we will know the consequences before the computer takes action. And so the science-fiction tragedy of the supersmart machine causing widespread social havoc through unforeseen complications is unlikely.

But all this is very much like a discussion of how to make rabbit stew without knowing how to catch rabbits. We must learn a lot more about artificial intelligence before we face decisions about its use.

The Quandary Over Quarks

By Robert H. March

With distinctive style, each of three theoretical physicists gives reasons why predicted fundamental units of the universe continue to elude detection

The argument began more than 2,400 years ago in the busy seaport towns of ancient Greece. The topic was the obvious starting point for any science of the physical world–"What are things made of?" Anaxagoras, a Greek philosopher, argued that all matter must be infinitely divisible, while Democritus, the leading spokesman for one of several rival schools, viewed matter as arising from combinations of indestructible building blocks that he called atoms. Relying solely on their unaided senses, these men had some remarkable insights that are still relevant to 20th-century physics.

Today, scientists probing the structure of matter with the help of powerful particle accelerators, popularly known as atom smashers, are sharply divided over fundamental questions very similar to those that tantalized the Greeks. Now, as then, rival camps have sprung up in a many-sided debate. Much of the controversy centers on three leading contenders, theoretical physicists Richard Feynman and Murray Gell-

John huehnergarth

Mann of the California Institute of Technology (Caltech), and Geoffrey Chew of the University of California, Berkeley.

Physicists once hoped that experimental data from particle accelerators—data that reveals a trillion times more detail than can be seen by the naked eye—would quickly settle all questions. In these experiments, particles such as protons or electrons that make up atoms are boosted to nearly the speed of light, then smashed into other particles going the opposite way or into chunks of ordinary matter such as iron. The collisions produce showers of short-lived particles. These particles travel a short distance during the millionth to a billionth of a billionth of a second that they exist, then change into still other particles.

Collision experiments such as these are the lifeblood of experimental work. Building ever larger and more powerful accelerators to boost the particles to yet faster speeds or designing increasingly sensitive detectors, such as bubble chambers in which the fleeting particles leave visible tracks, challenges the ingenuity of experimental physicists. But a triumph for the experimenter frequently means a headache for the theorist. With each increase in particle speed, the collision debris becomes more abundant. Over 200 fleeting particles had been produced by 1974, all with different combinations of mass, electric charge, and other physical properties.

In grappling with these complex experimental results, Feynman, Gell-Mann, and Chew use mathematics that was unknown to the ancient Greeks. But formulas alone rarely point the way to a deeper understanding of nature. The minds that invent the theories must be guided by a personal vision of the nature of things, and every good theorist has a unique personal style. As with other creative artists, they hold passionately to their ideas because they believe them to be beautiful. To understand this, we must first look closely at the ideas of Democritus and Anaxagoras, then briefly trace the evolution of these ideas down through the centuries.

Democritus believed that anything really important ought to be simple. Since any child can see that we live in what appears to be a very complicated world, simplicity must rest beyond what meets the eye. He concluded that the motions and combinations of large numbers of indestructible, indivisible particles of a few simple geometric shapes could combine to produce all of the world's complexities.

Anaxagoras believed that some sort of atoms might exist, but he warned that the search for them would be a walk on an endless treadmill. He argued that atoms could be subdivided indefinitely, producing an endless succession of "seeds within seeds." Each part would prove as complex as the whole.

At first, the search for fundamental particles ran close to the script of Democritus. In 1808, the English chemist John Dalton showed that the fixed, unalterable recipes for forming chemical compounds could be explained by assuming that the known elements were made of atoms. By weighing the elements that combine to form compounds, he

The author:
Robert H. March is a professor of physics at the University of Wisconsin. He contributes the Science File article, Physics, Elementary Particles.

deduced the relative weights of the atoms of many chemical elements. Following the arrangement of the elements into an orderly periodic table by Russian chemist Dmitri Mendeleev in 1859, Democritus' dream seemed to have been realized.

But the concept of atoms as the fundamental building blocks of nature was shattered by the end of the century. A lightweight subunit of the atom, the electron, was found in 1897 by the British physicist Joseph J. Thompson. By the early 1930s, the model of an atom as a dense nucleus of protons and neutrons orbited by distant electrons was well understood. These atomic constituents briefly reigned as the new ultimate particles. But even in the 1930s, other particles were detected in cosmic radiation, and the accelerators of the 1950s and 1960s have produced hundreds more. Which of these, if any, are fundamental?

Fans of Sherlock Holmes have some idea how the mind of Murray Gell-Mann answers this question. Out of a confusing welter of clues, pick a few seemingly unrelated or contradictory facts and make a wild guess. Of course, you must guess right, and Gell-Mann has been right with uncanny regularity for more than 20 years.

Though at 44 his hair is peppered with gray, Gell-Mann has changed little from the days when he earned a Ph.D. degree from the Massachusetts Institute of Technology at the remarkable age of 21. Start a conversation on any topic, from modern literature to French wines or the psychology of gorillas, and Gell-Mann will probably dominate by drawing on a combination of encyclopedic knowledge and brash confidence that can simultaneously delight and infuriate his

Colleagues struggle to match the pace set by Murray Gell-Mann, whether on a mountain trail or the frontiers of theoretical physics.

listeners. A more modest man could hardly have proposed some of the ideas he has given to physics. He drives his fireplug body as hard as his mind, as anyone who has tried to keep up with him on a mountain trail can testify. One admirer summarizes the Gell-Mann style thus: "He has the guts of a burglar and a mind like a steel trap."

Gell-Mann first gained acclaim by guessing right about the puzzling behavior of 10 new particles discovered between 1947 and 1955. They all were found to live a million million times longer than predicted by the best theory known at the time. Gell-Mann suggested that all particles carry a whole-number amount of some mysterious property, just as they carry some multiple of the basic electric charge unit. They might carry +1 of these mysterious units, −2 units, or 0 units, for example, but each particle would always appear with its characteristic amount.

With the refreshing irreverence toward scientific terminology that marks his style, Gell-Mann called his mysterious property strangeness. But strangeness was much more than a way of joking about these puzzling particles. This powerful concept allowed physicists to predict which particles could be produced in particle-accelerator experiments, and which other particles these debris particles could change into. Gell-Mann's theory said that the puzzling, long-lived particles are changed into other particles by processes which change the total amount of strangeness. It was an audacious shot in the dark, especially since strangeness cannot be measured directly as can electric charge. But the guess solved the mystery of the 10 new particles.

By 1961, the list of known particles had grown to about 30, and Gell-Mann took the lead in proposing a classification scheme similar to the periodic table of the elements. In this system, dubbed the Eightfold Way, particles with similar properties are grouped in families whose members are close to one another in mass but differ in other properties such as electric charge and strangeness. The existence of undiscovered families, and the properties of missing members of established ones, were then predicted and soon found by experimentalists. Characteristically, Gell-Mann conceived the Eightfold Way—for which he won a Nobel prize in 1969—when only about one-tenth of the presently known particles had been discovered. By comparison, Mendeleev had more than 50 of the 92 elements to go on when he authored the chemists' periodic table.

By the mid-1960s, Gell-Mann had left the completion of this classification scheme to others and was again breaking new ground. Searching for the simplest combination of subparticles that could account for the existence of the known families, he found that he could generate them all by combining only three new building blocks. He called them quarks, a name he borrowed from the Irish writer James Joyce. But these new particles would have to be radically different from any object that had ever been detected. Gell-Mann's quarks would possess an electric charge of $-\frac{1}{3}$ or $+\frac{2}{3}$ of the charge carried by the proton.

Because experimentalists for decades had been measuring charged objects and finding only positive or negative multiples of the proton's charge, never fractions of it, a less bold theorist might never have proposed the idea.

But Gell-Mann said quarks and their antiparticles, antiquarks, combine in only two ways. Both ways produce only whole-charge particles. In the first way, quarks combine with each other in groups of three. The particles produced in this way are known as baryons, the proton being the lightest baryon. There are 10 such possible combinations, so for baryons, the basic family is a decet. A second type of baryon family has eight members. In the second way, quarks combine with antiquarks, which have opposite charge and strangeness. These

The Elementary-Particle Building Blocks

Gell-Mann's quarks explain the elementary-particle families in his Eightfold Way classification system. They combine by threes to form a 10-member family, the baryon decet. Their relative motions give rise to decets at higher energies, or mass. They also form 8-member baryon families. Researchers have found missing family members predicted by the system, but not a quark, despite its telltale fractional electric charge.

Gell-Mann's Three Quarks

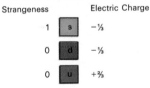

Strangeness		Electric Charge
1	s	$-\frac{1}{3}$
0	d	$-\frac{1}{3}$
0	u	$+\frac{2}{3}$

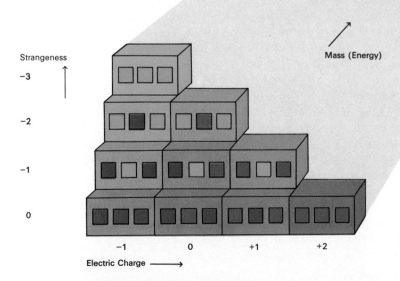

quark-antiquark combinations are called mesons, and occur in families with nine members, called nonets. The lightest meson, the pi-meson, has about one-seventh the mass of a proton.

Gell-Mann's suggestion set off a wild stampede by experimenters to be the first to find a quark. Their search, which continues to this day, is one of the most bizarre chapters in the history of physics. Some studied photographs of cosmic rays passing through cloud chambers, looking for faint tracks that would identify particles with a less-than-normal electric charge. Others put accelerator beams through magnetic obstacle courses that only a fractionally charged particle could survive. Still others searched for quarks that had attached themselves to ordinary atoms, giving these atoms surplus fractional electric charge. One such research group even ground up thousands of oysters looking for quarks, because these delectable creatures feed by filtering large quantities of seawater and might concentrate quark-bearing atoms. But no matter how unusual or refined the experiments, they have all failed to find quarks.

Almost from the outset, Gell-Mann surprised everyone by suggesting that these searches might well be in vain. Some experimenters suspected that he was merely hedging his bets to save his theory in case the quarks failed to materialize. But Gell-Mann would really be happier if no quark were ever found. He no longer views quarks as tiny bits of matter which can exist by themselves. Instead, he gives quarks the quality of becoming, rather than being; they represent processes by which the fundamental forces of nature create, destroy, and transform baryons and mesons.

Once again, he has made a bold leap. This personal view of quarks promises to unite the two distinct views of the physical world that physicists have accepted for over 100 years—particles of matter and fields of force such as gravity and magnetism. Ever since Albert Einstein discovered the equivalence of energy and mass, expressed in the formula $E=mc^2$, physicists have dreamed that someday matter might be shown to be concentrations of energy created by the basic forces. Every attempt to realize this dream has run into mathematical problems, and Gell-Mann's quark theory is no exception. For almost the first time in his life, he has tackled a problem he cannot solve quickly and completely, and is forced to dig in for a long battle.

If Murray Gell-Mann is the brash "boy wonder" of physics, 56-year-old Richard Feynman is its irrepressible merry prankster who insists that good physics must also be good entertainment. He has been known to dismiss a complicated rival theory on the grounds that "if it turns out to be right, physics just ain't as much fun." He has a love for practical jokes. During World War II, for example, he demonstrated his lock-picking skills on a safe used for top-secret documents at the Los Alamos, N. Mex., atomic bomb laboratory.

Feynman's fun-loving nature and Cary-Grant good looks have brought him a large measure of popularity, even among the Hollywood set. At cocktail parties he would play bongo drums or, with a few simple drawings, explain complicated physical theories to other guests. He quickly gained legendary status as the playboy of modern physics by alternating sieges of intense work with bouts of high living.

Today Feynman no longer lives the life of a playboy, but he is still as fun-loving as ever. His idea of fun in physics is any game that is played by simple rules, so that the imagination has free rein. Simplicity has been the distinguishing mark of his contributions to physics. He views nature as a sort of cosmic chess game, with the scientists as observers trying to figure out the rules. Given enough time and ingenuity, they learn to identify the playing board, the pieces, and the moves, and they develop a rulebook like the one used by nature. Occasionally, something unexpected happens, like the chess move called castling, but that makes science all the more fun.

Feynman's first major work, for which he won a Nobel prize in 1965, is simple enough to be fun, but leads to some peculiar mathematical problems. A theory of electrical forces on the subatomic scale, it treats electrons as charged points having no size whatsoever. It would take an infinite amount of energy to concentrate the electron's charge at such a point. According to Einstein's famous energy-mass formula, the electron would then have an infinite mass, rendering it incapable of motion. To get around this problem, Feynman invented a rule called renormalization that enables the theorist to ignore these infinities. Whenever they appear in a calculation, the infinite terms are deleted and the experimentally observed values for the electron charge and mass are substituted. Modified in this way, the theory works in every detail.

Feynman is famous for lecturing on abstract topics without recourse to elaborate mathematical equations. A few simple pictures on the chalkboard and dramatic hand gestures usually suffice. The way he explained his Nobel prizewinning work illustrates this knack. He published his results in 1948 in a physics journal which, like most scientific journals, is filled with papers as difficult to decipher as a code message. Feynman's paper was a notable exception. It began by explaining the theory through simple analogies, and ended with what amounts to a do-it-yourself manual for the theoretical physicist. His simple, pictorial views of subatomic processes, called Feynman diagrams, give exact prescriptions for how the physicist should do his calculations, and are used widely today to describe interactions of elementary particles.

Given his love for simple theories, Feynman was bound to take quarks as tiny particles quite literally. It would be great fun if quarks, like electrons, were so small that their size was unimportant to the theory. To test this, Feynman, in 1968, suggested a way of interpreting violent collisions between electrons and protons, such as researchers are now studying at Stanford's linear electron accelerator (SLAC). Given sufficient speed, electrons can overcome the forces that hold the quarks together and rebound from one quark at a time. Analysis of the

Do-It-Yourself Physics
Feynman diagrams, such as these representing interactions between two electrons, top, and an electron and a positron, are also exact prescriptions that tell a theorist how to write correct mathematical formulas for the interactions.

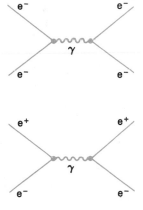

Richard Feynman uses his simple diagrams and a few dramatic hand gestures to explain scientific theories, whether to laymen or to his colleagues. He believes that physical theories must be simple in order to be correct.

rebounding electrons would then reveal not only the existence, but also the nature of quarks. In Feynman's words, "It is like studying a swarm of bees by radar." Stanford theorist James Bjorken had previously discovered a way of testing the data to see whether the quarks are truly small, and for nearly five years the Feynman-Bjorken theory successfully explained experiments run at SLAC.

But their theory has a serious loose end. If the forces binding quarks to one another can be overcome so easily, why is it that 10 years of exhaustive searching has not turned up a free quark? To Feynman, this is a delightful puzzle that merely adds to the fun of physics. It is a clear sign that the scientists' rulebook is not yet complete. And the more puzzling the situation, according to Feynman, the more important the message. Perhaps there is in the cosmic chess game a yet undiscovered rule that makes quarks inseparable.

But late in 1973 the game stopped being so amusing. The Feynman-Bjorken predictions failed disastrously when applied to SLAC studies of head-on collisions between electrons and their antiparticles called positrons. To make matters worse, scientists at the Fermi National Accelerator Laboratory in Batavia, Ill., observed what seemed to be similar effects. The probes there are particles called high-energy muons, which are similar to SLAC's electrons, but capable of revealing finer detail in the proton. If these results hold true, Feynman's quarks may be as large as $1/100$ the size of the proton itself. This is far too large for a theory as simple as he would like.

The news threw Feynman into a state of depression that he described as "almost suicidal." However, it would be premature to count him out of the game. In 1957, a theory he had co-authored with Gell-Mann was in glaring contradiction with several experiments. He declared that the theory was "too pretty not to be true" and took off for Brazil to have a roaring good time "while the experimenters came to their senses." By the time he returned, tanned and rested, refinement of the experiments had vindicated his theory. So we have probably not heard the last from Dick Feynman.

The experiments that spoiled Feynman's game came as no surprise to Geoffrey Chew, though he is far too polite to say "I told you so." Chew's personality, as well as his view of nature, contrasts sharply with the flamboyance of Feynman and Gell-Mann. Although tall and ruggedly athletic, he tends to be soft-spoken and introspective almost to the point of shyness. In many respects, he bears the mark of a reluctant hero who never expected to get very far in the world.

Geoffrey Chew indoctrinates younger theoretical physicists in his theory of elementary-particle democracy. He sees no reason to treat some particles as more basic than others.

He was a star on the baseball team at George Washington University in Washington, D.C., in the early 1940s. But Chew, now 50, never considered a baseball career because he doubted that he was good enough to make the major leagues. If this appraisal of his athletic prowess was as far off the mark as his youthful estimate of his scientific potential, he might well have become a superstar. He started out majoring in chemistry because it seemed to be a sound way for a man of modest ability to earn a steady income. Physics seemed far too difficult, a risky meal ticket. But he took a modern physics course from the late nuclear physicist George Gamow, renowned as a spellbinding lecturer and author, who persuaded him to switch majors.

Chew's scientific concepts have been formed, not through sudden flashes of inspiration, but through a gradual process of transformation. Throughout the 1950s, he gradually became convinced that the slow progress in understanding the ever growing numbers of particles was caused by a basic flaw in the existing ideas. The flaw lay in treating some particles as elementary, and others as composites of the elementary ones, when there was no basis in theory or experiment for making any such distinction. While most theorists felt that the reason for this would be clear once the truly elementary particles were found, Chew rebelled against this approach.

In search of a theory that satisfied his ideas of particle democracy, Chew, in 1961, settled on a mathematical tool called the scattering matrix (S-matrix). Other theorists had used this device, regarding it as merely a convenient, temporary way of cataloging the results of collision experiments until a more basic theory could explain them. Though Chew had borrowed an old idea, he took it much further than its authors ever intended.

The S-matrix can be thought of as a table similar to the intercity mileage tables found on road maps. However, instead of city names, symbols for groups of elementary particles head each horizontal row and vertical column of the S-matrix. Row headings are combinations of particles that come together in collision; column headings are all the different combinations of debris particles that might be produced.

Just as entries in the mileage table link two cities by giving the mileage between them, S-matrix entries give the chance that colliding particles (rows) produce the debris particles (columns). For example, one reads across the row labeled $p + p$ (proton plus proton) to see how often different possible particle combinations are produced when two protons collide over and over again. On the diagonal of the table, where the $p + p$ row and $p + p$ column meet, the entry shows the odds that the protons will simply rebound unchanged, say 1 chance in 5. The next column, marked $p + p + \pi°$; shows the chance that some of the protons' collision energy is converted to mass in the form of a pi-zero meson. Here the chance might be 1 in 10. Other entries give the chances of other possible outcomes. The possibilities are infinite.

Actually, entries in the S-matrix are formulas, not numbers, be-

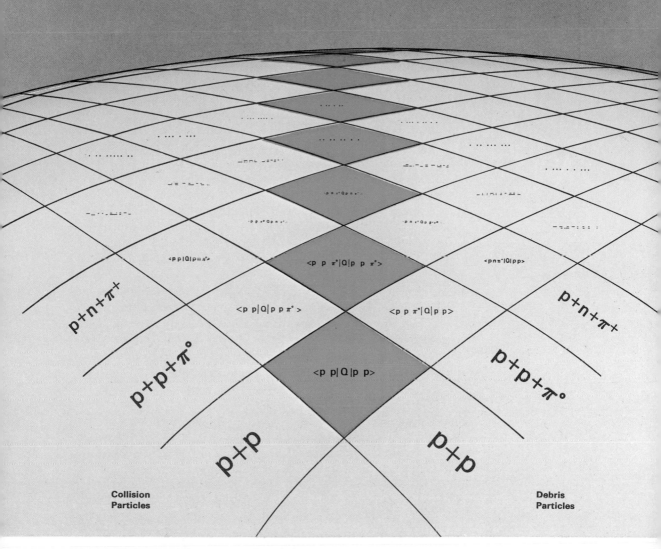

p+n+π+

p+p+π°

p+p

<p p|Q|p n π°>

<p p|Q|p p π°>

<p p π°|Q|p p π°>

<p p|Q|p p π°>

<p p π°|Q|p p>

<p p|Q|p p>

<pnπ°|Q|pp>

p+n+π+

p+p+π°

p+p

Collision Particles

Debris Particles

Equal Rights for Elementary Particles

The S-matrix mathematically expresses Chew's notion that no elementary particles are fundamental. It can be viewed as an infinitely large table whose entries link collision and debris particles formed in particle accelerator experiments. Its entries are tied together in a tight web of physical and mathematical interdependence, so that a change in any entry requires that many other S-matrix entries must also be changed.

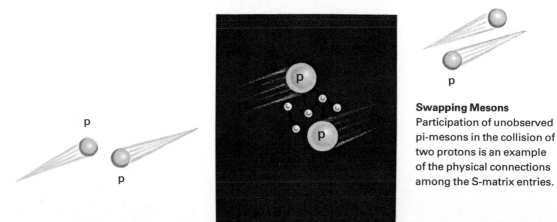

p

p

p

p

p

p

Swapping Mesons

Participation of unobserved pi-mesons in the collision of two protons is an example of the physical connections among the S-matrix entries.

cause the odds change with changes in the energies of the colliding particles. These formulas were developed by Chew and others, notably his Berkeley co-worker Stanley Mandelstam and Tulio Regge, an Italian theoretical physicist. To fill in the table, a physicist selects formulas that agree with measurements made in collision experiments. The formulas he selects must also meet certain mathematical rules of the S-matrix that tie its entries to one another, in much the same way that entries in a mileage table between successive cities along a common route must add up to the distance between the cities at each end.

A physical link between entries in the S-matrix is that particles can influence reactions in which they are not actually observed by briefly appearing during the moment of collision. For example, when two protons collide, a meson can be created by one and absorbed by the other. A large number of individual mesons, or combinations of them, may appear, and they can interact with one another while in transit between protons. Consequently, the properties of every meson, or combination of mesons, can affect the simple rebound of one proton off another. Protons may play a similar role when mesons collide, so the table is tied together in a tight web of mutual dependence. Each new measurement changes one entry, which in turn affects many other entries in the table, like ripples spreading on a pond.

Interdependence is the core of Chew's thinking. The simple fact that all particles are related should be enough to determine everything. If we study hard enough, Chew maintains, we will find that the masses and electric charges of all particles, and the strengths of the forces between them, are exactly what they are because no other arrangement would be logically and mathematically self-consistent. This theory is known as the bootstrap, because it suggests that physics can pull itself up by its bootstraps. Assume nothing, prove everything.

Since 1961, Chew has argued for the bootstrap theory with increasing boldness, and indoctrinated dozens of graduate and postdoctoral students at Berkeley in the mathematics and philosophy of S-matrix theory. He rejects Feynman's renormalization, even though it works, because it uses such numbers as the measured charge and mass of the electron without explaining them. A proper theory, in his view, needs no such add-ons.

To see what Chew means by a self-consistent S-matrix, imagine that a physicist has written down what he believes to be the correct version. To test it, he changes one of the entries by a small amount. Ripples of change spread through the table and eventually return, requiring him to change the entry he started from again. The changed table is not self-consistent. If the returning ripples do not require a change, then that entry is correct. The process must be repeated for many entries. Because there are so many particles, it will be years, possibly decades, before all the possible collisions can be studied.

The effort to build up the S-matrix has spawned a new breed of particle physicists, teams of experiment-minded theorists and theory-minded experimenters called phenomenologists. As collision-experiment results flow into their laboratories from accelerators around the world, the phenomenologists put the data on computer tapes and run elaborate programs to test the refined S-matrix. As the S-matrix grows more accurate, it also becomes larger and more complex, which is why Feynman finds this approach unattractive.

Though hundreds of physicists, many of whom are former students of Chew, use the techniques he developed, not all of them share his philosophical viewpoint. Many suspect that his approach may be unscientific, possibly even antiscientific. Most scientists prefer theories that continually face crucial experimental tests, the failure of any one being enough to prove a theory wrong. But it is hard to see how the bootstrap theory could meet such a moment of truth. Each new fact is simply swallowed up by the S-matrix, contributing its part to the total picture. The bootstrap theory can only prevail through slow refinement, and the gradual disillusionment of physicists with the failure to explain things by other means.

Chew accepts this criticism willingly. He claims that he wants to go beyond science, at least as it is presently defined. When asked to be more specific about what this means, he replies almost mystically: "I have a pretty clear gut feeling for where we ought to be going, but if I try to translate the feeling into words, my training as a scientist makes it come out twisted and distorted."

But in general terms, it is not hard to see where Chew is headed. Science is based on the faith that nature makes sense. Modern science, since the time of Galileo, has made sense of nature one piece at a time. For four centuries, this method has been a spectacular success. Chew believes that science by pieces has finally exhausted its potential. It has come square up against a fundamental truth—ultimately, nature makes sense only when taken as a whole. Viewed in this way, we should not expect nature to be simple. The most we can hope for is that its complexity makes sense in terms of a few simple ideas.

Science has known such confrontation before, and learned that the end result need not be a triumph for one theory over the others. Indeed, Gell-Mann believes that his theory and Chew's may be saying the same thing in different words, though Chew strongly disagrees. In any case, their styles have converged somewhat as each has matured. Chew has developed the nerve to paint in bolder strokes, while Gell-Mann has acquired the patience to stick with a theory that promises no quick payoff. Anaxagoras would probably applaud their efforts. Feynman has clung stubbornly to his insistence on simplicity, and Democritus would find in him a kindred spirit.

Perhaps the quandary over quarks will be solved in our time. Modern science has laid to rest some questions raised by the ancient Greeks, left others open, and shown still others to be irrelevant. But this clash of ideas—and of the minds and hearts that give them birth—makes science a supreme creative adventure of the human spirit.

Science
On the Ice

By Peter Gwynne

Researchers from 12 nations have turned Antarctica's ice-covered wasteland into a laboratory for many important studies

Bacteria frozen in the ice of Antarctica for at least 10,000 years were brought to life recently by a United States research team headed by Roy E. Cameron of the Jet Propulsion Laboratory. They reported in April, 1974, that they had revived the microscopic organisms by placing them in nutrient fluids in a laboratory on the subzero continent. This is just one of many scientific accomplishments coming from Antarctica, once the earth's most unexplored frontier.

Less than two decades after U.S. Admiral George Dufek landed at the South Pole to inaugurate the International Geophysical Year (1957-1958), the continent has become a giant laboratory providing scientists with data about the overall functioning of planet earth. About 3,000 scientists and support personnel from a dozen nations are scattered across the continent at a score of bases. They are engaged in a variety of tasks ranging from meteorological observations to a census of seals.

Under terms of the Antarctic Treaty of 1961, the continent is to be used "for peaceful purposes only." Scientific investigation is encouraged, and scientists move freely among the expeditions and bases. On Dec. 14, 1973, for example, a flight

from the U.S. McMurdo Station took American scientists to Russia's Vostok Station. They were greeted with "Merry Christmas" signs and vodka toasts. When the plane returned to McMurdo later that day, it carried four Russian scientists who spent two weeks at U.S. research sites. One American stayed behind for a year of study.

Most of the scientists work on Antarctica only during the summer, a time of continuous daylight. But even in the dark Antarctic winter, about a hundred researchers stay at their posts on the frigid continent, with radios their only link to the rest of the world.

The Antarctic land mass, which lies almost entirely within the Antarctic Circle, covers a larger area than the United States and Mexico combined. The towering Antarctic Mountains, with peaks as high as 15,000 feet (4,600 meters), divide the continent into two distinct parts, East and West Antarctica. It is a land of scenic wonders, of enormous glaciers and delicately colored ice. It is also a stormy land where blizzards explode with frightening fury. Not a single common plant or animal lives on the icy continent, and even the native life forms that have adapted to the conditions there—such as penguins, seals, and skua gulls—rely on the seas that surround Antarctica for their sustenance. Indeed, apart from an occasional minor insect, only one living creature has adapted to life in the frigid, gale-wracked interior of the Antarctic continent—man.

Much of the scientific interest in Antarctica focuses on two different south poles. The geographic south pole is the point at which the earth's axis of rotation cuts through the surface of the Southern Hemisphere. Its position with respect to the land mass of Antarctica is permanently fixed, but because the icecap that covers the continent is gradually sliding north across those rocks, in the general direction of the Azores, the position of the pole on the ice is gradually changing. As a result, a barber's pole erected outside the U.S. Amundsen-Scott station in 1957 to mark the position of the geographic south pole at that time is now slightly more than a mile from the true location. A new U.S. station to replace the original one is being built about a quarter mile from the pole's actual position in anticipation that the ice will carry the station directly over the pole about five years after it goes into operation.

Of perhaps more scientific importance is the south magnetic pole— the point in the Southern Hemisphere at which a south-seeking compass needle points straight down. The lines of force of the earth's magnetic field converge at this pole, producing a gap in the atmosphere through which cosmic rays from outer space can readily penetrate to the earth's surface. There, scientists are conducting cosmic ray surveys to determine the number that reach the earth.

The most practical scientific work at the Antarctic stations has to do with daily weather observations. These are important to meteorological stations in other parts of the world, because Antarctica helps generate weather patterns for all of the Southern Hemisphere. Cool air

The author:
Peter Gwynne is an associate editor for *Newsweek* magazine, specializing in science. He visited Antarctica in the winter of 1973 to observe the scientific work in progress there.

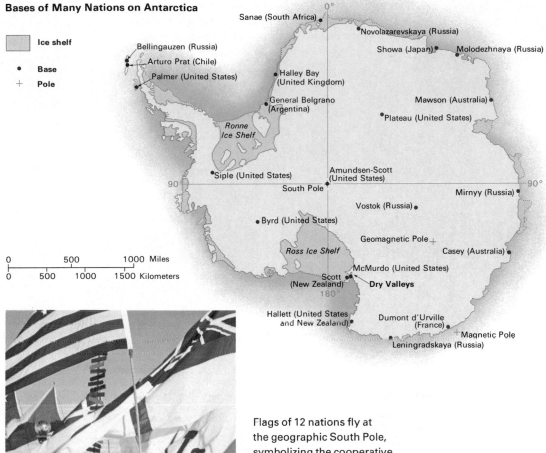

Bases of Many Nations on Antarctica

Ice shelf

• Base

+ Pole

Sanae (South Africa)

Novolazarevskaya (Russia)

Bellingauzen (Russia)

Showa (Japan)

Molodezhnaya (Russia)

Arturo Prat (Chile)

Palmer (United States)

Halley Bay
(United Kingdom)

Mawson (Australia)

General Belgrano
(Argentina)

Plateau (United States)

Ronne
Ice Shelf

Siple (United States)

Amundsen-Scott
(United States)

Mirnyy (Russia)

South Pole

Vostok (Russia)

Byrd (United States)

Geomagnetic Pole +

Casey (Australia)

Ross Ice Shelf

McMurdo (United States)

Scott
(New Zealand)

Dry Valleys

Hallett (United States
and New Zealand)

Dumont d'Urville
(France)

+ Magnetic Pole

Leningradskaya (Russia)

0   500   1000 Miles

0   500   1000   1500 Kilometers

Flags of 12 nations fly at
the geographic South Pole,
symbolizing the cooperative
nature of the international
scientific program on the
frozen continent. Research
stations of the countries
are distributed throughout
the Antarctic land mass.

flows north from there toward the tropics, gradually warms up and
rises, then flows back toward Antarctica, setting up a global circulation of the atmosphere. The Antarctic stations monitoring and reporting the details of this process fill in what would otherwise be a huge
gap for meteorologists.

The National Oceanic and Atmospheric Administration (NOAA)
oversees weather observations at the South Pole. Each day, scientists
launch two small radiosonde balloons that carry instruments to measure temperatures, pressures, and the amount of electricity in the atmosphere. They also record the amount of sunshine and snowfall.

The air circulation pattern from the Antarctic to the tropics and
back includes a huge heat-absorbing area in the atmosphere over

Hostile and foreboding environment is also varied as seen at scientific working centers such as Vanda, which stands among stark rocks; Vostok, usually covered by snow; and beautiful Anver Island, at the edge of the frigid sea.

Antarctica. Meteorologists call the area a heat sink and believe that detailed knowledge of it will help them to understand world-wide weather processes. The heat sink covers the whole Antarctic plateau and extends more than 7 miles (11 kilometers) above it.

During the Antarctic winter, the heat sink produces a large mass of cold air that registers as low as -100°F. (-74°C.), directly above the inland icecap. The force of its own weight drives this air mass down the plateau toward the Antarctic coast. By the time it reaches the coast, the air is traveling at about 20 miles per hour. On the way, it picks up large amounts of snow from the ground and carries it out to sea. Here, the snowflakes fall and act as nuclei on which the seawater starts to freeze. The winds from the interior of the continent thus play a direct role in the production of sea ice around Antarctica.

Balancing the outward flow of cold air from the interior is a mass of relatively warm (-40°F.), moist air that drifts in from the sea at higher altitudes than the cold air. As it moves in above the frigid Antarctic plateau, it cools, and the water in it freezes into ice crystals, which sink to the ground as snow. This precipitation is unusual, because there are no clouds in the sky to produce it, as are necessary for snowfalls else-where in the world. Meteorologists are currently trying to determine

what proportion of the continent's precipitation is produced in this way. If, as many experts suspect, this process produces most of the continent's snowfall, then it will offer scientists a relatively simple means of measuring the effectiveness of the Antarctic heat sink. The number of ice crystals will indicate the amount of heat taken out of the atmospheric moisture by the action of the heat sink.

Meteorologists are now in the early years of a project, designed to last until 1978, to identify and set up means for monitoring the heat sink. Already, weathermen from the University of California, at Davis, and the University of Innsbruck in Austria are studying the exchange of energy between the snow surface and the atmosphere by measuring heat radiation from the surface and the polarization of light in the sky. Other scientists from the universities of Alaska and Nevada are measuring the distribution of ice crystals in the sky with such instruments as photometers and lidars, or laser radars. And meteorologists from the University of Wisconsin and Australia's University of Melbourne are measuring and analyzing the winds from the polar plateau to the Antarctic coast. The U.S. National Science Foundation also plans to study the past effects of the heat sink by measuring the layers of snow and ice laid down year by year at the pole.

The Antarctic heat sink is easier for meteorologists to study than a similar sink at the Arctic. It has simpler weather patterns, because it is farther from centers of population and the resulting pollution from automobiles and factories. This factor also makes Antarctica a natural center for global studies of atmospheric pollutants. The continent's air is so clean that any pollutant, such as radioactive dust from nuclear bomb tests or trace metals from poorly controlled industrial processes, can be detected easily. "Any increase in global pollution should give a very much larger jump in our measurements than in measurements anywhere else in the world," explains Gene Mroz of the University of Maryland, one of a team of environmental monitors.

This team, made up of physicists from the University of Rhode Island, the Lawrence Livermore Laboratory in California, and the University of Maryland, is measuring the concentrations of radioactive trace elements in the polar atmosphere. Their base, Scott Station, is part of a world-wide network that also includes installations in Bermuda; Providence, R.I.; American Samoa; Fort McPherson in Canada's Northwest Territories; and aboard the University of Rhode Island research vessel *Trident*. The South Pole group collects atmospheric particles by pumping air through plastic filters, and then chemically analyzes the matter trapped on the filters.

Particles are not the only types of pollutants under investigation at the South Pole. NOAA scientists are also measuring the amounts of carbon dioxide and ozone in air samples to determine how burning fossil fuels affects the temperature of the atmosphere. As a check on atmospheric radioactivity, they also sample the atmosphere for the presence of the radioactive isotope carbon-14.

For geophysicists, the major point of interest in Antarctica is Siple Station, a small, remote base close to the bottom of the Antarctic

Antennas rising from Siple Station are used to beam radio signals to the upper atmosphere in a continuing study of the natural effects on the signal reception.

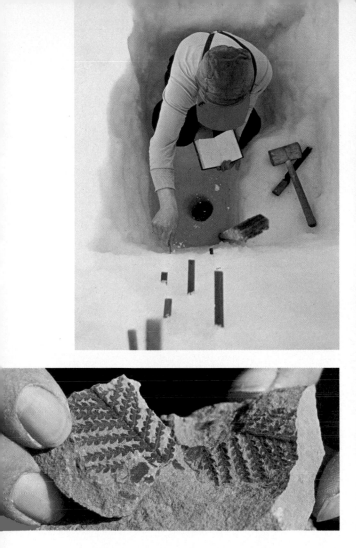

Antarctic science studies include surveys of glacial ice, observations of volcanic activity on Deception Island, and excavations of fossil plants that grew millions of years ago in a more hospitable climate.

peninsula. Siple is located at 60° magnetic latitude, and the magnetic lines of force that strike the earth there produce some unexpected communications effects. When low-frequency radio waves are beamed up from the station, they are reflected back amplified 1,000 times. The amplified signals are also received at a station in Roberval, Que., which lies at the northern end of the same magnetic lines of force.

These lines of force pass through the upper atmosphere to the plasmapause, a zone about 300 miles (480 kilometers) thick at an altitude of about 12,000 miles (19,320 kilometers). Across this zone the density of the atmosphere thins a hundredfold. Scientists believe that electrochemical reactions in the plasmapause cause the amplification of the radio waves. The phenomenon is somewhat like the action of an amplifying device called a maser, although it is not as consistent.

The first studies on this atmospheric effect were made in January, 1971. At that time scientists began to record natural, very-low-frequency signals in the Siple area. Stanford University physicists monitored these signals on the ground, while scintillation counters were sent aloft on a balloon by a University of Maryland team. These

Scientists at the Dry Valley Drilling Project, *above,* and in a makeshift laboratory, *left,* study freshwater and terrestrial ecosystems of the frigid continent. They also examine core samples of the rocks and soil, *below,* in the hope of someday reconstructing the history of Antarctica.

counters detected X rays that the scientists believe were produced in the plasmapause. The two teams found a direct relationship between the number of low-frequency signals and the number of X rays. In December, 1973, the Stanford group transmitted radio signals from Siple while University of Maryland physicists, headed by Theodore J. Rosenberg, sent a scintillation counter aloft to see if the amplification of the signals could also be related to the X-ray production. Results are still being analyzed.

The land of Antarctica is, of course, of as much research interest as the atmosphere above it. Geologists see Antarctica as virgin territory, and they have drilled all over the area. Early in 1973, the deep-sea drilling ship *Glomar Challenger,* which was taking core samples from the ocean bottom, detected natural gas in sediments beneath the Ross Sea. Experts have little doubt that oil fields, possibly huge ones, lie close by.

For the geologist, however, the most exciting drilling sites are in the dry valleys, located in a 4,000-square-mile (10,400-square-kilometer) area some 60 miles (97 kilometers) west of McMurdo Station. There, the heavy layer of ice that covers 98 per cent of the continent is absent. The landscape consists of chocolate-colored rocks interspersed with a thin ice cover, and occasional glacier-fed lakes and ponds, which are among the most scientifically important bodies of water in the world. Geologists believe a complete record of the history of Antarctica lies beneath the valleys. Moreover, this record should provide a guide to geological changes over thousands of years throughout the world. The work is being conducted by the Dry Valley Drilling Project (DVDP) that is sponsored by the U.S. National Science Foundation and similar agencies in Japan and New Zealand.

Each of the dry valley lakes has unique characteristics, in terms of chemical composition and physical features. Don Juan Pond, for example, is so salty that its water does not freeze even when its temperature is -70°F. (-57°C.). Only one species of bacteria is found in its waters, and DVDP scientists consider it "to be the single aquatic body on earth most closely approximating the presumed environmental conditions for aquatic bodies on Mars."

Lake Vanda is covered by 10 feet (3 meters) of ice, but the temperature of the water at its bottom, 200 feet (60 meters) beneath the ice, is close to 80°F. (27°C.). Geologists argued for years over the reason for this peculiarity. Some believed that the water was heated from below by some kind of geothermal effect, and others theorized that the sun's rays, focused by Vanda's ice cover, produced the extraordinary temperature. In November, 1973, DVDP drillers bored down through the ice and water of Lake Vanda and into the sediments below it, and settled the question. The bottom waters of the lake were warm, but the sediments on which they rested were quite cold, making it evident that the sun is responsible for the heating.

The Vanda drilling effort produced more than the simple answer to a simple question. The drillers bored more than 50 feet (15 meters)

Bacteria that are more than 10,000 years old were found in a layer of ice at McMurdo Station. Some revived and even reproduced in an Antarctic laboratory.

beneath the bottom of the lake, pulling up cores which, according to geologist Samuel B. Treves of the University of Nebraska, "contain the record of the entire period from when the dry valleys were marine fiords to when they became an icy desert." Understanding this process may lead geologists to an overall grasp of what causes successive ice ages elsewhere on earth. As an example, geochemist Nobuki Nakai of Nagoya University in Japan is searching in the cores retrieved from beneath Lake Vanda for evidence linking the onset of ice ages to reversals in earth's magnetic field.

The dry valley drilling research is notable in another way. It is the first drilling project in which strict environmental guidelines control every move. Because the Antarctic environment is so simple, it provides a perfect model for the more complex environments in which we live. But any outside factor, such as human waste, cigarette ashes, or even a rock from another part of the dry valley region, could ruin the area's value as a model. As a result, an environmental monitor accompanies every drilling team in the valley to ensure that no drilling fluid, food, fuel, or other substance from the outside is left at the site.

At times, the monitors' decisions have caused the geologists great disappointment. For example, the crew drilling under Don Juan Pond hit a boulder about 10 feet (3 meters) down in late November, 1973. They put a special bit on the drill and drilled about 6 inches (15 centimeters) into the boulder. Suddenly, water from beneath the lake bottom started to rise up the drill column. The local monitor, biologist Frank Morelli of the Jet Propulsion Laboratory, ordered drilling halted and the hole plugged. "If the water had gotten into the lake," explained Treves, "it would have ruined its geochemical uniqueness."

A remarkable scientific dividend from this environmental caution occurred in December, 1973, when monitors routinely added specimens of rock to nutrient solutions designed to foster the growth of bacteria. They did this to check any possible transfer of microorganisms from the drilling team to the rocks. When Morelli noticed live bacteria in a solution prepared using rock drilled from a depth of 420 feet (128 meters), he suspected such contamination. But a series of checks showed the bacteria to be entirely different from any associated with the drillers, the drill site, or the laboratory in which the nutrient solution was housed. These were the 10,000-year-old bacteria, and further study of them should lead to greater understanding of the origin of life on the earth and other planets. Discovery of the Rip Van Winkle-like creatures may also have particular significance in the search for life on Mars (see CLIMATES AND PLANETS). Morelli believes that, even if living things do not appear on the surface of the red planet, they may well turn up beneath that planet's surface, just as the Antarctic bacteria did.

A major ecological study at Lake Bonney, another dry valley lake, is aimed at producing a mathematical model of one of the simplest ecosystems known on earth. Unlike most lakes, Bonney's waters do not mix from top to bottom, so the microscopic forms of life in the water do not compete with each other for food. The microscopic life forms are both small and simple, and there are few nutrients to feed them. The food chain that keeps this lake life going has only three stages, rather than many, as in other lakes. Nutrients are consumed by simple algae, which are eaten by a more complex algae that die and produce the nutrients that feed the simple algae.

"In the past, scientists have tried to understand more complex lakes by simplifying them," explains botany professor Bruce C. Parker of Virginia Polytechnic Institute and State University, who heads the Bonney investigations. "We hope to take a simple lake and understand it thoroughly, thus perhaps learning more about how other, more complex, lakes function."

Scientists in Antarctica are also studying the region's unique animals. Zoologist Donald B. Siniff of the University of Minnesota is conducting a census of the seal population along the shores of the continent. This census could confirm that the huge mammals are numerous enough to warrant a carefully controlled annual harvesting for their fur, blubber, and meat. Studies are also being made of the habits and life cycle of the animals. Since seals spend a great deal of their time in the water under the ice, the census involves much more work than simply counting those basking on the ice. Technicians have devised sonic transmitters that can be strapped to the seals' rear flippers with surgical tape. The scientists then position three hydrophones

Ice-fishing biologists Yuan and Arthur DeVries use a cable to catch specimens of 150-pound Antarctic cod for their research. The fish has natural antifreeze in its blood that scientists hope to synthesize for use as preservative.

on the ice in a triangular array and monitor the movements of the
tagged seals. They can record the sonic signals at distances of a quarter
mile and a depth of about 30 feet (9 meters). This setup does not
record the seals' depth, however, and the electronics experts are now
developing a transmitter that responds to water pressure to provide
this information. Researchers have also lowered television cameras
through holes in the ice that the seals use when they come up for air to
study the seals at close range in the icy waters.

Krill, a tiny shrimplike animal high in protein, is one of the major
sources of food for the seals in Antarctic waters. These tiny creatures
are so plentiful that they could probably be used as human food, but
scientists know little about them. Researchers from DePaul University
in Chicago have been studying the physiology and seasonal behavior
of krill since 1973. Two of the scientists, biologists Mary Alice Mc-
Whinnie and Sister Mary Odile Cahoon, were the first American
women to spend a winter at an Antarctic base.

In another project, a husband-and-wife team of biologists from the
Scripps Institution of Oceanography in La Jolla, Calif., is studying a
type of natural antifreeze found in the blood of Antarctic fishes, who
have to survive sea temperatures below the freezing temperature of
fresh water. Arthur L. and Yuan DeVries catch Antarctic cod, 150-
pound fish known scientifically as *Dissostichus mawsoni*, extract their
blood, isolate the antifreeze, and study it. The substance is a glycopro-
tein somewhat similar to the ethylene glycol in commercial antifreeze.
It may someday be used to prevent the growth of ice during low-
temperature preservation of organic materials such as sperm, blood,
and organs for transplantation.

Emperor penguins, probably the most familiar Antarctic animals,
are also being studied by Antarctic scientists. For example, Duke University researchers, headed by biologist Mike Fedak, are exercising
penguins on treadmills to measure the oxygen they take in and the
carbon dioxide they give off. From this, they calculate the energy the
birds expend as they walk. Other experiments are designed to study
the penguins' metabolism to determine how they can live in such
extreme temperatures.

Since the International Geophysical Year, both scientific understanding and international cooperation have advanced tremendously
in Antarctica. "We've taken an unknown continent and made it
known in 20 years," says geologist Treves. With jet planes, helicopters,
and snowmobiles to transport them, and comfortable, insulated quarters to house them, the scientists now avoid many of the discomforts
suffered by Antarctic pioneers. Yet Antarctica still seems a hostile
frontier. Even for the most worldly-wise scientists, living and working
on the continent fulfills a sense of adventure and excitement.

Cancer Clues at The Cell's Surface

By Garth L. Nicolson

Comparing the membranes of normal and tumor cells may uncover ways to check uncontrolled cell growth

Judy Campbell of Panama City, Fla., turned 29 in 1974, and it was a happy milestone. That birthday marked her fifth healthy year since a surgeon used a new and daring technique to save her from malignant melanoma, one of the deadliest of all cancers.

Judy's treatment began with surgery. But instead of the massive operation usually performed to try to kill melanoma cells that might have spread from the main tumors, Dr. Edward T. Krementz of Tulane University removed only the tumors themselves. Then he used the removed tumors to make a vaccine that immunized Judy against her remaining cancer cells.

Unfortunately, such vaccines, little more than the patient's own cancer cells isolated, grown, and then killed, have had only limited success since Judy's case. Yet, they emphasize the view of most cancer researchers: The secret of controlling human cancer lies in understanding how our bodies identify and kill most cancer cells at an early stage and why some cancer cells escape destruction. This understand-

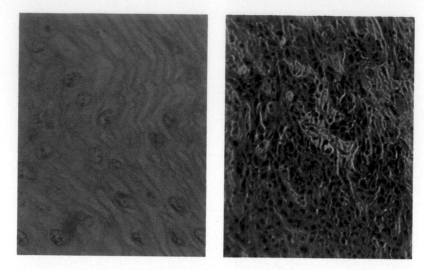

Normal cells are orderly, *right,* because they stop multiplying when their plasma membranes touch. Cancer cells, *far right,* continue to multiply and pile up in a disorderly crush.

The author:
Garth L. Nicolson is head of the Cancer Council Laboratory and director of the Electron Microscopy Laboratory at The Salk Institute for Biological Studies, La Jolla, Calif.

ing can come only with more information on the structure and organization of both normal and cancer cells.

Human cells exist in many different forms and in a variety of complex interrelationships with other cells. Some cells are organized into masses that form tissues such as muscle, skin, and bone. Others lead a solitary existence as part of the blood and lymph fluids. Each cell has a specific task to perform in maintaining tissues, the organs they form, and ultimately, the whole body. And each cell knows how, when, and where to perform these tasks, including when to grow, when to stop growing, and, finally, when to die.

The interaction between cells has been called their "social behavior," and it is at least as complex as the behavior in a large human society. The overwhelming proportion of cells rigidly adhere to their proper social behavior. But sometimes some become abnormal and, with little regard to neighboring normal cells, they proliferate and grow over and around them, using up valuable nutrients that the normal cells need to survive. This is the overriding characteristic of cells that have become cancerous; they proliferate in an unrestrained and uncoordinated manner that threatens the whole organism.

Many scientists interested in why cells become cancerous have lately focused their attention on the surface "skin," or plasma membrane, of the cell, where communication with neighboring cells and the rest of the environment occurs. Most of these scientists now think that the disorderly, uncoordinated growth that is typical of cancer cells is caused by a change in the controls that regulate the cells' genes. This change, in turn, alters the plasma membrane in such a way that normal communications go either unnoticed or unheeded. Consequently, scientists in many laboratories throughout the world are now carefully comparing the plasma membranes of normal and cancer cells in the hope that the differences they find will help them to develop methods to identify and destroy cancer cells.

Proteins Adrift in a Lipid Sea

It was only a few years ago that scientists began to realize the importance of the plasma membrane. Previously, they lacked instruments and techniques sensitive and sophisticated enough to work with. Also, the cell's contents—including the nucleus, with its genes; the mitochondria, which generate the body's energy; and the ribosomes, which help fashion enzymes and other vital proteins—seemed much more important than the plasma membrane. This flimsy "plastic bag" appeared to do little more than passively surround them.

And flimsy it is by almost any standard—only about one-half millionth of an inch thick. Yet, it provides the cell with a remarkably effective barrier that keeps needed materials in and unneeded or dangerous ones out. It is made up of several kinds of molecules—proteins,

The cell's plasma membrane is composed of two layers of fatty or oily molecules (blue). Protein molecules (pink), with short chains of sugar molecules (green) attached, penetrate into the two layers to varying degrees.

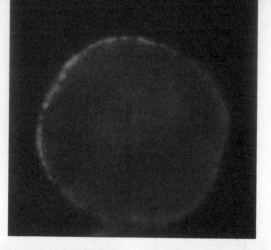

Green- and red-tagged membrane proteins of two cells separate immediately after fusion forms one cell, *left*. But less than an hour later, views of the same cell through two filters show that the proteins have spread, *below left* and *below*, proving that membrane components roam the cell surface.

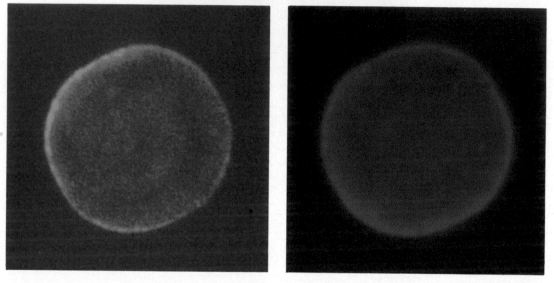

short chains of sugar molecules called oligosaccharides, and fatty or oily ones called lipids. At first, scientists thought these components were arranged in a "sandwich" structure with the proteins and oligosaccharides on either side of a double layer of lipid molecules. However, most biochemists and cell biologists now accept the membrane model which cell biologist S. Jonathan Singer of the University of California, San Diego, and I proposed in 1972. In this model, the membrane's proteins poke into the double layer of lipid molecules, penetrating to various depths, from slightly to completely through it. The oligosaccharides are found only on the outside of the membrane and are connected to certain of the protein and lipid molecules.

Perhaps the most important feature in our model is the constant motion of the plasma membrane's lipid and protein molecules. This movement, always parallel to the surface of the membrane, indicates that the membrane is a fluid structure. Just as a thin layer of oil on top of water acts effectively as a fluid membrane separating the water beneath from the air above, the cell membrane separates the inside of the cell from the outside environment.

Singer and I knew that the membrane was fluid from the results of several experiments. One of the earliest was reported in 1970 by cell biologists Michael Edidin and John Frye of Johns Hopkins University in Baltimore. They fused two cells—one with membrane proteins chemically marked to fluoresce red, the other with membrane proteins marked to fluoresce green—to form one giant cell. They found that the cells' membrane proteins had completely intermixed over the giant cell's surface 40 minutes later.

Although such movement of membrane components appears to be a natural property of every cell's plasma membrane, I suspected that the rate and pattern of movement of some of the components might be altered when a cell becomes cancerous. This may change the cell's reactions to other cells or to its environment. In 1972, cytologist Monique Lacorbiere and I began to study the mobility of certain membrane components on normal and cancer cells at The Salk Institute for Biological Studies in La Jolla, Calif. With an electron microscope, it is possible to observe the thin plasma membrane, but not its individual molecules. However, because it is observable in minute quantities, a substance called ferritin would be an ideal marker for such molecules

Ten minutes after sugar molecules are treated with a substance that causes them to appear as black dots and to begin clumping, they are still evenly dispersed across membrane of a normal cell, *left*. On cancer cell, *below*, they have already clumped. Membranes magnified about 130,000 times.

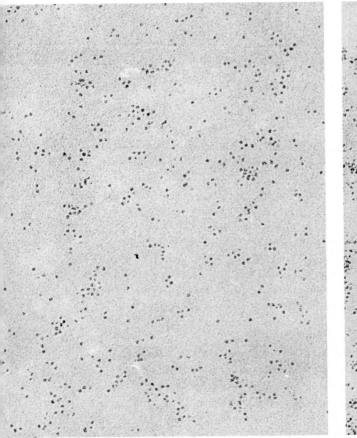

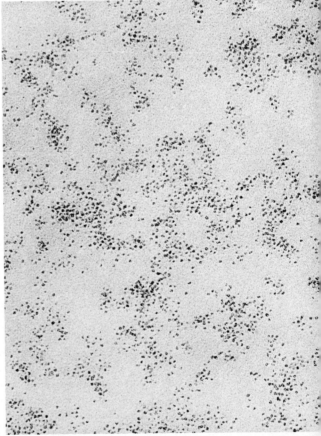

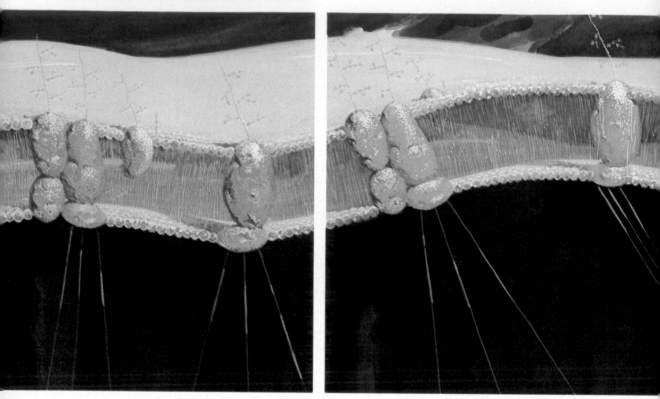

if it could be attached to them somehow. We chemically coupled ferritin to certain plant proteins, called lectins. These bind to specific sugar molecules and sometimes cause them to clump. With the resulting ferritin-lectin material, we could mark certain oligosaccharides located in the membrane.

We added the ferritin-lectin material to both normal and cancerous mouse cells. After 10 minutes, we added a chemical that stops the movement of the membrane's molecules. Next, we carefully broke the cells, collected their plasma membranes, and mounted them on thin plastic films for viewing with the electron microscope.

We found that the ferritin-marked oligosaccharides on normal cells were still dispersed evenly across the cell membrane, but those on the cancer cells had already been clumped by the lectin of the ferritin-lectin material, creating a clearly discernible patchy distribution. This experiment, a second experiment that we performed later in 1972 and in 1973 with fluorescent markers, and several experiments by other scientists demonstrated that certain components of the cancer cell's plasma membrane move more rapidly than those of normal cells. It is possible that this might alter the way in which one cell recognizes another, accounting in part for the tendency of cancer cells to grow without regard for their neighbors.

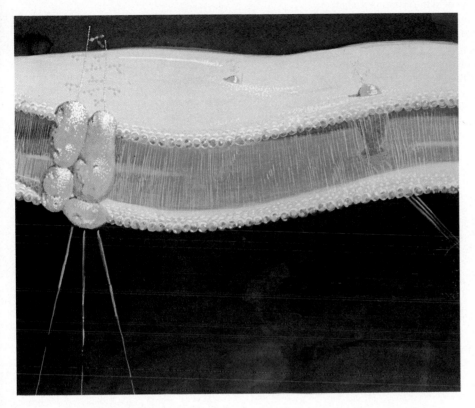

The cell membrane is a sea in constant motion. Sugar molecules (green) bob and weave among the fatty (blue) and protein (pink) molecules they are attached to. Some proteins are anchored by rodlike microfilaments that allow them only to bob and turn. Others drift freely. Still others, pulled by microfilaments, plow through the rolling sea.

In other experiments at The Salk Institute in 1973 and 1974, we found that structures within the cell seem to control the movement of some of the membrane components, and that these structures are altered when a cell becomes cancerous. Most of the structures that interact directly or indirectly with the plasma membrane are microfilaments and microtubules. Microfilaments are long, parallel fibers, some of which run directly under and probably bind to the inner surface of the plasma membrane. Microtubules, very long tubular structures that are thicker than microfilaments, sometimes run almost the length of a cell. They are associated with, and probably anchored to, other structures within the cell. Microtubules do not appear to bind directly to the plasma membrane's inner surface, so they probably influence it only indirectly.

Microfilaments and microtubules provide a skeletonlike structure for the cell as a whole. They are probably involved in a variety of functions, including cell motion, changes in cell shape, and interactions between cells. Microfilaments, in particular, appear to be capable of acting as tiny cellular muscles that can pull parts of the cell around. They may also be a very important link between the cell's surface and its interior, including, perhaps, the nucleus. If this is so, microfilaments might be one of the pathways by which events at the

A Deadly Escape

A cancer cell, *right,* reveals itself to the immune system through tumor-specific proteins, or antigens, (pink). Normally, this seals the cell's doom; antibodies (orange) grab and clump the antigens, an early step in the immune response. However, when microfilaments suck the antigens and antibodies into the cell, the immune response is short circuited and the cell escapes destruction. The initial and final steps in this process, called endocytosis, are clearly visible in an electron photomicrograph of a cell enlarged 140,000 times, *below,* with proteins marked to appear dark.

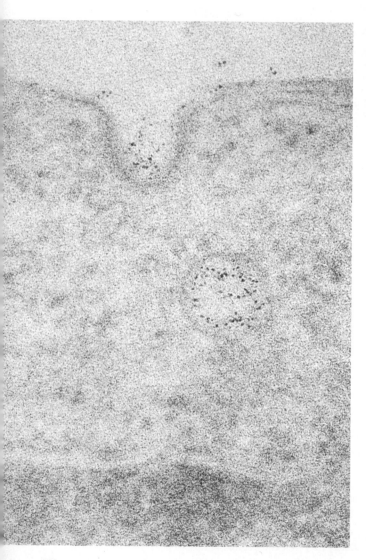

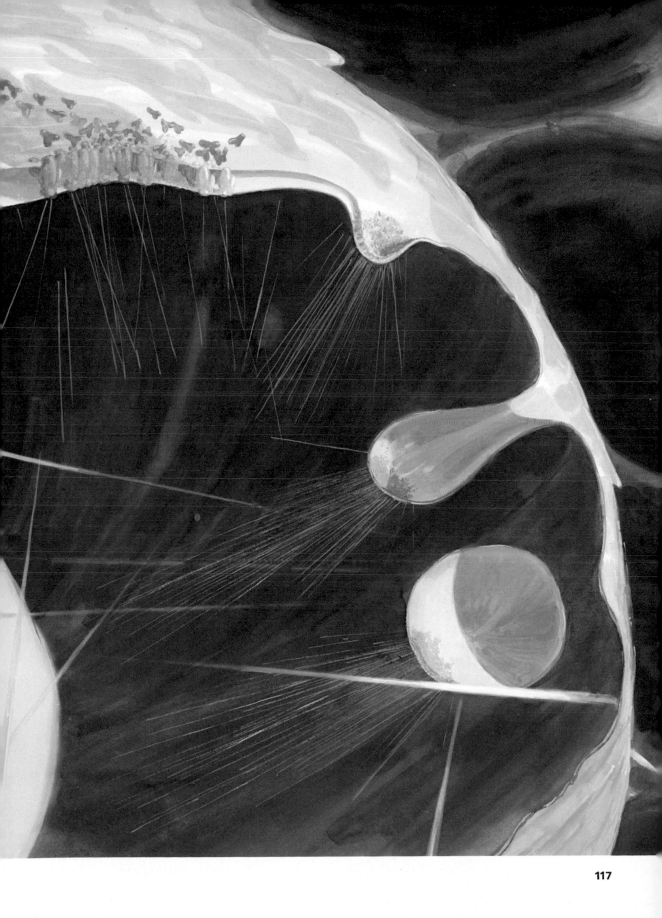

cell surface signal the nucleus to begin or cease duplicating genetic material, which starts or stops cell proliferation.

A few research groups, including mine, have found evidence of this. At Salk, we compared the internal structure of normal and cancerous mouse cells. We found that the microfilaments associated with the inner surface of the membrane increase in number and form complex networks when normal cells touch one another. This does not happen in cancer cells, however. Does the build-up of the microfilament networks stimulated by cell contact somehow signal the cell to stop growing, or does the build-up occur after the signal has passed into the cell? We do not know yet.

However, we do know that another signal system that is probably involved in controlling cell proliferation also affects the microfilaments and microtubules. This system is regulated by the concentrations of several small molecules such as cyclic-AMP and cyclic-GMP. These molecules, along with the cell-energy molecules called ATP and GTP, can start or stop cell proliferation, and they also can control the movements of microfilaments and microtubules.

Nobody yet knows how to tie all this together to explain how cell proliferation is controlled, but it might work this way: Contact between cells may cause certain surface receptors in the membrane to activate membrane enzymes that change the concentrations of molecules such as cyclic-AMP and cyclic-GMP within the cell. This, in turn, stops or starts many cell processes, including motions of the microfilaments and microtubules. Although we only suspect that this may affect the cell nucleus, we are sure that it affects certain membrane molecules that transport food and a number of other substances that cells need if they are to proliferate.

Cell proliferation apparently may also be regulated by changing the concentration of certain growth molecules in the serum surrounding the cells. Nobel prizewinning biochemist Robert Holley and his Salk Institute collaborators, cell biologists Dieter Paul and Josephine Kiernan, think cell proliferation is regulated mainly in this way. In experiments performed from 1971 to 1973, they showed that cancer cells do not require nearly as high a concentration of growth molecules as do their normal counterparts. As a result, cancer cells continue to grow at growth-molecule concentrations where normal cells stop growing. But does this explain why normal cells stop growing when they have formed a single layer? Are the serum growth molecules sufficiently expended at this time to account for it? This does not seem to be the complete answer; experiments on normal cells show that continually replacing these molecules by providing fresh serum does not stimulate continued growth once they have formed their single layer. It may be that the changes triggered at the membrane surface when normal cells contact one another modify the cells' response to the growth molecules. Cancer cells, with their responses to both cell contact and growth molecules altered, are insensitive to crowding.

Beyond their possible role in carrying messages from the cell's surface to its interior, microfilaments and microtubules serve other important cell-membrane functions. One particularly important role is in endocytosis. In this process, damaged portions of the cell surface and even potentially damaging substances that bind to it are sucked, or endocytosed, into the cell. Endocytosis depends particularly on microfilaments, which contract at the affected region of the membrane and pull it into the cell's interior. The cell then pinches off the internalized membrane region, leaving it as a free vesicle, or sac, that is eventually destroyed.

Endocytosis is usually a protective process, but in the case of cancer, it may act against us. Cancer cells have altered surface molecules called tumor-specific antigens that allow the host's immune system to identify the cancer cells and attack them before they can form a tumor. There are basically two kinds of immune attack. In one, molecules called antibodies combine with the tumor-specific antigens and attract substances called complement, which then dissolve portions of the cancer cell's membrane. In the other, killer cells (white blood cells called lymphocytes and macrophages) recognize the tumor-specific antigens on the cancer cell and kill it. When the antibodies combine with the tumor-specific antigens of the cancer cell, they cause them to cluster. Unfortunately, this sometimes signals the cancer cell to contract its microfilaments and endocytose the region where clustering has taken place, before the complement or the killer cells can destroy the cancer cell. Thus, the cell is saved from the initial immune attack, and it cannot be recognized for further attack because the tumor-specific antigens have been removed from the cell surface.

Cancer cells also escape immune mechanisms in other ways. In one found by medical researchers Karl and Ingegerd Hellstrom of the University of Washington in Seattle, they secrete "blocking substances" (probably tumor-specific antigens) that circulate outside the tumor cells and somehow stop killer cells. Many immunologists believe that the blocking substances attach to and jam the sites that recognize tumor-specific antigens on the killer cells' surface.

Cancer researchers are seeking several ways to keep cancer cells from escaping host immunity. Judy Campbell's malignant melanoma was probably controlled because the vaccine from her tumor cells stimulated a lagging immune response. But other exciting research approaches focus more directly on the cell surface. Preventing endocytosis at the cell surface so cancer cells cannot hide their identities, using substances that kill cancer cells selectively because they recognize the differences between their cell membranes and those of normal cells, and removing circulating blocking substances will all be tested soon. Hopefully, one or more of these techniques can help to control the incidence and spread of cancer in human beings. Then, like Judy Campbell, others will have a fighting chance in the battle against their own wayward cells.

Cataloging the Whole Earth

By Edward G. Nash

Satellite eyes are scanning the planet, providing us with down-to-earth data on our resources

How many acres of popcorn are growing in Holt County, Nebraska? How many of wheat in Kansas? Of timber in Oregon? Are there unknown deposits of copper in Nevada? Or untapped water sources in the Sahara? Where are the fish in the South Atlantic's Falkland Current? Such questions may ultimately be vital to human survival. And their importance can be summed up in two general questions: What and where are the resources of earth? Are we using them wisely and efficiently?

The Earth Resources Survey Program of the National Aeronautics and Space Administration (NASA) is beginning to provide some answers. The program, still in its experimental stage, employs ground measurements and observations, aerial photography, and satellite cameras and sensors in an effort to gain the most comprehensive view humans have ever had of their home planet.

A major key to the success of the program has been the development of multispectral scanners (MSS) which, in effect, enlarge the visual window of the human eye. Objects reflect many different wave lengths of electromagnetic radiation, only some of which are visible light. In

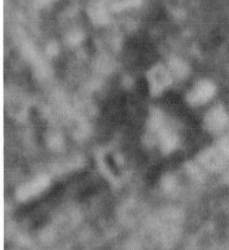

Skylab Looks at Washington, D.C.
Washington-Baltimore area appears in amazing detail in a photo taken from 270 miles up, *top left*. Highways and Chesapeake Bay Bridge are clearly visible. Enlarged view, *left*, shows the parklike Mall. The U.S. Capitol is enlarged further, *above*.

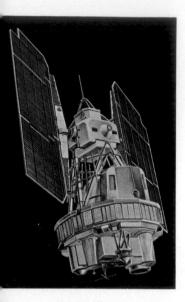

Like a space-age moth, ERTS-1 spreads solar panel wings and turns a searching gaze on earth.

addition to visible light, MSS can also pick up infrared and other invisible wave lengths and translate them into visible images of an object or area. By comparing images of the same area made in different wave length bands, or channels, of radiation, scientists can learn more about the features of an area than they can by using only visible light and ordinary photography.

NASA launched its first experimental survey satellite, the Earth Resources Technology Satellite (ERTS-1), on July 23, 1972. ERTS-1 was designed to test the MSS equipment in some 300 experiments. Later, an Earth Resources Experimental Package (EREP) with MSS and photographic equipment was placed on board Skylab. Both have been resounding successes.

ERTS-1 was placed in a near-polar orbit 570 miles above the earth. This orbit allows the satellite to view more than 90 per cent of the earth's surface, providing repetitive coverage of an area at the same time of day every 18 days.

The satellite's MSS scans the earth in four wave length bands, two visible and two infrared. The information produced can be manipulated in a number of ways. For some studies, single band images are useful, for others, two or three bands may be combined in a "false color" image (so called because colors are arbitrarily assigned for various wave length bands). Computers that can interpret subtle differences in the radiation are used to enhance certain details in the images, such as differences in kinds of crops, or in water densities.

ERTS-1 also carries equipment that collects information from unattended ground stations, such as local water depth, stream flow, soil moisture, temperature, and humidity. This information is transmitted by the satellite to NASA receiving stations.

The satellite has generated an astonishing mass of data. In its two years, it has sent nearly 100,000 images of earth, as well as relayed 800,000 readings from remote ground stations. A data-processing facility at Goddard Space Flight Center in Greenbelt, Md., has been established to handle more than 9,000 image prints a week.

The Skylab equipment included a 13-band MSS, a land terrain camera, and a multispectral photographic device, as well as other sensors. With a lower orbit, more frequent coverage of a smaller area, more sophisticated equipment, and human operators, the Skylab experiments complemented those of ERTS-1. More than 40,000 photographs and about 40 miles of data-filled magnetic tape were acquired during the program (see RESEARCH IN ORBIT).

Even though the two projects are experimental, the results and benefits have been impressive. Valuable information has been gained in agriculture, forestry and range resources, oceanography and water resources, minerals and land resources, mapping, and environmental studies. Only one more ERTS satellite is presently planned, to be launched in late 1974 or early 1975, but a permanent, operational system, combining satellites, aircraft, and ground stations, would be of

The author:
Edward G. Nash
is a senior editor
for *Science Year*
and *The World Book
Year Book.*

great value to government, business, and science. By providing more complete data than are presently available for rational decisions about world resources and their uses, such a system might help to improve the quality of life on earth.

Meanwhile, in the summer of 1974, ERTS-1, long past its expected one-year lifetime, was still looking down on a changing earth: It was watching the progress of the seasons—the spring floods, the summer droughts, and the winter storms. Over cities, farmland, and forests, it was measuring man's mark on his planet. And every 18 days, it returned to the popcorn fields of Holt County.

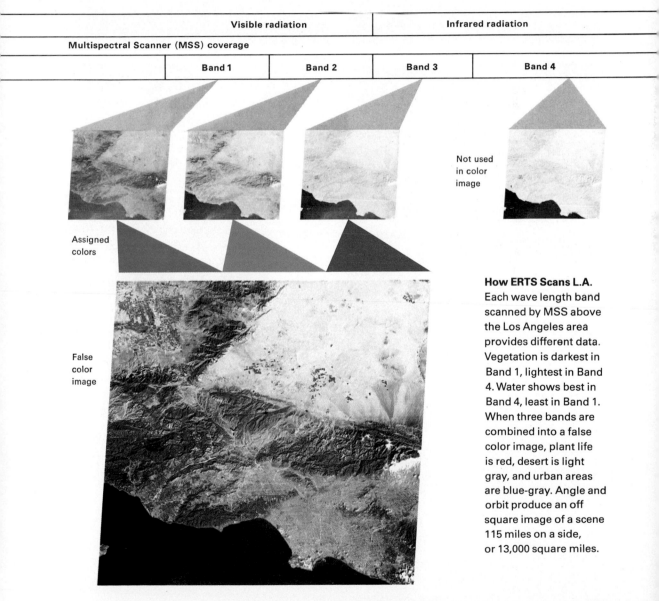

		Visible radiation		Infrared radiation	
Multispectral Scanner (MSS) coverage					
		Band 1	Band 2	Band 3	Band 4

Not used in color image

Assigned colors

False color image

How ERTS Scans L.A. Each wave length band scanned by MSS above the Los Angeles area provides different data. Vegetation is darkest in Band 1, lightest in Band 4. Water shows best in Band 4, least in Band 1. When three bands are combined into a false color image, plant life is red, desert is light gray, and urban areas are blue-gray. Angle and orbit produce an off square image of a scene 115 miles on a side, or 13,000 square miles.

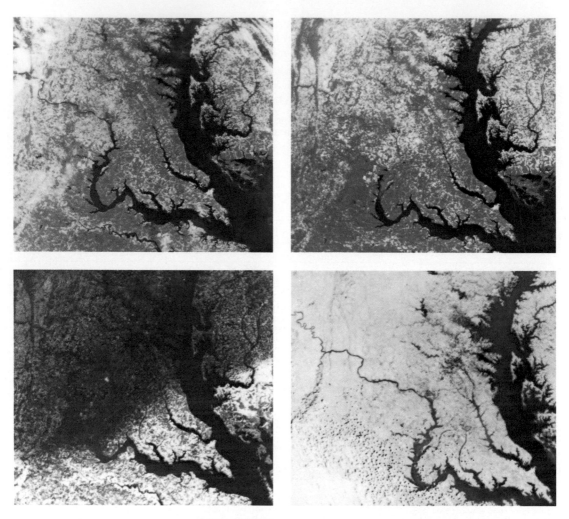

A Year of Observation
ERTS scanner records in false colors the seasonal changes in the Middle Atlantic area. Baltimore, on the Patapsco River, and Washington, on the Potomac, are blue-gray spots west of Chesapeake Bay. Summer and fall vegetation is rich red, *top left and right.* Run-off sediment from an October storm causes light-blue color in the Potomac. Snow blanketing countryside south of Washington, *bottom left,* brightens the dark winter landscape. A delicate pink signals the return of spring greenery, *bottom right.* Such year-round coverage reveals changes in land-use patterns.

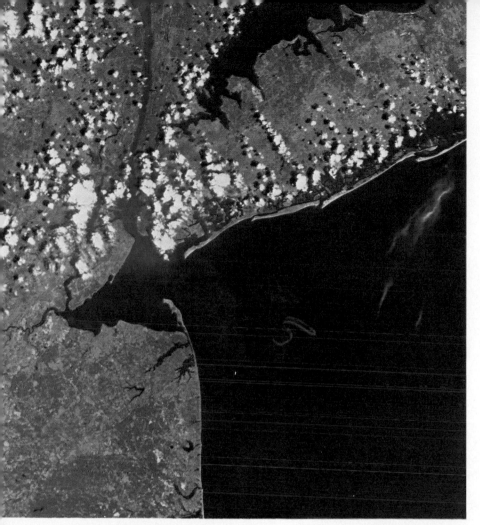

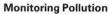

Monitoring Pollution
ERTS saw faint hairpin
feature, *left,* on Aug. 16,
1972, off New York Bay
near New Jersey shore.
It proved to be acid
wastes dumped from
zigzagging barge on the
day before. In single
band image, *bottom left,*
acid showed clearly;
computer enhancement,
below, allowed scientists
to check acid density
and dispersion rate.
Such ERTS images have
been used as evidence
in pollution disputes.

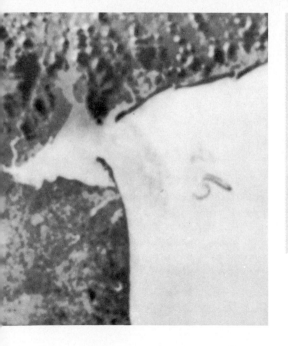

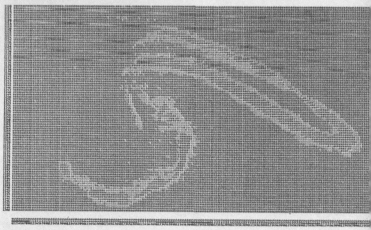

Forest Resources
The snow-covered peaks of Mount St. Helens, lower left, and Mount Adams, right, dominate true-color Skylab photo of a small section of Gifford Pinchot National Forest in Washington. Federal forestlands are an important source for lumber industry, but must be used wisely to preserve beauty and renew timber. Ground survey of forests would be time-consuming, but large areas can be mapped quickly from space.

A Skylab MSS view of the area highlights important information when bands are assigned colors and combined to aid resource survey. Clear-cut forest areas, seen on opposite page as light-colored shapes, stand out vividly as red geometric forms against forest-green background of living trees. The technique also produces odd effects — yellow-green water in reservoirs north and south of Mount St. Helens; magenta snow on peaks.

Firewatch from Space
Forest fires rage north of Fairbanks, Alaska. Older burned areas and cloud shadows can be seen in west, south of meandering river. ERTS can help to assess damage from fires, floods, and other natural disasters.

Food from the Sea
Drifting northward on the Falkland Current in the South Atlantic, a plankton cloud hints at the presence of fish, which feed on these tiny organisms. The Skylab photo also shows a "red tide" of poisonous algae, seen faintly at left. Such large-scale ocean observations can greatly benefit world fishing.

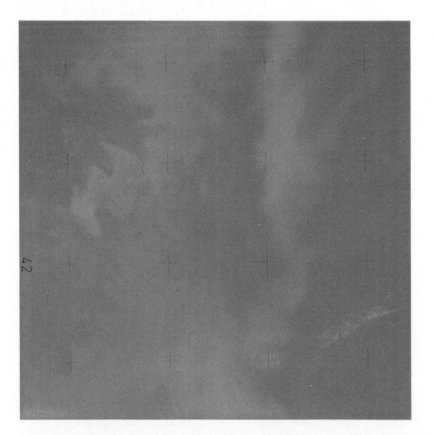

Food from the Land
ERTS view of Holt County, Nebraska, from 570 miles up, is dotted red
by thousands of acres of cultivated fields. Circular red fields to the
west are irrigated by pipes, which rotate around the center of each field.

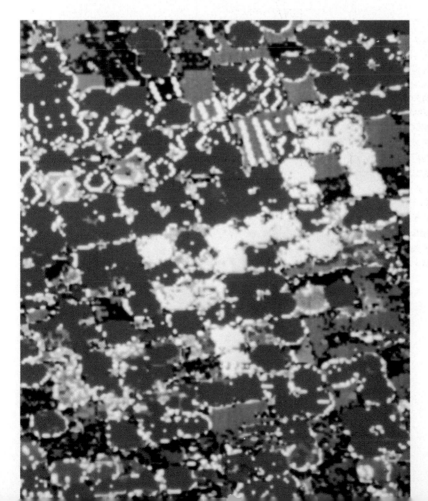

Computer-enhanced differences that escape the human eye provide this crop breakdown of a part of Holt County. Colors are assigned to distinguish crops. Each small unit is about an acre. Among crops seen here are field corn (red), popcorn (yellow), sorghum (blue), and alfalfa (black). Such surveys have proved to be 90 to 95 per cent accurate when they are verified on the ground.

Image Interpretation

The first requirement in interpreting pictures from space is a good map. Comparing map and image will help you to orient an area. Look for major features—mountains, lakes, and cities. Consider when the image was made; most areas in temperate zones show marked changes in vegetation from season to season. Remember, too, that nature rarely makes straight lines. Most regularly shaped features are roads, fields, dams, and bridges. Here are two practice views to use:

Salt Lake City area. More than 80 per cent of Utah's people live in the 115- by 130-mile area, *left*. In this false color ERTS photo, the cross-shaped blue-gray area between Great Salt Lake, northwest, and Utah Lake is Salt Lake City. Ogden lies just east of Great Salt Lake. The crests of the Wasatch Mountains are snow-covered, but the slopes and farms are bright red, suggesting it is spring or autumn. The color change across the lake is a change in water density made by a railroad causeway, which interferes with lake circulation.

Chicago area. From Gary, Ind., to its northern suburbs, metropolitan Chicago hugs the Lake Michigan shoreline in a true color Skylab photo, *above*. City streets and interstate highways are clearly seen. Navy Pier, a half-mile long, juts into the lake near the center of the city. Far to the west is the mile-wide main ring of the Fermi National Accelerator Laboratory.

ERTS and Skylab pictures of the United States and Canada are available at modest cost. To learn what your area looks like from space, write to: EROS Data Center, Sioux Falls, S. Dak. 57198.

Research In Orbit

By William J. Cromie

Skylab astronauts proved that man can live and work for months in space, gathering valuable data for earthbound scientists

Early in the morning of Sept. 7, 1973, a mass of hot gas and charged particles 10 times the size of the earth erupted from the sun. A world-wide sun-watching network spotted the solar flare traveling toward earth at 35,000 miles (56,000 kilometers) per second. It would collide violently with the earth's magnetic field in about 45 minutes.

Orbiting 270 miles (435 kilometers) above the earth was a space station with a $121-million complex of solar telescopes and sensing equipment. The station's crew of three astronauts were thus in a unique position to observe a well-known but little-understood phenomenon which exerts widespread effects on weather and communications on our planet. But could they be alerted in time to man the controls of the solar observatory?

Hopes fell when the space station orbited beyond radio range of the ground station at Guam before a message could be sent. A communication problem prevented contact by the next station, the U.S.N.S. *Vanguard,* cruising in the South Atlantic Ocean.

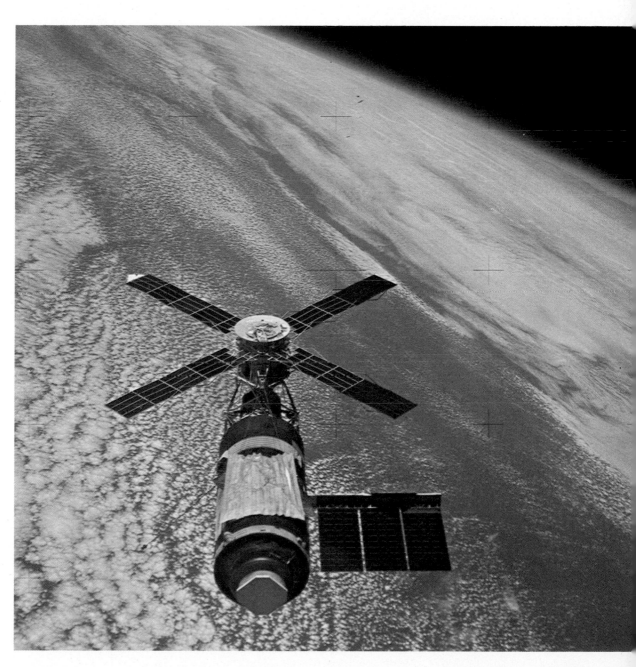

Finally, ground teams on Ascension Island in the South Atlantic contacted mission commander Alan L. Bean. "It's the big daddy," he said, referring to the solar flare. The astronauts had been taking data on the flare since the sun became visible to them that morning.

"The crew observed the flare exactly the way everybody wanted them to do it," recalled James Milligan, a solar physicist with the National Aeronautics and Space Administration (NASA).

To Milligan, and to the vast majority of NASA scientists, Bean's performance proved the value of manned space flights. But not everyone shared this view when the United States launched its first experimental space station, called Skylab, on May 14, 1973. During the next nine months, it was both home and laboratory to three separate crews. The last crew boarded Skylab in November, 1973, and spent a record-breaking 84 days in the roomy, gravity-free station that had become man's first space colony.

Skylab marked a turning point from missions of exploration and testing in space to missions where men lived and worked in orbit on a routine basis. It represented a step from small to large spacecraft, from short- to long-duration missions. Instead of being primarily explorers, Skylab astronauts functioned as scientists, technicians, and observers.

The nine Skylab astronauts spent a total of 172 days in the 117-foot (35-meter)-long space laboratory, which contained as much living and working space as a small 3-bedroom house. They measured their own physical performance during prolonged exposure to weightlessness. Circling above the earth's atmosphere, which hinders landbound astronomers because it scatters light and absorbs ultraviolet radiation and X rays, they trained their telescopes not only on the sun, but on comets, stars, and galactic bodies as well. In this way, they collected data which observatories on earth could not obtain. Working in the weightlessness and vacuum of space orbit, the astronauts experimented with materials. For example, they grew crystals and joined metals together. And passing over 75 per cent of earth's surface, they surveyed its resources and gathered information that could be used by pecan growers in Sequin, Tex., as well as by geologists, oceanographers, and many other earth scientists.

NASA's $2.6-billion Skylab project was a highly ambitious undertaking considering that, barely 12 years earlier, many medical experts doubted that man could survive at all in space. Prior to Skylab, the longest U.S. mission–Gemini 7 in 1965–had lasted only 14 days. In 1971, three Russian cosmonauts died during their return to earth following 24 days in an orbiting spacecraft. Although the deaths were attributed to a leaky hatch seal, scientists wondered whether deterioration of the cosmonauts' physical and mental condition, caused by their lengthy stay in space, might have contributed to the tragedy.

American astronauts who had flown to the moon lost weight, plasma and red cells from their blood, and calcium from their bones. Aerospace doctors feared that, on longer missions, a man's cardiovas-

The author:
William J. Cromie is Director of Research and Development for Field Enterprises Educational Corporation, and a frequent *Science Year* contributor.

cular system would deteriorate because his heart would not have to pump the blood against the pull of gravity. They also worried about the difficulties of readapting to earth's gravity. "Maybe you could live out there for five years, then die when you re-enter because readaptation is what kills you and not the other way around," NASA medical officer Jerry R. Hordinsky commented.

The key question to be answered by Skylab was, "Can man survive long-duration flights without compromising his ability to work in space?" To find out, the astronauts shared their living compartment with biomedical equipment that monitored changes in their physiological condition. Experiments checked sleep patterns; changes in muscle and the cardiovascular system; losses of blood plasma, red cells, and body fluids; nervous system responses such as balance and orientation; and energy expenditure. The astronauts weighed all the food they ate, as well as all body wastes. Samples of the latter were frozen and brought back for analysis. Once each week, they drew blood samples and partially processed them for later study on earth.

One major medical experiment was carried out in a cylindrical chamber resembling an iron lung. Each day, one of the crew lowered his feet, legs, and lower trunk into this lower body negative pressure device (LBNPD). Sealed at the waist to form an airtight chamber, the LBNPD was pumped down to one pound per square inch (0.7 newton per square centimeter) below cabin pressure. Sensors monitored the astronaut's vital signs as his heart began pumping harder to prevent blood from pooling in his legs.

This simulated a return to earth, where gravity would cause blood to shift into the lower parts of the body. By monitoring the response of the cardiovascular system to this stress, physicians on earth could detect any deterioration in the heart and blood vessels.

Results of such experiments gave doctors the answers they sought. "We didn't see any appreciable muscle atrophy [wasting away]," said W. Royce Hawkins, deputy director for medical operations at NASA's Lyndon B. Johnson Space Center near Houston. "Losses of bone calcium were not large enough to cause bone fractures or weakness. The astronauts' hearts did not deteriorate significantly. Before we flew Skylab, I thought we would see far greater changes in the astronauts' cardiovascular systems. But what we saw in space were crews looking more or less like they did during preflight."

However, physicians did discover at least one startling physical effect. Careful measurements showed that the third crew—astronauts Gerald P. Carr, Edward G. Gibson, and William R. Pogue—gained up to 2 inches (5 centimeters) in height after they left earth. "The same thing must have happened on earlier missions, but we didn't find it until the last flight," said Hordinsky, who attributes the change to a lengthening of the spinal column. Weightlessness removes the gravitational force that normally compresses the spine. The disks between the vertebrae expand, the spinal column lengthens, and the astronaut

Key to Skylab

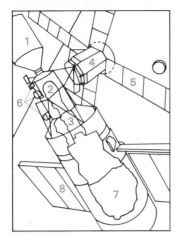

1. Command and Service Module. 2. Multiple Docking Adapter. 3. Airlock Module. 4. Apollo Telescope Mount. 5. Solar Arrays. 6. Earth Resources Sensors. 7. Crew Quarters. 8. Solar Array.

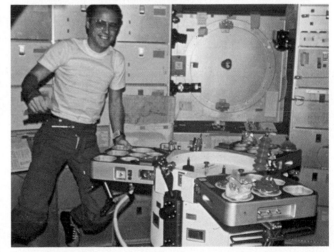

Orbiting 270 miles above the earth's surface, Skylab astronauts learned to cope with prolonged weightlessness. Gerald P. Carr and William R. Pogue put out the trash, *top.* Jack R. Lousma takes a hot shower in space, *above left,* and Edward G. Gibson cooks a meal in the space galley, *above.* Joseph Kerwin is strapped in for the night, *left,* his headgear monitoring the quality of his sleep.

"grows." When he returns to earth, the force of gravity "shrinks" him to his preflight height in two days or less.

While the Skylab astronauts may have gained in length, they lost weight—as much as 8 pounds (3½ kilograms). This was due to loss of fluids. Other physical changes were due to fluid shifts. Blood and body fluids moved upward, producing feelings of fullness in the head during the first few days in space. The shift caused their calves to shrink in circumference by as much as 1½ inches (4 centimeters). It also produced changes in heart size. "Overall, the crews showed a decrease of from 1 to 3 per cent in heart size as measured by the cardiothoracic area ratio," said Hawkins, "but this was not statistically significant." He believes that the shrinkage was caused by a reduction of as much as 15 per cent in the volume of blood plasma that the astronaut's heart pumped, not by a loss of heart muscle.

From data on previous manned space flights, NASA physicians expected most of these medical changes. The nagging question that only Skylab could answer was whether the changes would level off after a period of adaptation. Blood plasma loss, calcium loss, and other medical changes did level off after about 40 days in orbit. After this, further significant medical changes could no longer be detected. The astronauts felt that they adapted even sooner. "After 25 days, we seemed to hit a groove," said Bean. "After that point, we felt we could have stayed up indefinitely."

A dramatic difference was observed in the time it took the crews to return to their preflight condition. Charles Conrad, Jr., Joseph P. Kerwin, and Paul J. Weitz—the first crew—spent 28 days in orbit. It required 21 days before their cardiovascular system and muscles readapted to earth's gravity. Alan L. Bean, Owen K. Garriott, and Jack R. Lousma spent almost 60 days in space, yet they reached the same preflight condition in five days. The third crew, who orbited for 84 days, had their heart and muscles back in preflight condition in about four days. In other respects, such as regaining lost blood cells and normal calf girth, they recovered faster than the second crew.

The best explanation for the quicker recovery involves the amount of exercise while in orbit. During the first mission, astronauts exercised 30 minutes each day. The second crew increased this to 60 minutes. The third crew worked out for 90 minutes each day on equipment such as a stationary bicycle, or ergometer, and a treadmill device carried up to Skylab by the third crew.

"Exercise definitely played a significant role in the recovery condition of the astronauts," said Hawkins. "Exercise and more time for body functions to stabilize, or adapt to weightlessness, were the big differences from one flight to the next.

"From what we learn from Skylab," continued Hawkins, "we'll develop criteria and standards for selecting nonastronauts, including women, as working passengers on flights in the 1980s. We've learned that the human body is sufficiently adaptive so that the average healthy person can make space flights of up to 30 days, with enough exercise to maintain him or her."

But even if average, healthy men and women can stay fit through 30 days of space flight, is there really any good reason for putting them in orbit? Scientists who participated in Skylab experiments think there is. Many were once skeptical about Skylab's value. For example, Leo Goldberg, director of the Kitt Peak Observatory near Tucson, Ariz., first regarded the program as "a mere exercise in manned space flight." However, Goldberg told a 1973 meeting of the American Astronomical Society that "the scientific gains from Skylab have been tremendous." He called the program "one of the most important events in solar physics."

Goldberg's enthusiasm and that of other solar physicists for Skylab comes from thousands of detailed solar observations. Operating controls located in a compartment called the multiple docking adapter,

Skylab structures and the earth below reflect from Jack Lousma's helmet visor as he erects an umbrella to shade the Orbital Workshop. Solar cell array, background, generated electric power for solar instruments.

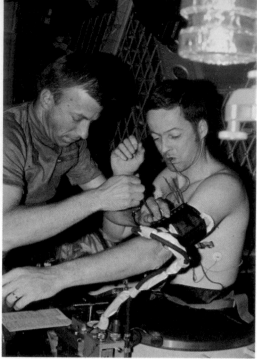

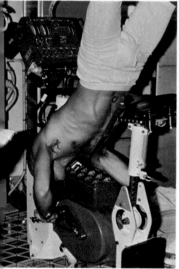

Astronauts exercised and checked vital signs daily. Charles Conrad pedals stationary cycle with his hands, *above,* and Alan Bean "weighs" himself, *top.* Paul Weitz helps Kerwin take his blood pressure while under stress, *top right.*

astronauts aimed eight precisely aligned instruments at specific target areas on the sun. These instruments were part of the Apollo Telescope Mount (ATM) set up on a truss structure perpendicular to the cylindrical space station. Five ATM instruments were sensitive to ultraviolet (UV) and X rays. Cameras attached to two other telescopes took television and still photographs of red light emitted by hydrogen atoms, the most abundant element on the sun. The eighth instrument, a coronagraph, artificially eclipsed the bright solar disk so that the sun's corona, or outer atmosphere, which is only one 10-billionth as bright as the main disk, was visible.

These experiments produced so much data that solar physicists will be analyzing it through 1975, or longer. This new information should result in a much clearer picture of what goes on in the sun. Already solar scientists are sketching a more detailed and dynamic picture of the sun's atmosphere than previously imagined.

Examining ATM X-ray images, researchers saw for the first time that the entire solar disk is peppered with bright points, each about 15,000 miles (24,000 kilometers) in diameter. Solar theorists interpret these features as the upper ends of magnetic field lines along which mass and energy travel outward from the inner reaches of the sun to the corona. They suspect that these bright points are involved in the surprising rise in temperature from about 10,000°F. (6000°C.) at the sun's visible surface to 2,000,000°F. (1,100,000°C.) thousands of miles above in the sun's gaseous corona.

Below the corona lies the chromosphere, or lower atmosphere. Skylab data produced the first evidence that cells of hot gas, up to 20,000 miles (32,000 kilometers) in diameter, extend up into the chromosphere from lower regions. Scientists see these supergranulated cells, as they are called, as the tops of convection currents bringing energy up from the center of the sun where it is generated by nuclear fusion. Rising from the outer margins of supergranulated cells, luminous jets of gas, or spicules, shoot up thousands of miles. Solar scientists suspect a close tie between spicules and bright points. The key to the nature of this tie may lie in Skylab observational data. If it does, one of the biggest mysteries of the universe will be solved—how energy is transferred from the inner furnace of a star to its atmosphere, then outward to make planets warm enough for life to arise and thrive.

Before Skylab, scientists visualized the corona as a continuous blanket of gas and charged particles which expanded uniformly as it became heated from below. This expansion, they thought, produced the rarefied solar wind, which blows across the void between the sun and earth at speeds of 300 miles (500 kilometers) a second. Skylab data clearly reveals that the corona contains dark regions called coronal holes—areas in the sun's outer atmosphere which are devoid of material. These areas are extremely stable, lasting for several months. Researchers generally agree that coronal holes are regions where closed magnetic field lines channel a solar wind of hydrogen gas and charged particles outward into the solar system.

Stuart Jordan, chief of solar physics for NASA's Office of Space Science, suspects that these channels cause changes in weather on earth. "Statistically significant evidence indicates that a reduction in severe storms occurs when the magnetic boundaries [of coronal holes] contact our atmosphere," he says.

"Sitting" at the Apollo Telescope Mount console in Skylab's Multiple Docking Adapter, science pilot Garriott gets ready to make solar observations.

The ability of ATM instruments to view the sun simultaneously at many wave lengths, Jordan points out, "allows theoreticians to build up a 3-dimensional model of the whole solar atmosphere." Such a model would be of value to a much broader range of scientists than just solar physicists. "Because our sun is a fairly typical star, understanding it would allow astronomers to learn a lot about most of the stars in the universe," he explains. "And by understanding why magnetic structures like coronal holes are stable over a long period of time, fusion energy researchers will have knowledge that may help them to develop fusion energy on the earth."

The third Skylab crew used the ATM telescopes, together with a special UV camera they had carried aloft, to gather information about Comet Kohoutek. In the first above-atmosphere observation of a comet by man, they monitored Kohoutek daily from late November, 1973, to late January, 1974. The UV camera was used outside the station during spacewalks on December 25 and December 29. See A COSMIC LABORATORY.

Solar researchers and comet watchers were not the only scientists elated by Skylab findings. A complex of cameras and sensors aboard the space station comprised the most sophisticated earth-monitoring system sent into space to date. Called EREP (Earth Resources Experiment Package), the six instruments gathered data for 137 scientists in 19 countries. This information provided oceanographers, meteorologists, urban planners, forest managers, fishermen, mapmakers, and prospectors with data not otherwise available. See CATALOGING THE WHOLE EARTH.

Skylab's EREP program was designed to test the value of different types of earth-monitoring sensors, so scientists could decide which instruments to use on future manned and unmanned space missions. EREP sensors recorded in different wave lengths in the visible, infrared, and microwave portion of the spectrum. They recorded data on photographic film and magnetic tape. For example, one EREP experiment, the Multispectral Photographic Cameras, contained six cameras precisely aligned to view the same 100-mile (161-kilometer) square of earth. Each camera was fitted with filters and film responsive to only one band of visible or infrared radiation.

Each object on the surface emits a characteristic pattern of radiation, which changes with the physical condition of the object. Scientists call these characteristic patterns spectral signatures, and use them to determine, for example, whether a field contains ripe green soybeans or a mixture of brown and green grass.

EREP experiments extended the spectral range and resolution of sensors aboard unmanned earth resources satellites and added microwave data. By recording two separate frequencies of microwaves, the effect of clouds on data recorded by the EREP instruments could be measured. This had the effect of allowing a visible light or infrared instrument to "see" through clouds.

An enormous solar eruption sent helium from the sun's surface arching 500,000 miles into the hot solar corona, and was recorded, *below,* on film during the third mission. Color processing makes the denser parts of the eruption appear darker in color, *right.*

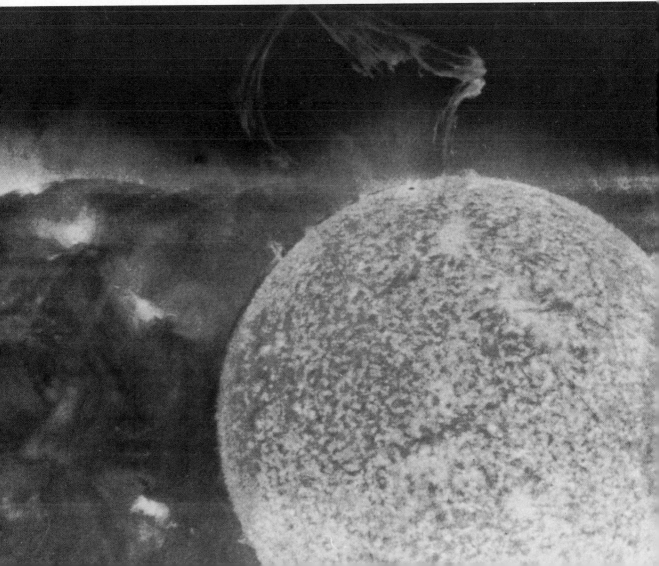

EREP also included radar and microwave devices to measure wave heights and sea surface temperatures. Astronauts monitored two hurricanes and one of the largest storms in a decade in the North Atlantic. Observations of Hurricane Ava off the west coast of Mexico, on June 6, 1973, recorded wind speeds ranging from 15 to 150 miles (24 to 240 kilometers) per hour, conditions ranging from clear skies to cloud systems characteristic of intense hurricanes, and sea conditions ranging from calm to 45-foot (14-meter) waves. "The equivalent coverage," stated a NASA report, "could only have been obtained by either hundreds of specially instrumented buoys and ships, or several fleets of aircraft." The Skylab data will help NASA planners determine the best sensors to use in future weather and oceanographic satellites.

In addition to evaluating sensors, NASA wanted to determine how much scientific data could be obtained by astronauts using a hand-held camera and looking out Skylab's single 18-inch (46-centimeter)-diameter window. Experts in 18 different disciplines trained the third crew to make observations of such things as geological faults, sand dune patterns, snow and ice cover, pollution sources, cloud cover, and sea conditions. The more than 800 observations they made turned out to be of much greater interest than expected.

Examining photographs taken on the first Skylab mission, oceanographer Robert E. Stevenson of the Office of Naval Research, La Jolla, Calif., spotted large eddies, circular patterns of surface water, in the Yucatán Current off the east coast of Mexico. About 40 to 50 miles (64 to 80 kilometers) across, these eddies mark ocean upwellings, areas where cold water rises from depths of 400 feet (122 meters) or more to the surface. Stevenson asked the third crew to take more photographs of the Yucatán eddies. They did this, and also spotted eddies in many other locations—off both coasts of South America, off Australia and New Zealand, off Africa, and off the Hawaiian Islands. Two of these—one off the east coast of New Zealand and another in the vicinity of French Frigate Shoal in the Hawaiian Island chain—were unknown before Skylab. Stevenson called the finding that eddies occur worldwide and mark ocean upwellings "the biggest discovery in oceanography in the past decade."

Because ocean upwellings bring up nutrients from deep waters, they establish potentially rich fishing grounds. Microscopic floating plants and animals called plankton feed on these nutrients, and in turn form the basic food source for larger marine animals. Upwellings also play a major role in the exchange of heat energy between the ocean and the atmosphere. This exchange governs changes in the weather and, over the long term, the global heat balance. The cold water may particularly influence the behavior of hurricanes. These storms draw their energy from heat fed into the air from warmer water, and they become weakened when passing over colder water.

When not making observations of themselves, the sun, and earth, Skylab astronauts spent time at a unique work station in the multiple

Science Fairs in Orbit

In January, 1972, the National Aeronautics and Space Administration (NASA) asked high school students to propose experiments that Skylab astronauts could perform in orbit. Working through the National Science Teachers Association (NSTA), the space agency sponsored a national competition to select the 25 best proposals. NSTA reviewed 3,409 applications and selected the winners in April, 1972.

Nineteen of these experiments were performed on the three Skylab missions. They ranged from looking for a new planet between Mercury and the sun to establishing a method of predicting volcanic activity.

Students designed the only Skylab experiment involving plants. Cheryl A. Peltz of Littleton, Colo., designed an experiment to see if weightlessness affects the movement of a plant cell's cytoplasm, the jellylike fluid in which most of the cell's activity takes place. In Skylab, on Nov. 26, 1973, astronaut Edward Gibson mounted a leaf from the water plant *Elodea* on a glass slide, and took movies of the cytoplasm through a microscope. Although his pictures were of poor quality, the cytoplasm appeared to move in space the same way it does on earth. In another experiment, suggested by Joel G. Wordekemper of West Point, Nebr., and Donald W. Schlack of Downey, Calif., rice seeds grew normally and oriented toward light in the absence of gravity. These and other student experiments provided the first information for U.S. scientists on the feasibility of using plants on spacecraft for food, for maintaining oxygen in the air, and for recycling human and other organic wastes.

On November 25, the third Skylab crew tested eye-hand coordination in an experiment designed by student Kathy Jackson of Houston. The test required them to insert a thin stylus in a definite sequence into 119 small holes arranged in a maze. They performed the same test on the ground before and after the space flight, and the results showed that the astronauts' coordination did not deteriorate after a long period of weightlessness.

The student experiment receiving the most attention involved two female spiders—Anita and Arabella—who tried to spin webs without a sense of gravity, or up and down, to guide them. The idea for the experiment came from 17-year-old Judith S. Miles of Lexington, Mass. At first, the cross spiders—a common backyard variety—were disoriented in space. After refusing to come out of the vial in which she was carried aloft, Arabella finally emerged into her clear plastic cage. She spent a day bouncing from wall to wall with her legs flopping around, but the next day she began spinning small webs in the corners of her cage. She began to spin normal webs without gravity's guidance the next day—sooner than expected. Anita replaced Arabella in the cage on August 27, and she, too, adapted to weightlessness, but refused to eat and died of starvation in mid-September. Arabella died later.

The richness of information from the student projects surprised some NASA scientists. "Frankly, we didn't expect much in the way of scientific results," admitted John MacLeod, a NASA engineer and adviser on the project. "But we found the possibility of real scientific payoff in some areas." He cited an experiment designed by Terry C. Quist of San Antonio, Tex., to detect neutrons, the chargeless particles in atomic nuclei. For years, physicists have tried to measure the number of high-energy neutrons, which stream from the sun, are reflected from earth, and are released in cosmic-ray collisions. Because they possess such high energies and have no electric charge, the neutrons pass right through most detecting devices.

Quist suggested using Skylab's water-storage tanks to slow down the neutrons enough to allow them to be counted by conventional detectors. "I was amazed by the proposal when I received it," said MacLeod. Quist's plan worked. Twice as many neutrons were found as scientists had predicted. This discovery could be extremely significant in understanding what goes on in the space environment near earth.   [w.j.c.]

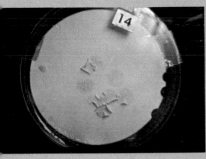

Web spinning by weightless spiders, *top,* and bacterial growth in space were two of the Skylab experiments suggested by students.

A large typhoon vortex centered southeast of New Zealand in the south central Pacific Ocean was photographed by the third Skylab crew.

docking adapter–the Materials Processing Facility. It provided a chamber and furnace in which experiments were performed under conditions of high vacuum and almost complete absence of gravity.

Most of the experiments involved heating metals and crystals in the cylindrical electric furnace designed to fit in the vacuum chamber. The first Skylab crew did three metals experiments. The second crew performed 11 crystal growth experiments, and the last crew repeated 7 experiments which showed the most interesting results.

According to William R. Lucas, director of the Marshall Space Flight Center (MSFC), Huntsville, Ala., the weightless condition aboard spacecraft eliminates mixing caused by gravity and convection. For example, on earth the hot parts of liquid crystals or metals tend to rise, while the cooler parts sink. Heavier metals in an alloy settle to the bottom of a container. Such separation and mixing make it impossible to obtain perfect crystals or evenly distributed additives. This affects the basic properties of materials, such as electrical conductivity or mechanical strength. Semiconductor crystals used in solid-state electronic products depend on the uniform spread of impurities, called dopants, throughout the crystals for their desired electrical properties. Better-structured crystals and more uniform distribution of dopants make possible smaller, cheaper, more efficient devices ranging from hand calculators and television sets to power-switching networks and cells to convert solar energy into electricity.

Absence of convection in Skylab produced the hoped-for chemical uniformity. The astronauts alloyed gold and germanium, two metals which do not mix well on earth. The gold-germanium alloy was found to be a superconductor at about 1.5°C. above absolute zero; that is, it lost all resistance to electric flow. Similar mixtures melted and resolidified on earth are not superconductive. Lucas sees in such findings a sign that "we are on the right track in pursuing the processing of materials in space as a practical matter."

Skylab's materials experiments also demonstrated the practicability of welding, brazing, and casting metals in space—important findings for future missions in which astronauts would assemble or repair large space stations in orbit. In one experiment, brazing of two steel tubes produced what investigator J. R. Williams of MSFC called "the most perfect braze joint I've ever seen."

In their varied roles, the three Skylab crews demonstrated that man can do useful work in space. Proponents of manned space flight argue that, if Skylab had been an unmanned program, it would have been a failure. Shortly before the uninhabited space station reached orbit in May, 1973, aerodynamic pressure ripped off a meteoroid and heat shield, tore away one large panel of power-generating solar cells, and jammed another panel in an unusable position. In a dramatic demonstration of skill and courage, astronauts Conrad, Kerwin, and Weitz boarded the crippled spacecraft on May 25, and they had corrected all the major problems by June 7. The three men then went on to complete 85 per cent of the scientific objectives that were originally planned for their 28-day space flight.

Despite valuable new data about the sun, the earth, and material processing, many scientists question the value of spending so much money to send men into space. They point to the astonishingly rich trove of scientific information collected by unmanned Mariner and Pioneer space probes on missions to Mars, Jupiter, Venus, and Mercury as examples of dollars better spent for space exploration. And most scientists involved in Skylab agree that the majority of its experiments could have been designed for unmanned operation. However, it would have required a far greater cost and a much higher degree of complexity to build an unmanned station with the same capabilities as Skylab. Nor would we now have the important biomedical data.

Skylab director William C. Schneider views manned and unmanned space flight as complementary, rather than contradictory, approaches. "When you understand almost all of what is going to happen on a mission, you can program a computer, and an unmanned mission is most economical," he says. "When you need decision-making ability, flexibility in selecting data, ability to handle unexpected situations and to make repairs, then you need a man up there."

The Climates Of Planets

By Carl Sagan

Seeking to prevent the earth from becoming another Mars or Venus, scientists turn to these other worlds for clues to the causes and cures of climatic change

Between 30 and 10 million years ago, it is thought, temperatures on the earth slowly declined, by just a few degrees. Vast forests receded toward more tropical latitudes, slowly removing the habitats of small, furry creatures, weighing only a few pounds, that had spent their days swinging from branch to branch. Some of the creatures followed the forests. With the forests gone, only those creatures able to survive on the grassy plains remained behind. Today, some tens of millions of years later, those creatures have left two kinds of descendants—baboons and men. We may owe our very existence to world temperature changes that, on the average, amount to only a few degrees.

The character of life on earth has been powerfully influenced by climate variations, which continue today. But earth is not alone in experiencing these changes. Other planets have climatic fluctuations, and some of the same factors that produce such fluctuations on earth also affect earth's nearest neighbors, Mars and Venus. Perhaps the

sharpest test of theories of climatology is that they be able to account for the climates of all three planets. Insights gained from the study of one planet will inevitably improve our understanding of the others.

There are many indications of past climate changes on earth. One approach, which may be valid for a million years back in time, is based on the ratio of two isotopes of oxygen—oxygen 18 to oxygen 16— in the carbonates of shells of fossil foraminifera, tiny, one-celled sea animals similar to species that can be studied today. The ratio varies with the temperature of the water in which these animals grew.

There are also more direct fossil indicators. For example, the widespread presence of figs, palms, and corals implies high temperatures in the epoch in which these organisms flourished. Similarly, the widespread remains of large hairy animals, such as mammoths, indicate a past period of low temperatures.

The geological record provides extensive evidence of glaciers—great flowing sheets of ice that leave characteristic boulders and traces of erosion. There is also clear evidence of beds of evaporites—regions where briny water has evaporated, leaving behind the salts. Such evaporation usually occurs in warm climates.

When this range of climatic information is put together, a complex pattern emerges of temperature variation with time. The average temperature of the earth today is roughly 57°F. (14°C.). At no time has the earth's average temperature dropped below the freezing point of water, and at no time has it even come close to the normal boiling point of water. But variations of several degrees are common over long periods of time and variations of many tens of degrees may have occurred locally in some places.

Fluctuations of several degrees characteristically occur over periods of tens of thousands of years. But climate also varies over much longer periods, some as long as 200 or 300 million years. Relatively warm periods appear to have occurred about 650 million and 270 million years ago. The most recent Ice Age began from 1 million to 1.5 million years ago, and has included four major periods of glaciation. At present, we are in an interglacial period, but by past climatic standards we are still in the midst of an Ice Age. The warm temperatures of the past few hundred years, far from being normal, are highly unusual. And there are signs that we may be plunging back into the cold worldwide temperatures characteristic of our epoch as seen from the perspective of geological time.

The energy for heating the earth comes almost exclusively from sunlight, the energy conducted to the earth's surface from its hot interior amounting to less than 0.001 per cent of the energy that arrives from the sun as visible light. But the earth does not absorb all the sunlight it receives. Some is reflected back to space by clouds, by polar ice, and by rocks and sand and water. The average albedo, or reflectivity, of the earth is about 35 per cent—as measured directly from satellites and indirectly from earthshine reflected off the moon.

The author:
Carl Sagan is director of the Laboratory for Planetary Studies, and professor of astronomy and space sciences at Cornell University in Ithaca, N.Y. One of his principal research activities is the study of planetary atmospheres.

Mars' Tilt with Time

Degrees of obliquity

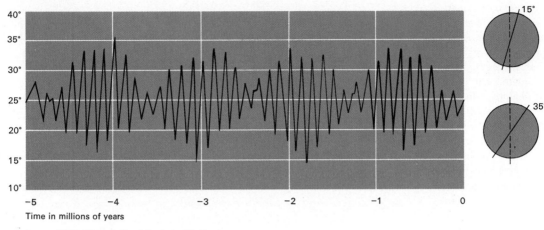

Time in millions of years

Source: William Ward, California Institute of Technology

The tilt, or obliquity, of the Martian axis has varied periodically from about
15° to 35° over the past 5 million years. At present, it is about 25°.
Major climatic changes may occur as the axis tips more toward the sun.

The 65 per cent of sunlight that is absorbed should, according to theory, heat the earth to a temperature of 0°F. (-18°C.), a temperature well below the freezing point of seawater (about 25°F.) and far colder than the earth's measured average temperature. This discrepancy is due to a phenomenon known as the greenhouse effect. Visible light from the sun easily penetrates the earth's transparent atmosphere to the surface. Because the surface is much colder than the sun, however, it radiates the energy back into space in the infrared. The atmosphere is not so transparent to infrared radiation, and at some wave lengths, the radiation travels only a few inches before being absorbed by atmospheric gases. Thermal radiation from the surface is impeded from escaping to space. In order to have a balance between the radiation received by the earth from the sun and the radiation emitted by the earth to space, the surface temperature must rise to a higher equilibrium value. This greenhouse effect on earth is due not to the major atmospheric constituents, such as oxygen and nitrogen, but almost entirely to minor constituents in the atmosphere, especially carbon dioxide (CO_2) and water vapor.

The observed average temperature of a planet can be explained quite well with the existing intensity of sunlight, global albedo, greenhouse effect, and *obliquity* (tilt of the planet's rotational axis from the perpendicular to the orbital plane). But these factors can vary, and climatic changes can be due to changes in any of them.

Certain feedback mechanisms probably have an effect. For example, suppose the earth's temperature dropped by 4 or 5 degrees. The

A Wobbling Top

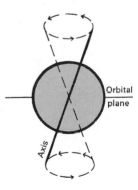

Mars' axis slowly traces circles in the sky, just as the axis of a top wobbles as it spins. This motion, called precession and caused by the tug of other planets, changes the angle at which sunlight falls on Mars' poles and equator.

151

The Delicate Balance

Part of the radiation received by a planet as visible sunlight is reflected back by the surface. The rest is absorbed sunlight, reradiated at infrared wave lengths. In an atmosphere, certain gases may absorb some of the infrared wave lengths. To maintain the equilibrium between the radiation received and that sent back to space, the planet's temperature must rise.

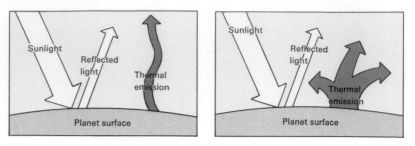

amount of water vapor in the atmosphere would also decline because at lower temperatures the air can hold less water. Less water vapor implies a smaller greenhouse effect and a still lower temperature, which may result in even less atmospheric water vapor, and so on. Likewise, a decline in temperature might increase the amount of polar ice, raising the albedo and decreasing the temperature still further. On the other hand, a decline in temperature may reduce cloudiness, decreasing the average albedo and increasing the temperature—perhaps enough to undo the initial temperature decline.

It is also possible that the plant and animal life on earth acts as a kind of thermostat to prevent extreme temperature variations that might have unpleasant consequences for global biology. For example, a temperature decline might encourage the growth of some species of hardy plant with extensive ground cover and low albedo, thus moderating the original temperature decline.

Over the years, there have been almost 100 different, and generally mutually exclusive, theories of climatic change on earth, and even today the subject is hardly marked by a unanimity of opinion. This is not because climatologists are by nature ignorant or contentious, but rather because the subject is exceedingly complex.

One of the more fashionable theories emphasizes astronomical factors that influence the amount of sunlight the earth receives and how it is distributed. One such factor is the obliquity of the earth, which is about 23½° today. It can change by perhaps several degrees over millions of years, thus alternately tipping the poles toward and away from more direct sunlight. Another factor is the precession of the equinoxes, in which the earth's axis slowly traces an imaginary circle in the sky over tens of thousands of years, in the same way that the axis of a spinning top slowly drifts in a circle. This also changes the angle at which sunlight falls on the equator and poles. Finally, the shape of the earth's orbit, which is today slightly elongated, or elliptical, varies over time due to the gravitational pulls and tugs of nearby planets. Detailed calculations of these three variations show that they can cause at least a few degrees of temperature change and, with possible feedbacks, this might be adequate to explain major climatic variations.

Another possible source of climatic change is albedo variation. One of the more striking causes for such variation is the injection of massive amounts of dust into the earth's atmosphere. The eruption of the Indonesian volcano, Krakatoa, in 1883, for example, spewed into the atmosphere vast amounts of dust that took several years to settle out. Such fine particles, distributed globally and slowly falling out of the stratosphere, seem to increase the earth's albedo and thus cool the planet. Sediment core samples indicate that past epochs of extensive volcanic activity coincided with glaciation and low temperatures.

Finally, some scientists have speculated that the sun's brightness may vary periodically and affect the climate. According to theories of solar evolution, the sun has been growing slowly but steadily brighter over many billions of years. But apart from this slow increase in solar luminosity, is it possible that fluctuations occur over shorter time spans? This is an important and unsolved problem. There is a continuing difficulty in detecting solar neutrinos, which, according to theory, should be emitted from the interior of the sun. A possible explanation is that periodic changes in the sun's core produce variations both in the number of neutrinos emitted and in solar brightness. The failure to detect neutrinos in the predicted amounts suggests that the sun is today in an abnormally dim period.

The inability to decide among alternative models of climatic change underlines the difficulties of this subject. When scientists are faced

Particles put into the air by volcanoes such as Japan's Sakurajima may change the climate by decreasing the amount of sunlight received.

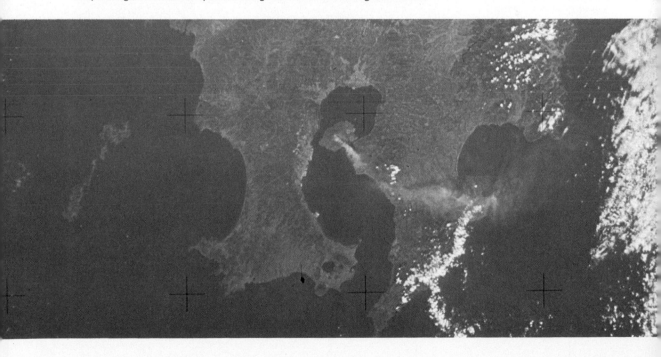

The Winds of Mars

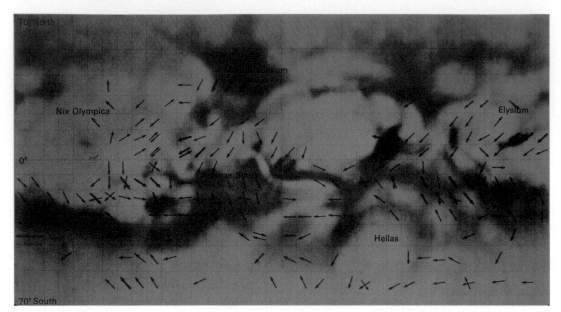

Source: Joseph Veverka and Carl Sagan, Cornell University

A Martian wind chart, *above,* derived when a major dust storm cleared in 1973, shows a basic circulation pattern that is strongly affected by topography. Prevailing summer winds on earth, *right,* show the more uniform flow patterns caused by temperature.

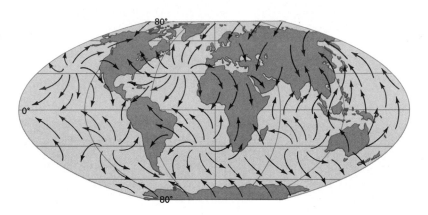

with difficult theoretical problems, they sometimes turn to experiments. Experimenting with the earth's climate, however, is difficult, expensive, and potentially dangerous. By the greatest good fortune, nature has provided us with nearby planets that display significantly different physical environments. They are superbly designed laboratories for studying climate variations.

Venus may be a case where the greenhouse effect has gotten out of hand. The surface temperature there has stabilized at about 900°F. (480°C.), and the atmosphere, composed primarily of CO_2, has a surface pressure about 90 times that at the surface of the earth. Water vapor is present only as a minor constituent of the atmosphere, perhaps 0.1 per cent. This amount of water vapor is about 0.03 per cent of that in the earth's oceans. The amount of CO_2 is about the same as that locked in the earth's crust as carbonates.

Apparently, the earth has so far escaped a climatic fate similar to that of Venus primarily because the earth is somewhat farther from the sun. Billions of years ago, when the planets first formed, the surface of Venus was probably warmer than that of the earth, resulting in larger quantities of atmospheric water vapor on Venus. The water vapor, through the greenhouse effect, caused the surface to be heated still higher, driving off more water vapor, and so on. The high temperatures also prevented the laying down of volcanic CO_2 as carbonates in the Venus crust. Finally, so much water vapor and CO_2 had collected in the primitive Venus atmosphere that the climate reached a point of no return. There was no chance that water vapor could condense on the hot surface or that much CO_2 could be laid down as carbonates. A runaway greenhouse effect ensued, stabilizing at the present conditions.

An estimated increase of from 10 to 20 per cent in the amount of sunlight absorbed by the earth for several centuries might be enough to convert it to a smoldering inferno similar to Venus. Venus may be a cautionary tale against recklessly changing the earth's environment.

Some of the most interesting hints about the nature of climatic change are coming from Mars, thanks to Mariner 9, which returned scientific data for a full year from its Martian orbit. When Mariner 9 arrived at Mars in November, 1971, no surface detail was visible because the planet was in the throes of a great dust storm. Mariner observations showed that atmospheric temperatures increased during the storm, while surface temperatures decreased. This simple observation provided a clear case of the cooling of a planet surface by the

Streaks of bright dust streaming from the Martian craters act as a sort of natural weather vane, pointing out the directions of the prevailing winds.

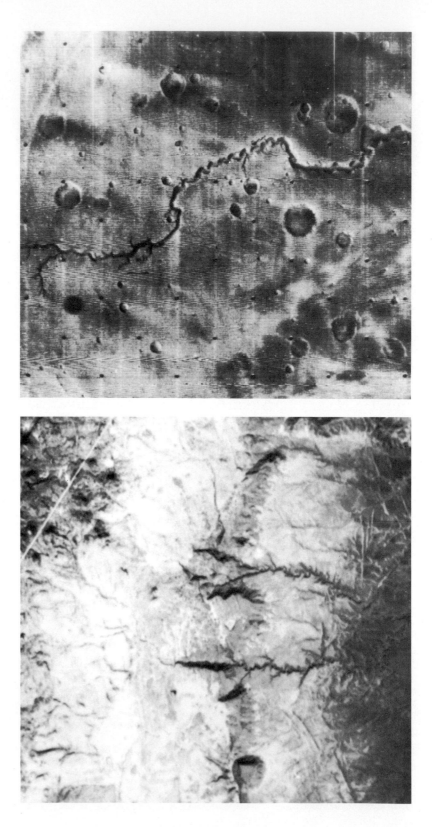

Many of the sinuous Martian channels have branching tributaries, *above right,* strikingly similar to patterns carved by rivers on earth, *right.* Many scientists believe this indicates that water once flowed on Mars.

massive injection of dust into its atmosphere. Scientists are now studying what happened on Mars in late 1971 to better understand what happens to the climate on earth when massive amounts of dust are put into the atmosphere.

An entirely unexpected finding was numerous sinuous channels, with tributaries, that cover the equatorial and middle latitudes of Mars. They seem to have flowed as streams do on earth–downhill. Some show braided patterns, sand bars, slumping banks, and stream-lined, teardrop-shaped islands, all of which are characteristics of river valleys on earth.

But there is a problem with interpreting the Martian channels as dry river valleys: Liquid water cannot exist on Mars today because the atmospheric pressure, only 0.5 per cent of that on earth, is simply too low. As a result, water can exist on Mars only as ice, snow, or vapor. This is why some geologists are reluctant to believe that the Martian channels were carved by liquid water.

Yet, they are dead ringers for terrestrial river valleys, and many of them do not resemble such other possible structures as collapsed lava tubes, which may be responsible for sinuous valleys on the moon. Furthermore, the channels are remarkably concentrated in the Martian equatorial region, the only region of Mars where the average daytime temperature rises above the freezing point of water. In addition, no other liquid fits the conditions of simultaneously being abundant throughout the universe, exhibiting low viscosity, and having a freezing point below Martian daytime equatorial temperatures.

If the channels are due to running water, that water must have run at a time when the Martian environment was significantly different. At some time in the past, Mars must have had a denser atmosphere, higher pressures, perhaps somewhat higher temperatures, and extensive running water. Such an environment might have been more hospitable to forms of life based on familiar biochemical principles than is the Mars of today.

One possible cause of major climate changes on Mars is a feedback mechanism known as advective instability. The present Martian atmosphere is composed primarily of CO_2, and the atmospheric pressure is quite close to the pressure of gaseous CO_2 in equilibrium with frozen CO_2 at -200°F. (-130°C.), the temperature of the winter Martian pole. The temperature at the winter pole thus may determine the total pressure on the planet.

On both earth and Mars, temperatures are colder at the poles than at the equator because sunlight generally falls more directly on the equator and more obliquely on the poles. On the earth, atmospheric circulation helps moderate the temperature difference; hot air rises at the equator and moves at high altitudes to the poles where it cools and settles, before returning at low altitudes to the equator. On Mars, however, the present atmosphere is so thin that the hot air carried from the equator has little effect in warming the poles.

Climate Runaway

Present equilibrium

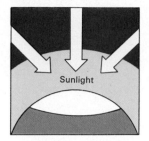

Future instability

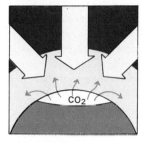

Future equilibrium

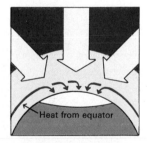

Atmospheric pressure on Mars today is in equilibrium with polar temperatures, *top.* But more sunlight, *middle,* releases carbon dioxide (CO_2) from the icecap. This raises the pressure, and increases the heat transported from the equator, *bottom,* to warm the poles further and free more CO_2. The process continues until pressures reach a new equilibrium with polar temperatures.

157

But now imagine that winter polar temperatures are somehow slightly increased. The higher temperatures would release some of the CO_2 frozen in the icecap, increasing the atmospheric pressure and thereby improving heat transport from equator to pole. Polar temperatures would increase still further, more CO_2 would be released, and a runaway to higher pressures might result. Pressures would stabilize either when all the frozen CO_2 was freed into the atmosphere, or when the atmospheric pressure reached an equilibrium with the increased polar temperature, including heat carried from the equator. If later the polar temperatures are somehow decreased, the atmospheric pressure would decline through the condensation of CO_2 at the poles. Less heat would be transported from the equator, and there could be a runaway to low pressures.

For Mars to experience a major increase in pressure, the polar regions must absorb 15 or 20 per cent more heat than they do now for at least a century. There are at least three possible sources of variation in the heating of the icecap. They are, interestingly enough, similar to three models of climate change on earth—changes in obliquity, albedo, and solar brightness.

Light and dark layers near the south pole of Mars suggest that large amounts of dust may have settled on the pole at various times in the past, significantly lowering the surface reflectivity to allow more sunlight to be absorbed at the poles.

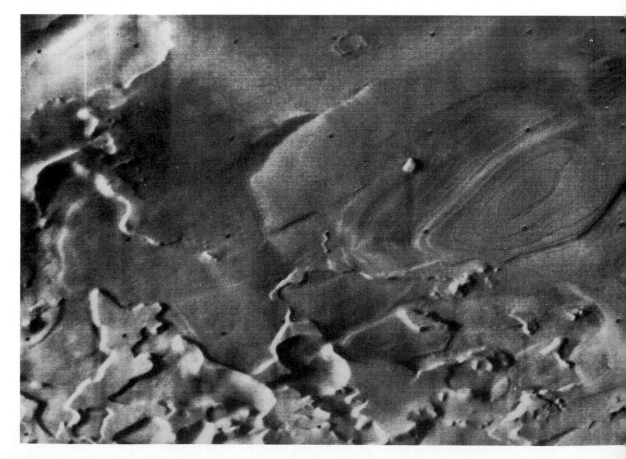

Obliquity variations for Mars are much more striking than for the earth because Mars is closer to Jupiter, the most massive planet in the solar system, and is much more affected by Jupiter's gravity. While the tilt of the earth's axis varies by only a few degrees from its present $23\frac{1}{2}°$, the obliquity of Mars may vary from about 15° to 35°. The Martian obliquity varies on a time scale of about 100,000 years. But the size of the variation itself changes on a time scale of about 1 million years. The obliquity of Mars today is about 25°. When the obliquity reaches about 30°, a major increase in pressure will occur. The last time this happened is calculated to be about 300,000 years ago.

Albedo variations in the polar regions also can cause major climatic variations. An increase in the sunlight absorbed can drive off large amounts of frozen CO_2. We already have seen substantial sand and dust storms on Mars. While in the air, the dust adds to the albedo and cools the planet. But when it settles in the polar areas, darkening the caps, it significantly lowers the polar albedo, allowing more sunlight to be absorbed at the caps. Perhaps we could make Mars more hospitable if we could develop a hardy species of plant that grows on dry ice, thereby lowering the polar albedo.

Variations in solar brightness may also affect the climate. The frequency of impact craters, produced by meteoritic bombardment, indicates roughly the age of certain areas on Mars—the more craters, the older the area. Crude dating of the Martian channels by this method indicates that some of the channels must be a few hundred million years old. This is consistent with the last epoch of high global temperatures on earth. It raises the captivating possibility that major variations in climate may have occurred on the earth and Mars at the same time, due to the same cause.

Further studies of the climatology of Mars should include extensive investigations of the polar regions, the dust storms, and particularly the channels. The Viking mission, which will land two space probes on Mars in 1976, may significantly improve our understanding.

If Viking works as intended, it will be the first time that a scientific laboratory has operated successfully on the surface of Mars. Both Viking landers, A and B, are biologically oriented and will search for Martian microbes. In addition, a gas chromatograph/mass spectrometer will examine the soil for organic chemicals, and two television cameras might conceivably detect larger organisms. Both microorganisms and larger organisms might be native to Mars today. There might also be living fossils, dormant organisms left from an earlier, wetter environment that have somehow survived to the present.

Viking A is scheduled to land on July 4, 1976, at a point where four major channels meet. Although it will have no facilities for radioactive dating of rocks, the combination of television pictures and inorganic chemistry experiments may provide important insights into the history of the area. A seismometer to detect Marsquakes may obtain data about the past geological history of Mars; and meteorological instruments, combined with orbital and lander television, may gather important information on the generation of dust storms.

Finally, two different mass spectrometers will search the Martian atmosphere for noble gases such as argon 40. Argon 40, like CO_2, is released by a volcanically active planet. But unlike CO_2 argon does not freeze out even at the cold poles. If Mars once had a much denser atmosphere, substantial quantities of argon should still be around today. Data from the USSR's Mars 6 descent module, which lost radio contact before landing on Mars in March, 1974, seemed to imply that from 10 to 40 per cent of the Martian atmosphere is composed of a noble gas, probably argon. Details of this experiment were not released by late spring, 1974, but the conclusions, if valid, would provide strong evidence of an earlier high-pressure Martian environment.

Our inability to decide among the alternative models of climatic change might appear to be nothing more than an unusually frustrating intellectual problem—except that climate variations appear to have certain immediate practical consequences.

The activities of man, for instance, may have drastic, and largely unexpected, effects on climate. Global temperature trends on earth show a slow rise from the late 1800s and the beginning of the Industrial Revolution to the mid-1940s, and an alarmingly steep decline thereafter. This pattern could be due to the increased burning of fossil fuels, which has two effects—it liberates CO_2 and, at the same time, injects fine particles into the atmosphere. The CO_2, through the greenhouse effect, raises temperatures; the fine particles, through their higher albedo, lower temperatures. Until 1940, the greenhouse effect may have been winning; after 1940, the increased albedo may have begun to dominate. Ominously, on a planet with declining temperatures, the increased burning of fossil fuels in a short-term attempt to stay warm may result in more rapid cooling over the long term.

There are other problems as well. We live on a planet where agricultural technology feeds more than a billion people. Yet the crops have not been bred for hardiness against climatic variations. Also, both mechanized farming and preindustrial slash-and-burn land clearing add considerably to the amount of dust put into the atmosphere, thus further influencing the climate. And, on a planet controlled largely by nation states, it is difficult or impossible for people to make great migrations in response to climatic change.

It is becoming increasingly clear that the earth's climate may not be nearly so stable as some had thought. Even tiny changes in climate may have profound human consequences. Our planet may be in a rather fragile equilibrium. A relatively small push might trigger an instability moving the earth toward the hostile environments of either Mars or Venus. Since man's activities may inadvertently alter the climate of the earth, it is imperative to understand the causes and cures of climatic variations. The study of the climates of other worlds is a unique method of understanding our own.

A Changing World

For centuries, man has speculated about the possibility of life on Mars. At first, his imagination peopled earth's neighbor with all manner of strange creatures, but as he learned more about the planet, the possibility of life existing there became more and more remote. Yet the speculation persists.

Today, Mars seems harsh and lifeless. Its thin atmosphere is primarily carbon dioxide; it has little oxygen and no liquid water. Deadly ultraviolet radiation beats upon its unprotected surface. Temperatures may range from only 70° F. (20° C.) at noon on the equator down to as low as -200° F. (-130° C.) at the poles at night.

But the discovery of winding channels, apparently carved by water, raises the possibility that Mars may have once had more atmosphere and a more clement climate. If water once flowed on Mars, some form of life may have emerged. Once present, Martian organisms may have been able to adapt as the atmosphere thinned and the water disappeared. In that case, they may still be present, perhaps in a sort of long-term hibernation, waiting only for a return of more agreeable conditions to awake and flourish once more.

How likely is it that Mars might see widespread climatic variations on a cyclical basis? Quite possible, according to some astronomers' speculations.

A number of factors could cause periodic climatic changes. One is a variation in the planet's obliquity, the angle that the equator makes with the plane of the planet's orbit. Today, that angle for Mars is about 25°, close to the obliquity of earth. But the Martian obliquity can vary from about 15° to about 35°, over time periods of 100,000 and 1 million years.

As the angle of obliquity increases, the poles tilt further from the perpendicular. This allows the sun's rays to fall more directly on the summer pole, heating the polar icecaps and releasing more gas into the planet's atmosphere. This, in turn, raises the atmospheric pressure, improving the circulation of heat from the equator, warming the poles further, and releasing still more gas into the atmosphere.

The end result is that the polar temperature would rise, and the atmospheric pressure might increase enough to allow liquid water to flow. And with water, Mars could see the revival of any organisms that might be sleeping out the long winter.

Some 300,000 years ago, the obliquity may have been great enough for Mars to experience a much more moderate climate than it knows today. And perhaps a few hundred thousand years from now, the planet again will be able to realize similar clement conditions.

An increase in the amount of energy put out by the sun might also trigger climatic change. There are indications that the sun's energy output varies periodically. At present, the sun seems to be in an unusually dim or cool state. But 100 million years ago, or 100 million years in the future, the sun's brightness might be raised by 10 to 20 per cent. Once again, Mars could have a period of higher pressures, warmer temperatures, and flowing water.

In this case, the pleasant climate might last 10 million years, or longer. The atmospheric density would approach that known on earth. With such an atmosphere, containing substantial quantities of carbon dioxide and water vapor, the greenhouse effect would come into play. Solar radiation, hitting the planet's surface at visible wave lengths, would be reradiated as heat at infrared wave lengths. Such wave lengths would be absorbed by the atmosphere, increasing the planet's temperatures still further. The temperature at the equator would rise again, for many hours a day. And low temperatures might be only slightly below the freezing point of water. For an earthling, the average temperature might still be a little chilly. But for a Martian organism, it would be a balmy springtime. Once again, Martian life could flourish and multiply, and perhaps evolve some quite sophisticated variations.

How to Use This Unit

To follow the changes in the Martian environment, first turn back this page. Then, place the two acetate overlays on the right-hand page so that the base page is unobstructed. Read the section, "A Martian Ice Age," then put down the first acetate overlay and read the accompanying text, "The Axis Tilts." Continue with the second overlay and its text, "The Sun Flickers."

A Martian Ice Age

Mars today is a dusty, arid, apparently lifeless planet. But its surface could be teeming with tiny, undetected microbes. Any future life must evolve from what is present there today, barring contamination from earth.

Near the Martian equator, a great volcano broods over a desert landscape pocked with craters. Because the atmosphere is only about 0.5 per cent as dense as that on earth, the wind often has barely enough force to lift the specks of sand and dust. But sometimes fierce winds of up to 300 miles per hour sweep across the surface. These winds can hurl the tiny grains against the rock and stone, wearing down the surface features with fine persistence.

There are few sharp edges on Mars. Canyons and craters are slumped and eroded. The volcano rises gradually to its towering peak, perhaps as much as 15 miles above the surface. To the left, erosion has worn away the shell of another volcano, leaving only the hardened lava plug, a stark sentry above the land.

The sun, some 140 million miles away, shines with only about half the intensity seen on earth. But, because of the thin atmosphere, shadows are crisp and black, and the sky color shades rapidly into black a short distance above the horizon. The only clouds are thin wisps that condense in waves near the top of the volcano.

At dawn, temperatures are still well below freezing. A thin film of frost, as yet untouched by the rising sun, coats the ground in the shadow of a great arch. Temperatures vary widely during the course of a day. At noon, they may briefly peak at about 70° F. (about 20° C.) at the equator, well above the freezing point of water. At night, temperatures at the equator may plummet to −115° F. (−80° C.); at the winter pole, they drop still lower.

The most unexpected feature of the landscape is a sinuous channel, with branching tributaries. The channel is dry and empty now, but it exhibits some curious characteristics — braids, sand bars, and teardrop-shaped islands. Such features could have been formed only by flowing water at some time in the past. The arch spanning one of the smaller tributaries was also carved originally by water. It has been eroded still further by wind and dust.

The Axis Tilts

Some 300,000 years from now, the Martian obliquity may reach 30° and the planet's poles would be tilted much more toward the plane of the orbit. The winter pole could absorb more sunlight, freeing some of the gases frozen in the icecaps to produce an atmosphere 10 times that of today, and about 5 per cent as dense as the atmosphere on earth.

The sky has become lighter, though still shading into dark blue relatively close to the horizon. Scattered clouds float above, not as often connected with the volcano. The sun still shines with the same intensity as before, but the denser atmosphere softens the shadows. Temperatures at the equator might be slightly cooler than before, due to the improved circu-

lation from the poles. But the temperature would remain at the high end of the range — about 45° F. (7° C.) — for a longer period each day, thus raising the average temperature. The nighttime low might range from −65° to −100° F. (about −55° to −75° C.).

Continuing erosion over the past 300,000 years has modified the landscape, although it still resembles the Mars we know today. The volcano has become slightly more slumped and eroded; the rock bridge has collapsed; the edges of some craters have slumped and softened; and the land has become less dusty.

Most important, the increase in atmospheric pressure allows water to remain a liquid. A muddy, brown trickle now flows down the once dry channel, slowly winding its way through the desert to some distant pool or small lake. The water may have been flowing for some thousands of years, long enough to have carved a new signature in the channel. Source of the water is the polar ice, evaporated and carried to the skies over the equator by clouds. In the distance, a rain squall pours the water down on the still thirsty land.

The most dramatic change in the equatorial landscape is the obvious presence of Martian life. Small, hardy, blue plants cluster along the watercourse, forming a thin band of color that traces the path of the stream into the distance. The plants, having evolved along different lines than terrestrial organisms and having, perhaps, descended from entirely different biochemical ancestors, resemble nothing that we know on earth.

The Blooming Of Mars: A Speculation

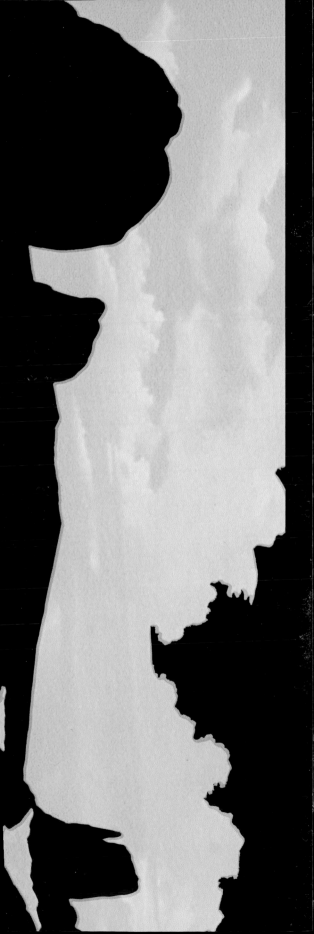

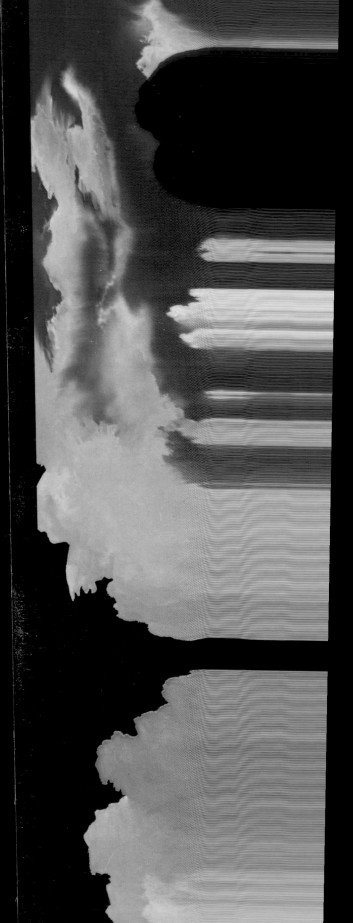

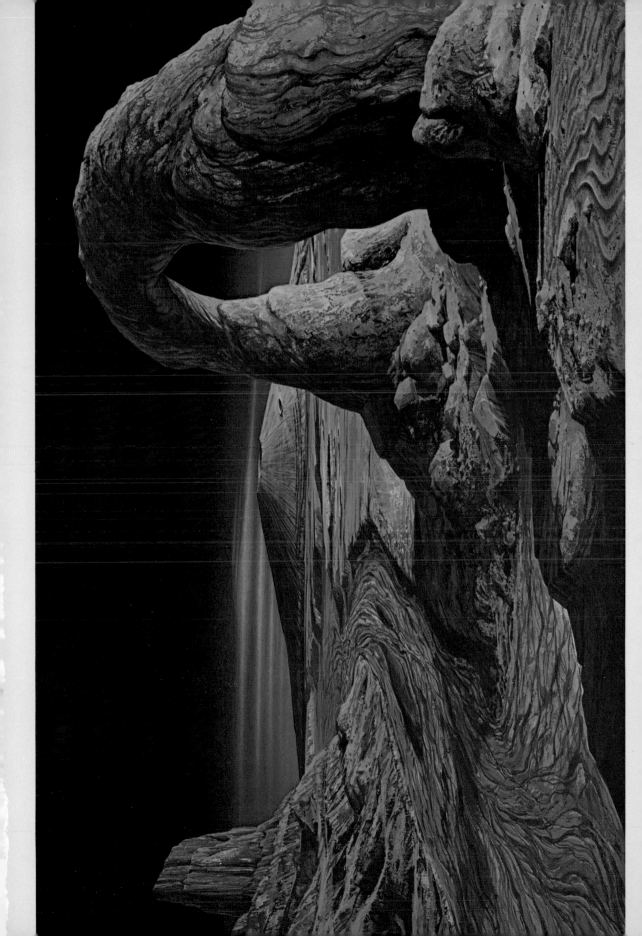

The Blooming
Of Mars:
A Speculation

The Sun Flickers

An increase in the sun's brightness, perhaps 100 million years from now, could bring another major change in the Martian climate. The sun may become as much as 20 per cent brighter, allowing more solar energy to reach the planet and be absorbed at the poles.

The atmosphere, still composed primarily of carbon dioxide, may become comparable to the earth's in pressure and density. Temperatures at the equator are mild and pleasant for Mars, although the climate resembles that of the Arctic region on earth. During the day, the high temperature at the equator hovers around 70°F. (20°C.), for many hours each day. At night, it may drop to 0°F. (−20°C.).

The terrain has seen major changes. Erosion has worn away the old volcano, leaving behind a lava plug, while a new, smaller volcano has appeared nearby. Traces of the old craters have all but disappeared. Above, the blue sky, with perhaps a 50 per cent cloud cover, resembles that of earth.

The channel now gushes with water, splashing along its course to run into a large lake. Slabs of ice in the water are evidence of the Arctic temperatures. Over the centuries, the watercourse has changed significantly—new tributaries have been carved and old ones have disappeared; the main channel itself has been deflected from its original course.

Vegetation is rife. Spreading away from the river, the ground cover has taken over and softened the rocky contours. Plants from the earlier era are much in the minority, having been superseded by more advanced species.

If there is life on Mars, it is probably formed of carbon compounds, as is life on earth. But native Martian organisms may have developed quite unfamiliar ways of carrying out the activities of life.

On earth, for example, plants use chlorophyll to aid in photosynthesis, the process of combining sunlight, water, and carbon dioxide to produce food substances. As plants evolve on Mars, they would also engage in photosynthesis, but they may use a different photosynthetic pigment. As chlorophyll gives earth plants their green color, the Martian substance turns plants some other color—shades of blue, ranging to purple.

Martian plants will face a number of problems not generally encountered on earth. To cope with the scarcity of water, plants need extensive, complex root systems. Ball-shaped water storage cells, able to shrink or expand according to the availability of water, help some plants survive periods of drought. Puffball seed pods are tossed about by the wind, gathering in rocky cul-de-sacs where only one may sprout and grow. Some plants have large, disk-shaped leaves that twist and turn to catch the sun's rays. Others spread wide during the day, then roll up at night to prevent the loss of heat. To protect them from the ultraviolet radiation, Martian plants are able to use silicates from the soil to grow a natural shield. In younger plants, this might be a sort of sheath or bubble, which is shed as they mature. Adult plants grow a toughened outer layer that is opaque to ultraviolet rays, but transparent to the visible sunlight which penetrates deep into the plant where photosynthesis occurs.

After 100 million years, some varieties of Martian plants have evolved to trees, 15 to 20 feet high, with a profusion of blue-bladed leaves spreading out to catch the sunlight. Ultraviolet radiation is still a problem and plants retain the protective silicate layer.

Animals, too, could evolve on Mars. One such animal is a leaping, leaf-eating treedweller. This three-legged animal has a transparent silicate skin. Its predominant color is blue, to blend in with the trees that nourish it and to protect it from some unseen flying predator. But its underside is a brilliant hue, to aid in attracting a mate. Four eyes give it a wide field of view, and a fine mesh opening on its underside allows it to breathe the carbon dioxide atmosphere, while straining out sand and dirt. Powerful hind legs, aided by the lower gravity on Mars, enable the animal to leap 15 feet or more into the trees on which it feeds. The trees, on the other hand, grow quite tall before branching out, to keep their tender leaves away from the animal's sharp teeth.

Seen at the peak of its climatic cycle, Mars is a lush and fertile planet. But eventually, the cycle will run its course. Temperatures will fall, the atmosphere will freeze out at the poles, running water will disappear, and Mars will revert to the desolate scene we see today.

Prepared by the editors of *Science Year,* The World Book Science Annual. Artist: Herb Herrick. Consultant: Carl Sagan, director of the Laboratory for Planetary Studies, Cornell University. Printed in U.S.A. by the Trans-Vision® Division, Milprint Incorporated.

Muscles And Motion

By C. Richard Taylor

The high-speed camera and the oxygen mask have revealed an economy of energy beneath the grace of a galloping animal

I have a few scars in my scalp to remind me that my studies of energy and animal locomotion, like all scientific research, should always be done with care. It was a cheetah—a tame cheetah, actually—that parted my hair. We had been working to accumulate data about her physical condition as she ran on a treadmill. As the day ended, I was in a hurry to head home. I removed a rectal temperature probe too abruptly, and she whirled and batted at me. Cheetahs' claws, unhappily, are not very retractable; whether she wanted to or not, she did about 20 stitches worth of damage.

My studies of running animals began in Africa with a more tractable species. Soon after I got my Ph.D. degree in biology in 1963, I received a grant to study the physiology of antelopes, particularly those living in the hot East African deserts. These animals seemed not just to survive, but to flourish in this harsh environment. And, curiously, explorers, naturalists, game wardens, farmers, and hunters had reported that the antelopes never drink water. I wanted to find out if these reports were true.

I soon recognized that I would have to study both resting and running animals because their water demands and use might be radically different. Most running animals dispose of their excess heat by sweating, or panting. The evaporating water cools them. But how could this work if they did not drink? To understand what was involved, I needed to find out how the animals coped with the heat from the hot desert sun and the heat that they generated when they ran. It is not too difficult to monitor physiological processes in resting animals. But making the needed measurements on running animals presented a larger problem.

I borrowed a truck from some British neighbors, and my staff and I jounced and jolted our way high into the bamboo forests of Mount Kenya. We spent a whole day cutting bamboo. The next day, we built a 12-foot-high bamboo fence around a makeshift 1/8-mile race track. In the center we built a high platform with a long boom that extended out over the track. Swinging a feed sack attached to the end of the boom, we could "chase" antelopes around the track at speeds of up to 30 miles (45 kilometers) per hour.

We attached to the animals radio-transmitter devices that monitored their temperature and sweat rate while they ran. Our most interesting discovery was that they got very hot internally when running at high speeds. Although their normal body temperature is about 97°F., we measured temperatures of up to 118°F. during a run. This would kill most animals. It looked as if antelopes simply store the heat, and later release it slowly. As a result, they do not need to evaporate water by sweating or panting.

My grant covered four years of research in Africa. During that time I found out a great deal about antelopes. Apparently, they do not drink, but get the water they need from the leaves and grasses they eat. In periods of extreme dryness they eat only at night when dew condenses on the foliage. But I never did discover how much energy antelopes use or how much heat they produce while running. The question became more and more a challenge. It also intrigued physiologist Knut Schmidt-Nielsen of Duke University, who had spent some time chasing African ostriches. He was aware of my work and had visited my lab in Kenya several times. It turned out that he, too, was interested in this problem of how much energy running animals use.

I left Africa in 1967 and went to work in Schmidt-Nielsen's lab at Duke. We began to look for general principles governing how much energy animals use when they run.

For many people, energy is a confusing term because it comes in several different forms—electrical, chemical, or physical, for example—and these forms are interchangeable. For our purposes energy is the ability to do work, and can be measured by the amount of force applied and the distance over which it acts.

Energy and work are most often thought of in connection with man-made machines, where petroleum products are the main source of

The author:
C. Richard Taylor is Alexander Agassiz Professor of Zoology at Harvard University and Director of its Concord Field Station.

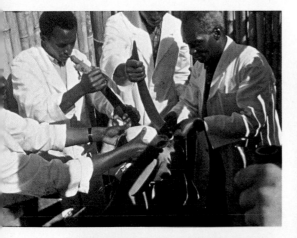

A bamboo-lined laboratory was built in the African desert to measure the heat generated by running antelopes. Radio transmitting equipment attached to the animals monitored their temperatures and sweat rates as they raced around the enclosure.

energy. As oil or gasoline burns, the chemical bonds between chains of carbon atoms are broken, releasing energy as heat. Water and carbon dioxide are produced at the same time. Machines such as internal-combustion engines or jet engines use the heat to do mechanical work, to provide some kind of motion. The energy in the petroleum is solar energy, trapped by plants which were buried and liquefied by the pressures of the earth over a long period of time.

Animals rely on this same form of plant-trapped solar energy for their own energy. Basically, an animal uses oxygen to "burn" its food —carbohydrates, proteins, and fats. The transformations within an animal as it digests its food and releases the chemical energy to do useful work are called metabolism. The end products of metabolism, like those when gasoline is burned in an engine, are heat, water, carbon dioxide, and work.

An animal's machine for converting the chemical energy trapped in foodstuffs into mechanical energy to do work—to move—is its muscles. Scientists believe that muscles use the energy to swing tiny cross bridges between neighboring filaments of protein, causing them to slide along each other and produce a force. British biologists Hugh E. Huxley and Andrew F. Huxley independently proposed this "sliding

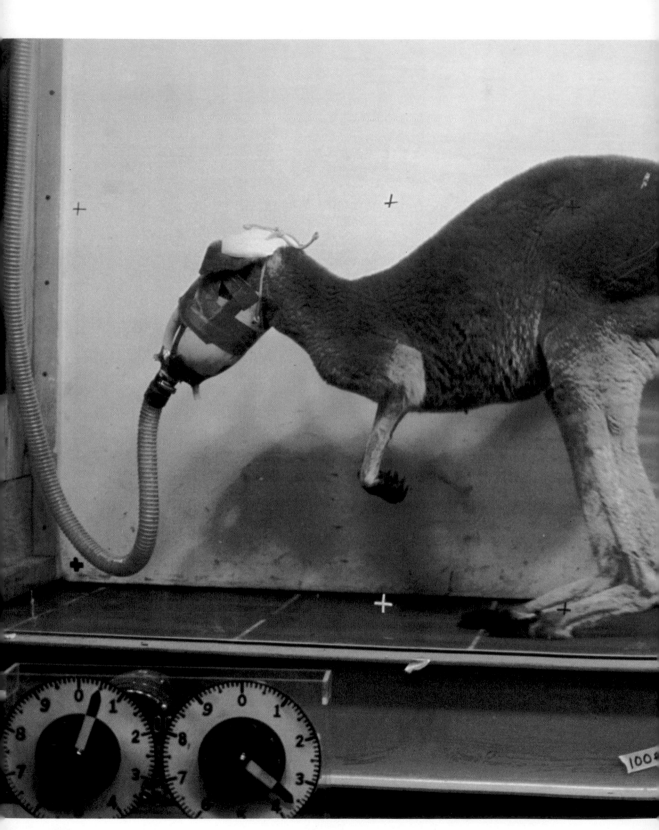

filament" theory of muscular contraction in 1954, based on highly magnified photographs of muscles in different stages of contraction. Subsequent studies have supported and expanded this theory. All vertebrate muscles appear to use this system of sliding protein fibers, and it now seems that all animal movement, even that of one-celled animals, involves a similar sliding system.

Thus it is not surprising that the mechanical properties of all vertebrate muscles seem so similar. British physiologist Archibald V. Hill played the major role in discovering these mechanical similarities, and shared the 1922 Nobel Prize in physiology for his work. Hill carefully dissected muscles from different animals and hooked them to delicate recording equipment, keeping their circulation intact so they were supplied with nutrients and oxygen. When he stimulated the muscles, usually by an electrical current to their nerve supply, he recorded the speed of their contraction and the weight they could lift. Each muscle contracted fastest when there was no weight attached. When he gradually added weights, he found that the contraction rate gradually slowed and stopped, marking the maximum force the muscle could develop. Hill plotted speeds against forces on a graph and found that for all animals the curves were similar. His findings can be summarized as follows:

■ All muscles can exert the same maximum force for a given cross-sectional area of muscle.
■ During each contraction, muscles of the same mass can do the same maximum amount of work, and they expend the same amount of energy doing it.
■ Every muscle has one speed at which its contractions are most efficient. Since each muscle is composed of many cells, or muscle fibers, the force of its contraction can be increased by adding to the number of its active fibers. The fibers' most efficient speed, however, can be changed very little.

We can measure the energy used by a combustion engine simply by measuring the amount of gasoline that it burns. The amount of energy in a gallon of gasoline and the efficiency with which it burns are fairly constant and known.

It is more difficult and less accurate to measure the energy an animal uses by measuring the food it eats. We would have to determine the amount of energy contained in the food, record how much the animal eats, and measure the energy lost in the animal's waste products. Not only would this be inconvenient, but it would be almost impossible to achieve the accuracy required to determine the extra energy used during short periods of running.

A much easier way is to measure the oxygen consumed as the food burns, because it is directly related to the amount of energy used. The amount of energy available from each milliliter of oxygen consumed is

Two-legged, as well as four-legged, animals trod the treadmill while their oxygen consumption is measured to determine their energy use.

almost the same, regardless of the type of foodstuff being burned. It varies only from about 4.7 calories per milliliter of oxygen for fats to 5.0 calories for carbohydrates.

For small animals, the easiest way to measure the oxygen consumed is to put the animal in a jar and measure the air flowing through it. The rate of air flow and the change in the air's oxygen content indicate the animal's oxygen consumption. Since oxygen used is proportional to calories burned, it is a simple matter to calculate the energy the animal released and used. For bigger animals, we simply put a face mask over the animal's mouth and nose, pump air through it at a measured rate, and determine the difference in oxygen content of the air inhaled and exhaled.

When scientists began to measure the oxygen consumption of animals, they found that a small animal expends energy much more rapidly and produces much more heat in proportion to its weight than a large animal. We might say, then, that mice are more energetic than elephants. The energy expended while resting–comparable to the cost of letting an automobile engine "idle"–varies according to the animal's weight. This relationship between resting mammals' metabolism and their body size is often referred to as the mouse-to-elephant curve. It lets us calculate the resting metabolism or "idling cost" of mammals simply from their weight. In 1938, Francis G. Benedict, then director of the Nutrition Laboratory of the Carnegie Institute of Washington, D.C., compared the resting, or basal, metabolism of a mouse and an

Measurements of oxygen used by animals at rest show that the smaller the animal, the higher its metabolism.

The Mouse-to-Elephant Curve

Oxygen consumption (mm³ per gram per hour)

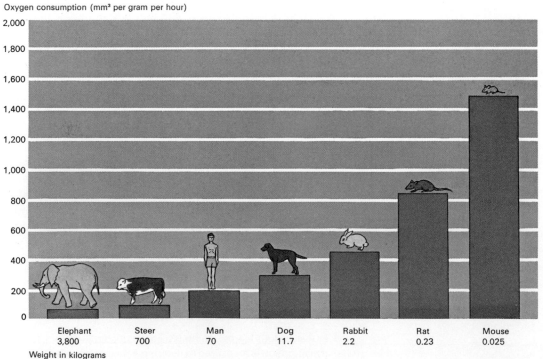

Weight in kilograms

Making Meat from a Ton of Hay

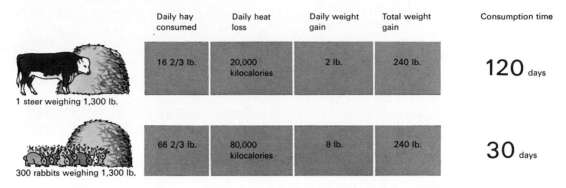

	Daily hay consumed	Daily heat loss	Daily weight gain	Total weight gain	Consumption time
1 steer weighing 1,300 lb.	16 2/3 lb.	20,000 kilocalories	2 lb.	240 lb.	**120** days
300 rabbits weighing 1,300 lb.	66 2/3 lb.	80,000 kilocalories	8 lb.	240 lb.	**30** days

Using more energy proportionately, smaller animals turn hay into meat more efficiently than can larger ones.

elephant. He found that a mouse, in proportion to its weight, consumes energy about 200 times as fast as an elephant. Small animals, plainly, have a very high idling cost. This has led people to believe that they are less efficient than large animals.

Physiologist Max Kleiber of the University of California, Davis, who spent the 1920s and 1930s experimenting on meat production, proposed a new view about the relationship between animals' size and their efficiency in using food. In one phase of his work, Kleiber compared cattle and rabbits. He figured that if a 1,300-pound steer and 300 rabbits weighing a total of 1,300 pounds are each given a ton of hay to eat, the rabbits will consume their ton much more quickly. And they will also produce heat much more rapidly. It turns out, however, that both the rabbits and the steer produce the same amount of meat. The rabbits simply do it more rapidly. We might say that the rabbits earn a higher rate of interest on the food they eat. As a result, Kleiber points out, their high idling cost does not mean their efficiency is low—at least in producing meat.

One thing is missing in Kleiber's experiments: The animals' food is brought to them. To understand the total flow of energy, we need to go beyond the idling cost. We also need to know the "freight cost"—the amount of energy an animal expends to move around in its search for food. And we need to know if its size, so important in determining its idling cost, is as important in measuring freight cost.

In 1950, Hill proposed a simple theory about relative energy expenditures for animals of different sizes that move in similar ways. He used the properties of muscles that he had found earlier—that muscles' maximum force is proportional to their mass; but each contracts most efficiently at its own specific speed.

Hill first studied the physical work that an animal does when it runs. Physical laws tell us that, once an accelerating animal reaches a constant speed, it need only work hard enough to overcome wind resistance and internal work (chemical and physical processes within the body) to maintain the speed. At the speeds animals run, however, neither wind nor internal work has very much effect. Hill therefore

High-speed photography
shows that a "scurrying"
mouse really gallops,
very much like a
graceful race horse.

concluded that a running animal uses most of its energy to alternately
accelerate and decelerate its legs during each stride.

Hill also concluded that small animals can move their limbs more
times per minute than large animals and that the maximum frequency
will increase predictably as size decreases. He had decided that a gram
of muscle expended the same amount of energy during each contraction, however, so he predicted that a small animal would expend
much more energy than a large one to move 1 gram 1 kilometer.

Hill's arguments indicated that it would take much more energy to
cover a given distance at a high speed than a low one. Experience supports this; we are exhausted after running a hundred-yard dash, but
we can jog a hundred yards and feel that we are just warming up.

Hill's arguments were very convincing—perhaps too convincing.
For some time, nobody took the trouble to measure the energy that
animals of different sizes consume as they run. Then, in 1969,
Schmidt-Nielsen, Jakob Raab, and I built some treadmills, fitted oxygen masks on a number of different animals, and began to measure the
oxygen consumption of animals as they ran at different speeds. In late
1970, I moved to Harvard University and built new treadmills.

The first surprise was finding that it costs a running animal almost
the same amount of energy per gram to travel a given distance at any
speed. Apparently the cost of speed is not as great as Hill thought.
Why we gasp after a high-speed run concerns the rate of chemical
transformations in our body, not the amount of energy we use. We did
confirm Hill's prediction that small running animals use more energy
than large ones do. Because for a given animal the running cost per

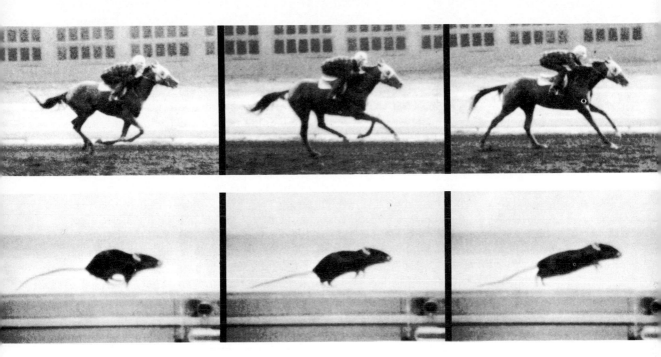

mile is the same, regardless of the speed, we developed a very simple mathematical equation, using the animal's weight, to predict the energy it would expend moving from one place to another.

We found this very exciting and useful. We can say, for example, that the more a predator roams, the bigger is his appetite. The equation also helps to explain many puzzling things I observed while watching animals. For example, why can a squirrel run up a tree trunk at nearly top speed while you and I slow down on a slight hill? Animals of any size must expend exactly the same amount of energy to lift a gram (of themselves) the same vertical distance. When running on the level, however, a squirrel already expends about 20 times as much energy as a man because its idling and freight costs are much higher. Thus, to overcome gravity, the squirrel would have to increase its energy consumption by only 5 per cent, while a man would have to increase his by 100 per cent.

I was still puzzled, however, about what it was that made energy cost so predictable. That prompted me to ask a simple-minded question that many biologists had asked before me. Does the amount of energy an animal uses to move from place to place depend on the way it is built? It seemed that comparing animals built to move in various ways could provide some insight into how they use energy when they run. And this might indicate why the amount used is so predictable.

Anthropologists have long believed that it requires less energy to move on two legs than on four. They suggest that this is one of the reasons modern man's hunting ancestors were so successful in the course of evolution. Not having to run on his forelegs (arms) freed

Finding a way to measure the energy consumption of a wriggling snake taxes the ingenuity of the experimenter.

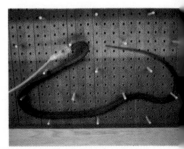

them for using weapons. However, the energy price man pays for using only two limbs to move about is not clear.

The first data from our study of four-legged animals in 1970 indicated that man's freight cost (determined from earlier treadmill studies) was about twice that of a four-legged animal of the same size. We decided then to look at another large two-legged animal—the ostrich-like bird called the rhea. We found that the rhea, like man, paid twice the price predicted for a four-legged animal of the same size. We next decided to look at several primates such as chimpanzees and cebus monkeys, that move either on two or four legs. Again we were surprised. Over a wide range of speeds, they used the same amount of energy whether moving on two or four legs. We are still investigating the energy-cost difference between two- and four-legged running.

In late 1973, Michael Fedak, Barry Pinshaw, and Schmidt-Nielsen at Duke finished a study of two-legged running in birds of different size. They found a regular relationship, but it differed from the simple, weight-dependent equation that we had found for four-legged running. For very small animals—those under 2 to 3 pounds (including most birds)—it is cheaper to move on two legs. Birds weighing 2 to 3 pounds use the same energy to move on two legs as other animals of the same size use to move on four. It costs larger birds more energy to move on two than on four legs. Man's place in the scale corresponds to that of large birds.

Comparative anatomists have argued that how an animal is designed could affect the efficiency of movement. Lizards, for example, with their sprawling posture, do not support their bodies with their limbs underneath them as do mammals. Their "elbows" and "knees" jut outward, so they must do a sort of continuous pushup as they move. Paleontologists have argued that the more upright posture of mammals is much more efficient. But in 1973, Robert Bakker, a graduate student working in my lab, came up with another surprise. Using the treadmill and oxygen-measuring apparatus, he found that the freight costs of lizards and mammals were exactly the same. He also found, however, that the lizards consumed less total energy because their idling cost was less. Thus, although the lizard cannot reach the same top speed as a mammal, it uses only one-third to one-half as much energy to move from point to point.

Anatomists have argued that animals with very light limbs and with muscles concentrated around the hip or shoulder joint have been designed to move cheaply. Moving light limbs requires less energy. And, at a given ground speed, the large muscle mass in the joints would not have to be moved fast or far in each stride. The heavy limbs of a cheetah or a lion, for example, are built to knock down prey. Those of an antelope or a goat are light and the muscles are concentrated around the joints. Despite such large differences in limb configuration, however, we found no difference in energy consumption as cheetahs and gazelles of the same weight traveled at the same speed. This probably means that once the animal achieves its speed, most of the energy is not going into moving the limbs. More work is needed to find out where it does go.

We have now more or less abandoned the comparative study of using animals that move in different ways or are built differently to help us explain the weight-related equation. Instead, we have shifted our focus to a much more basic question: How do animals use the energy they consume when they run?

With the help of William Bossert and two of his Harvard students in applied mathematics and engineering, we are using computers to help calculate the energy an animal expends to move its limbs as it runs at different speeds. We take very-high-speed movie films (200 frames per

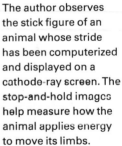

The author observes the stick figure of an animal whose stride has been computerized and displayed on a cathode-ray screen. The stop-and-hold images help measure how the animal applies energy to move its limbs.

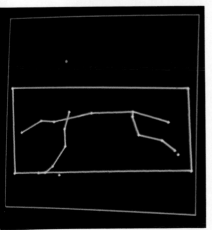
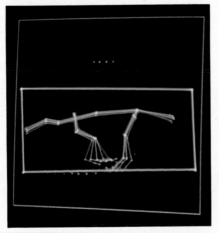
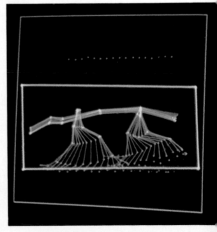

A system of force plates can show how much of an animal's energy goes into changing speed during each stride. Highly sensitive pressure devices measure force in three directions. Data from all hooves are recorded on tape and integrated in a computer.

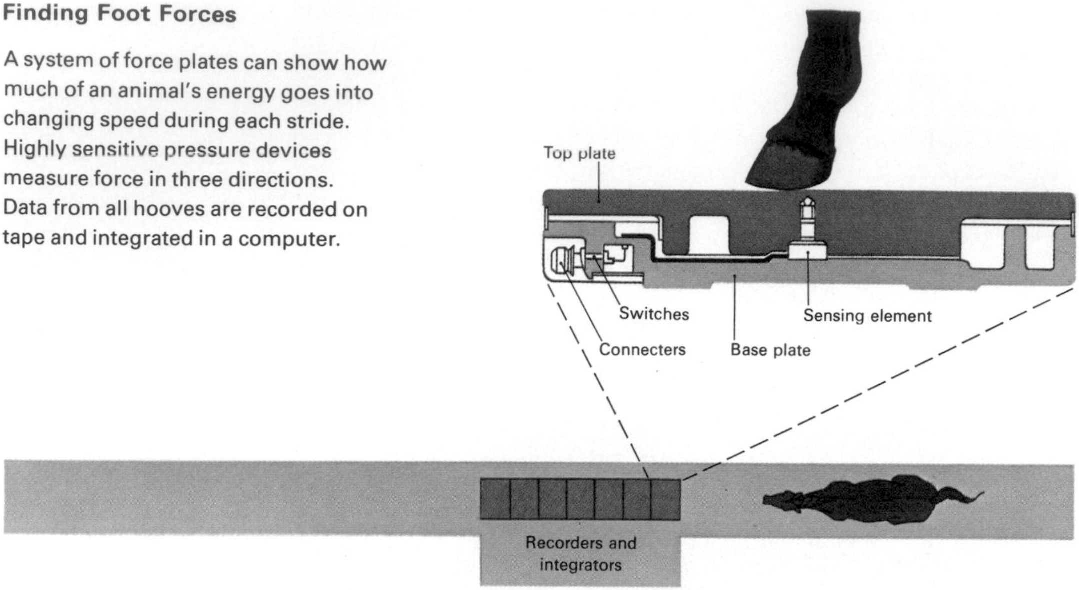

Top plate

Switches

Sensing element

Connecters

Base plate

Recorders and integrators

second) and then abstract the animal's image to a stick figure. From a series of stick figures covering several strides at 5-millisecond intervals, we can calculate the energy expended to move the limbs.

The camera has shown that an animal never runs at a constant speed; its body changes speed during each stride. These changes are so small that we cannot measure them accurately with our films, but they may require more energy than is spent in moving the limbs. To evaluate these changes, we need a "force plate," a device that measures the magnitude and direction of the forces the animal's legs exert on the ground. This information can tell us how much energy is needed to account for speed changes during each stride of different animals.

If, as we have learned, an animal's muscles contract most efficiently at one specific frequency, how does it manage to run at such a wide range of speed? An automobile engine also can operate most efficiently only within a limited range of speed. So the automobile extends the range by changing gears.

Do animals also change gears when they increase speed? To find out, we turned again to the high-speed camera. Films showed that stride frequency changed regularly with speed but that there were abrupt transitions when the animal switched from one gait to another. After an animal switches from a walk to a trot, more of its increase in speed comes from increasing stride length; frequency does not increase as rapidly. When an animal starts to gallop, it gains speed almost entirely by taking longer strides.

We think that changing gaits in animals has the effect of changing gears in automobiles. Apparently each group of muscles has a different frequency at which it operates most efficiently. As the animal's stride frequency begins to exceed the optimum for one group of muscles and its efficiency begins to drop, the animal shifts to a different group with a higher optimum speed of contraction.

It is meaningless to compare stride frequency of animals of very different size at the same speed. But we can compare their transition frequency—that at which an animal changes from one gait to another. In comparing stride frequency at the transition from trot to gallop as a function of the weight of an animal, a very regular relationship appears. Because the frequency within a gait changes very little as an animal increases speed, the trot-gallop transition frequency is also the maximum stride frequency. To check these gear-change theories, we plan to measure the activity of all the different muscles of animals' limbs while they run at different gaits.

When an animal gallops, it seems that something besides its muscles provides energy. A great deal of it may be stored in elastic elements such as tendons and ligaments. A galloping animal has all four legs off the ground during each stride. As it lands, it stretches its tendons, storing energy that it can use to launch the next stride.

To check this, Terry Dawson of the University of New South Wales, Australia, and I decided to investigate hopping energetics in kangaroos. A hopping kangaroo reminds one of a bouncing ball or a pogo stick. While its first hop might require lots of energy, subsequent hops could rely almost entirely on elastic rebound.

The treadmill and high-speed camera showed us that the stride frequency of hopping kangaroos remains nearly constant as they increase speed. Most of the gain in speed comes from longer strides, just as we had found in galloping animals. The proportion of each hopping stride that was spent on the ground decreased and the proportion spent off the ground increased. This gives the muscles involved in bringing the leg back on the recovery stroke, while the animal is off the ground, time to contract more slowly. Thus, the muscles can retain their optimum contraction speed, even though the animal's ground speed increases. The kangaroos' energy consumption remained constant or even decreased slightly as they increased their speed.

We are now trying to determine if this is also true in galloping animals. One reason we may not have seen it before is the difficulty of getting an animal to gallop long enough to measure its oxygen consumption. We may simply have missed it.

Over a decade of research into animal locomotion has revealed some surprises and spiked some venerable scientific theories. And it has raised many new questions. Someone might ask: "Why are we doing these studies?" For one thing, we want to understand how the same basic materials—muscles and bone—can be used to build animals of such different sizes and functions. We should be able to predict the amount of energy an animal needs to move. Further, we will be able to predict many things that depend on energy consumption, such as heart and respiration rates. And we may someday even learn why different animals have different life spans.

How the Salmon Comes Home

By Arthur D. Hasler

Scientists have solved the mystery of how salmon returning from the sea find their way to the stream of their birth

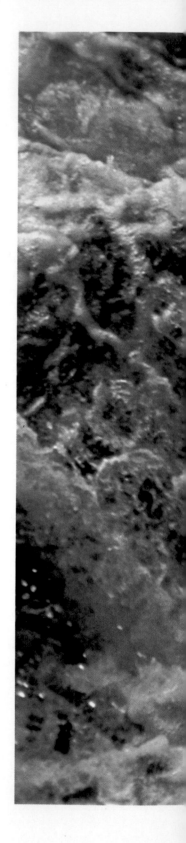

Our first salmon came back on Sept. 20, 1973. Only a few of the fish trickled into tiny Oak Creek in South Milwaukee, Wis., at first, but soon the trickle turned into a flood. By December, more than 1,600 had returned from hundreds of miles away in Lake Michigan. The statistics were impressive, but they could not compare to the actual sight of the spawning salmon, crowded together and splashing as they courted. Like most salmon returning after more than a year in open water, they were exhausted by the long journey home. But these fish were unique. They had come to a stream they had never seen before, drawn there by our knowledge of their homing secrets.

For me, it was a 30-year-old dream come true. As a young biologist, in the mid-1940s, testing the responses of fish to the smell of aquatic plants, I started work aimed at testing the theory that odor is the "underwater guidepost" that ultimately brings the salmon back from the sea to the stream of its birth. I thought that the young salmon might learn, or become imprinted with, the unique fragrance of the soils, plants, and animals in its native stream. The salmon that came to spawn in Oak Creek provided proof that this theory was right.

This discovery has opened up a whole range of exciting possibilities. Knowing that the salmon are guided by odors, man can conceivably bring them back to any spot that he chooses along their migration route, either by simulating the home-stream odor or by teaching

young salmon to home in on the odor of some man-made substance. Thus, the salmon could be concentrated in one place for the benefit of anglers or commercial fishermen.

But when my students, colleagues, and I at the University of Wisconsin started our studies, we were not thinking of practical applications. We simply knew that salmon were a precious natural resource whose numbers were dwindling as a result of pollution and power dams and other man-made obstructions along the routes to their home streams. So we felt that almost anything we found out about the salmon's biology might ultimately be of some use.

What challenged us initially was a curiosity about how animals manage to return over long distances to a specific spot. We knew, for example, that young coho, a kind of Pacific salmon, leave their home stream when they are about 1½ years old and migrate to the open sea, where they grow up. Then, after another year-and-a-half in the ocean, they somehow find their way back over thousands of miles of open water and up through a maze of rivers and streams to their birthplace, where they spawn and die.

My early research, together with what I had read about salmon and homing behavior in other animals, prepared me for an experience I had in 1946 while on vacation in Utah's Wasatch Mountains, where I grew up. As my children and I hiked along a path I had frequented as a boy, the familiar fragrances of columbine and mosses growing just ahead but out of sight triggered a whole flood of memories. The names of boyhood chums and visions of the nearby mountain meadow where we played ball vividly flashed across my mind. I thought, "Well, Art, you're a salmon coming home, and it smells like home."

The author:
Arthur D. Hasler is professor of zoology and director of the Laboratory of Limnology at the University of Wisconsin at Madison.

Clipping the fin of a young fish, *far left,* identifies it as imprinted with morpholine. Scientists use an electrical shocking device and nets, *center,* to catch fish as adults returning from the sea to a morpholine-treated stream. The author, *left,* checks a fish to see if it was imprinted.

Although it is not scientific to generalize what happens in a human being to another animal without rigorous testing, that experience planted the seed of the odor-migration theory in my mind. It also marked the beginning of the efforts at the University of Wisconsin to discover how a salmon finds its home stream.

In 1953, after a series of preparatory experiments, we were ready to try to find out if the salmon needed its nose to locate the stream in which it was born. Our research site was a scenic little Y-shaped stream about 15 miles from Seattle, Wash. Each branch of the stream had its own native salmon populations. We captured 300 of these fish as they entered their home branches, and we plugged the noses of half of them with cotton. Then, we put an identification tag on each fish to tell us in which branch we had caught it and released them all a little more than a mile below the fork of the stream.

As they repeated their journey upstream, the fish that had been deprived of their sense of smell became disoriented and confused, and many of them entered the wrong branch of the stream. But the fish that could smell chose their home tributary almost without error. The experiment was straightforward and the results dramatic. The sense of smell seemed crucial to the salmon's finding their home stream.

We felt then that the best way to show that salmon homed in on odor was to substitute some man-made chemical odor for the natural home-stream scents and then show that the fish would follow that odor. The chemical would have to be fairly stable, detectable in small quantities, completely new to the salmon, and one that would neither naturally repel nor attract the fish. Graduate student Warren Wisby, with the aid of undergraduate student Ross Horrall, screened likely substances for two years. Their tests turned up the right chemical, a colorless, acrid-smelling liquid called morpholine.

Despite this breakthrough, our experiments had reached an impasse. We now had the chemical we needed, but the stocks of salmon we wanted to study were on the Pacific Coast, and our working base lay 2,000 miles away, in Wisconsin. So Wisby and I published the details of our planned experiment in a scientific journal in 1951 in the hope that someone else would perform it. Although several scientists from other universities expressed interest, the work was never done.

Then, in the late 1960s, the Michigan and Wisconsin Departments of Natural Resources (DNR) introduced Pacific coho salmon into the Great Lakes to revitalize the local sports fishing. Tests had shown that these salt-water fish could adapt to the fresh water of the lakes and the streams that feed them. Fishermen were happy, but we were overjoyed. Suddenly, we had the fish we needed to do our experiment right in our own back yard.

With support from the National Sea Grant Program and the National Science Foundation, we began imprinting salmon in the spring of 1971. We transported 16,000 coho fingerlings—young fish about the size of a finger—from the DNR Wild Rose Fish Hatchery in central Wisconsin to a water filtration plant in South Milwaukee. We held the fish there for about 30 days, during their smolting period—the stage in nature that marks the beginning of their movement downstream to the sea. All the fish were held in tanks with water piped in from Lake Michigan, which contained no detectable home-stream scents. We dripped morpholine in a quantity equal to about 1 drop to 125 thousand gallons of water into the tanks containing half of the fish. The rest of the fish were not treated, to serve as a control group. The fish from each of the groups were then marked for identification and released in May into Lake Michigan near the mouth of Oak Creek.

During the spawning season that fall, we created what we hoped would be an artificial home stream for the salmon by dripping small amounts of morpholine into the waters of Oak Creek. Using several techniques to catch returning fish, we captured 31 that had been imprinted with morpholine. These were precocious males that had returned a year early. The following fall, the bulk of the returning adults came back. There were 185 more morpholine-imprinted fish and only 27 from the control group. Since only between 1 and 2 per cent of the fish raised and released from a hatchery are normally expected to return, these returns were very good and certainly supported our hypothesis that the imprinted fish recognized and homed in on the morpholine scent. Nevertheless, we decided it would be best to collect even more data.

During the spring of 1972, our team worked with a larger number of smolts. We exposed 18,200 to the morpholine and left 20,000 unexposed as our control group. This time, we released the fish at three different points along the Lake Michigan shoreline.

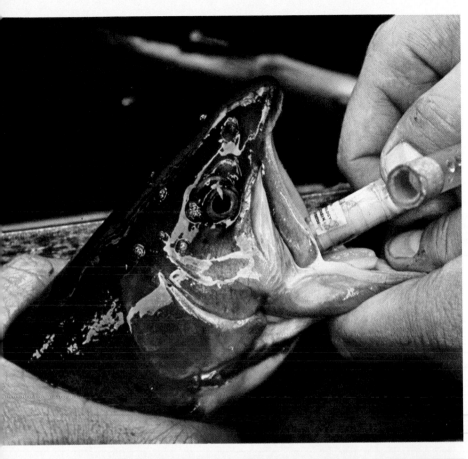

The Scent of Home?

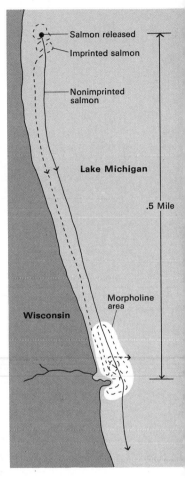

Salmon released
Imprinted salmon
Nonimprinted salmon

Lake Michigan

.5 Mile

Morpholine area

Wisconsin

Radio transmitters inserted into fishes' stomachs help scientists to track the fish with an underwater receiver, *left.* Typically, morpholine-imprinted salmon stopped and milled about an area containing the chemical, *above.* Nonimprinted salmon swam right by.

Electrodes implanted in a fish's brain, *right,* monitor the animal's responses when test solutions are squirted into its nostrils. The responses, recorded electronically, *below and below right,* show morpholine-imprinted fish reacts most strongly to morpholine, not at all to water from Oak Creek, but strongly to morpholine in Oak Creek water.

What the Nose Tells the Brain

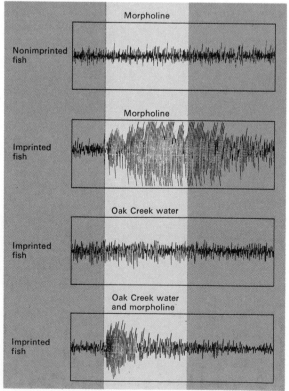

Nonimprinted fish — Morpholine

Imprinted fish — Morpholine

Imprinted fish — Oak Creek water

Imprinted fish — Oak Creek water and morpholine

When these fish began to show up in Oak Creek in the fall of 1973, we were tingling with excitement. We eventually caught 1,485 imprinted fish and only 163 controls—a ratio of nearly 10 to 1. Not only did the numbers seem to substantiate our theory, but they also showed an astounding, and as yet unexplainable, 8 to 9 per cent return of the fish we had imprinted.

Two other experiments performed at the same time strengthened our already strong evidence for the odor-homing theory. During the 1972 and 1973 spawning seasons, zoologists Ross Horrall and Dale Madison and field assistant Allan Scholz from my laboratory captured fish that were returning to Oak Creek. After inserting small ultrasonic transmitters into the fishes' stomachs, the men took them out in a boat and released them along the coastline, one at a time. Madison and Scholz then used a hydrophone and receiver to track each fish as it swam along the coastline. Meanwhile, men in another boat dripped a small quantity of morpholine into the water along the fish's path. When the imprinted fish reached the area containing the morpholine, they stopped short and milled around. Control fish, however, swam right on by. If the chemical was not dripped into the water, the imprinted fish also swam by without hesitating.

Meanwhile, in my laboratory, graduate student Jon Cooper performed a delicate operation on some of our coho that were captured at the mouth of Oak Creek. Cooper bathed each fish's nose in such substances as phenethyl alcohol, distilled water, home-stream (Oak Creek) water that contained morpholine, and dilute morpholine in pure distilled water. Tiny electrodes planted in the olfactory bulb, or smell center, of the fish's brain sensed the animal's reactions to each substance. Cooper found that the responses were most intense when imprinted fish were exposed to the morpholine in distilled water and that these fish also reacted very strongly when exposed to the home stream-morpholine mixture.

Now, with data from these different types of experiments, we feel we can say with certainty that odor is the invisible element that guides the salmon back from just beyond the shoreline to the stream of its birth. How the fish navigate in the open ocean to reach a point where they can pick up the crucial scent is still a mystery. However, with the knowledge we have now, we stand a better chance of protecting the salmon's dwindling populations. For example, if power dams or pollution should ruin a salmon stream as a spawning site, perhaps man can decoy the fish back to a cleaner or more accessible point downstream. This could be accomplished either by simulating home-stream odors or by "training" the fish as we did.

Surely any step toward saving them is worthwhile, for salmon are a gift from nature to man. We neither feed them nor take care of them in any other way. Yet, as young fish, they go out to sea where they grow fat on the ocean's "rangeland" and then deliver themselves, free of charge, to our back door for the catching and eating.

The Biologists Bite Back

By John F. Henahan

Drawing from nature's arsenal, scientists are amassing an amazing array of arms against the deadliest insect of all

From swamps in Nigeria to flooded rice fields in California, man has been losing the war against an age-old enemy he once thought he had vanquished—the mosquito. More than just a nuisance, mosquitoes spread some of the worst of man's diseases, including malaria, which has killed more people than have all other infectious diseases combined. Widely used chemical insecticides have proved ineffective against many new varieties of mosquitoes. Worse yet, many of the mosquito's natural enemies are killed by the poisons meant for the mosquitoes. In addition, the use of these powerful poisons had to be limited because they take an unintended toll in wildlife.

Against this background, an 11-man panel of mosquito-control experts formed by the National Academy of Sciences (NAS) concluded in 1973, "Mosquito control is in a state of crisis." After detailed consideration of all known alternatives, the panel decided that one way out of the crisis might be to complement selective chemical control with biological controls—natural agents that act specifically against mosquitoes without disrupting the ecology of the surrounding area. Initial tests of this strategy had already shown its great promise even before the NAS panel met. Harrison Brown, former foreign secretary of NAS, put it this way: "Recent findings justify a prediction that significant breakthroughs in biological control can be expected within five years, given adequate support and sustained research efforts."

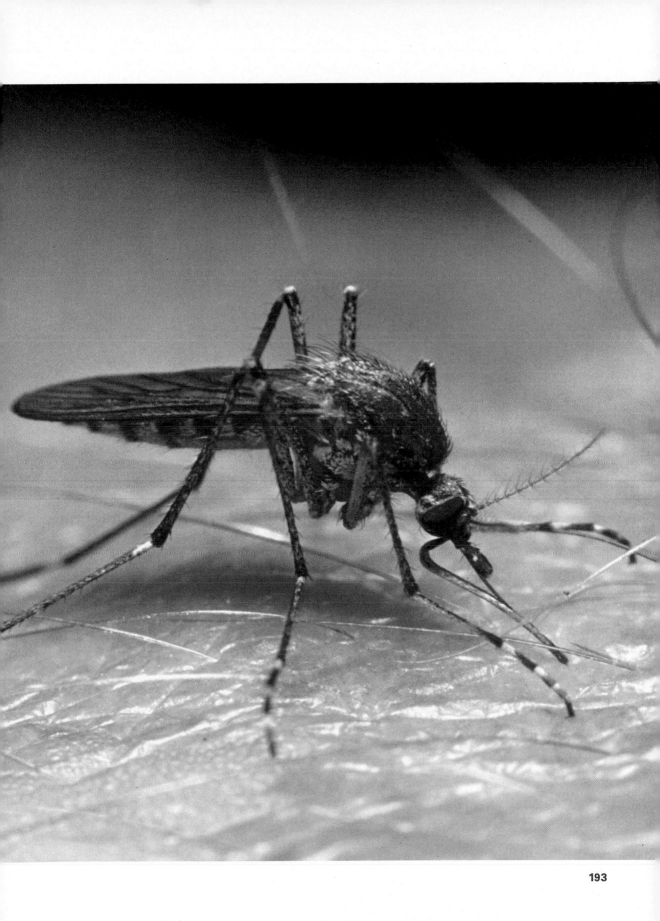

So the basic plan for the new attack on mosquitoes has been determined. This time, the weapons will come from nature's arsenal, not from man's alone. Prime targets for the impending biological onslaught are the three major types of disease-carrying mosquitoes: *Anopheles,* which spreads malaria; *Culex,* which transmits encephalitis; and *Aedes,* which carries yellow fever.

Anopheles mosquitoes reach overwhelming numbers in Asia, Central and South America, and large portions of Africa. Millions of the 2 to 3 billion people on these continents have malaria, and the disease claims more than 1 million lives each year. This occurs in spite of the millions of tons of insecticides applied to combat *Anopheles.*

Like all female mosquitoes, the female *Anopheles* must suck her victim's blood in order to develop her eggs. She spreads malaria when she draws blood from an infected human or animal, then bites others.

Culex mosquitoes transmit filariasis, a disease that causes grotesque swelling of the body and other debilitating symptoms, in the same way. Although filariasis is usually not fatal, it afflicts more than 250-million people, mainly in Africa and Southeast Asia. *Culex* mosquitoes also transmit viral encephalitis to people in these countries. This disease, which attacks both man and beast, causes inflammation of the brain and such symptoms as fever and headache. In more severe cases, convulsions, coma, and even death follow.

Aedes mosquitoes spread not only yellow fever, but also dengue, or "breakbone fever." Yellow fever's chief symptoms are yellowing skin and high fever, but it often progresses to bleeding gums and stomach and sometimes results in delirium, coma, and death. All but eliminated in Central and South America, yellow fever still incapacitates or kills millions of people in Africa. Dengue is marked by high fever and stiff joints. One form of the disease has been killing one of every five children that it attacks in Southeast Asia, according to the World Health Organization (WHO).

Mosquitoes have a four-phase life cycle which biologists must fully understand in order to develop biological controls. Each adult female lays her eggs in water areas ranging in size from a muddy hoof mark or flower vase to a large swamp or rice paddy. From each mosquito egg, a tiny, wormlike larva emerges. The larva then enters the cocoon or pupa phase. The life cycle is completed when a mature, winged adult emerges from the pupa, flies off across the countryside, and lays its own eggs. The entire cycle takes about 12 days.

A major advantage of the chemical insecticides is that they kill susceptible mosquitoes in every phase of their life cycle. But both larvae and adults gradually develop resistance. The scientists who are developing the new, natural methods of destroying the insects have focused in on the larval and the pupal stages, when they are more or less sitting targets.

One of the most promising of these methods is application of a hormone that prevents mosquito larvae from developing into adults.

The author:
John F. Henahan is a science writer and former editor of *Chemical and Engineering News.* He wrote "The Power Above, the Power Below" in the 1974 edition of *Science Year.*

In 1956, biologist Carroll Williams of Harvard University isolated such a hormone from a caterpillar, the larva of a moth or butterfly. It was called juvenile hormone (JH).

If JH is applied to a larva, the larva will enter the pupal stage, but it will never develop properly and emerge as an adult. Williams speculates that the JH somehow blocks the genes that normally guide the developing insect to adulthood.

Armed with this knowledge, biologists theorized that they might control mosquitoes in nature by applying large quantities of mosquito JH to their breeding grounds. But using natural JH on a commercial scale was clearly out of the question: It cost too much to produce, it was too unstable for use in the field, and, from a financial point of view, it could not be patented. So chemists began synthesizing thousands of chemical relatives of mosquito JH in a search for one that would be commercially useful.

After synthesizing some 1,500 variants of the natural product, a team of chemists headed by John Siddal and Clive Hendricks at Zoecon Corporation in Palo Alto, Calif., finally produced an amber liquid that proved to be about 2,000 times more potent and 5 times more stable than the natural insect JH.

Because the synthetic JH breaks down after a few hours in water, it goes through a special process before it is applied. It is mixed with

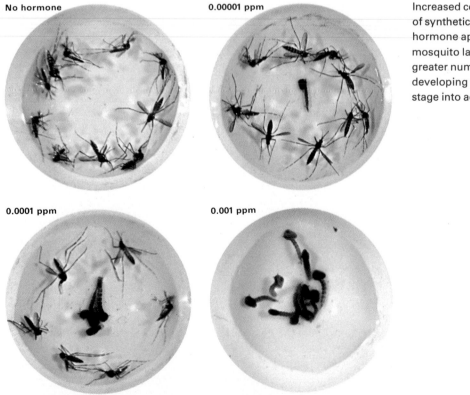

No hormone

0.00001 ppm

0.0001 ppm

0.001 ppm

Increased concentration of synthetic juvenile hormone applied to mosquito larvae keeps greater numbers from developing past pupal stage into adulthood.

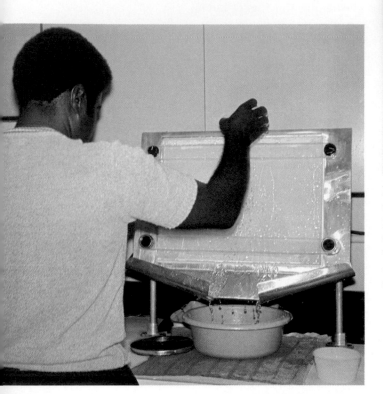

A technician pours male and female pupae through a glass-sided wedge that opens just wide enough at bottom to let only smaller, male pupae pass. Male pupae on wire screens, *above*, are ready for rinsing after having been exposed to Thiotepa, a chemical which produces sterile adults.

water, the chemical building blocks for a plastic, and a catalyst. This recipe produces a unique suspension of tiny particles, which are actually time-release capsules of the man-made JH. The watery suspension, which strongly resembles white latex paint, can be applied easily with conventional insecticide sprayers.

But chemists still could not answer some questions, among them: Would the synthetic JH actually eradicate mosquitoes in the field? And does it have harmful side effects? To find out, the Environmental Protection Agency has licensed small-scale field tests of synthetic JH.

Although still considered an experimental material, synthetic JH has already proved its worth in Florida and in the Central Valley of California, near San Francisco, where the *Culex* mosquitoes are highly resistant to DDT and other chemical insecticides. It has also been tested with promising results against *Aedes* and *Anopheles* mosquitoes in about 30 foreign countries, and is currently under study by the WHO.

The question of the hormone's safety is not easily answered. Because it is new, its long-term effects are still unknown. But, in experiments, large doses fed for 90 days or more to dogs, rats, rabbits, chickens, ducks, and fish produced no noticeable effects.

Siddal admits that even though the synthetic JH appears to be both effective and safe, mosquitoes may develop resistance to it, as they have done to chemical insecticides. But he points out that the synthetic substance is so similar to the insect's natural JH that any defense the mosquito might develop would probably be self-destructive.

Another promising biological control interferes with the mosquito's life cycle at an even earlier stage than does the synthetic JH. In fact, it prevents egg fertilization. In the first successful use of this technique, in the late 1950s, scientists of the United States Department of Agriculture (USDA) used radiation to sexually sterilize billions of male screwworm flies. The sterile cattle pests were then released over a 10,000-square-mile area in the southeastern United States, and the screwworm population was rapidly erased. Apparently, sterile flies so outnumbered their fertile brothers in the treated area that they mated with most of the females. Because no eggs would hatch from such unions, the female screwworm flies—which mate only once in a lifetime—died leaving no offspring.

The same technique has been tested successfully against *Anopheles* and *Culex* mosquitoes in Florida and Central America. Donald E. Weidhaas, an entomologist at the USDA research laboratories in Gainesville, Fla., is in charge of the mosquito sterilization tests. Weidhaas found early that male mosquitoes sterilized with radiation lost much of their mating drive. So he tested Thiotepa, a chemical known to cause sterilization. He found that the chemical sterilized male mosquitoes without appreciably decreasing their mating drive.

The mosquitoes are treated in their pupal stage. Male pupae are smaller than females, and so the sexes can be separated. Weidhaas treated millions of male mosquito pupae with a dilute solution of Thiotepa, then shipped them in small plastic boxes to Sea Horse Key, a small island off the Florida coast, and isolated Lake Apastpeque in El Salvador in 1971 and 1972. There the sterile males emerged and mated, unproductively, with the local female mosquitoes. Five months later, virtually all of the *Anopheles* mosquitoes in the El Salvador test area were eliminated. The *Culex* mosquitoes on Sea Horse Key were almost entirely eliminated in 10 weeks.

Even though the sterilization technique worked dramatically in these small isolated areas, Weidhaas is not sure that his method will be widely accepted. Many people will fight any move to introduce perhaps billions of mosquitoes near their homes, even though it might eventually mean a drastic reduction in the insects and, subsequently, in disease. Weidhaas therefore sees the sterile male technique being used primarily in sparsely inhabited breeding areas as a way to hold down mosquito population. He expects other methods, including the use of insecticides, to be used in other areas.

Other weapons that may be used with sterilization or JH application, or both, are under study by scientists in California and Florida. These biologists attack mosquitoes with the insects' natural enemies.

In some cases, the scientists are simply restoring the natural checks and balances that existed until insecticides aimed at the mosquito wiped out its predators instead. In other cases, the scientists have recruited foreign parasites and predators to help fight the war.

One of the most effective predators is the minnow called the mosquito fish, *Gambusia affinis*. Feeding mainly on larvae, this fish has all but eliminated the *Anopheles* mosquito from warm waters of the southeastern United States. It has also been credited with reducing the malaria incidence in Italy and other countries that have imported it for malaria control. A single female *Gambusia* will produce from 2,000 to 3,000 young per season, enough to gobble up mosquito larva infestations in breeding areas covering an acre or more.

But *Gambusia* is considered a mixed blessing in California, according to Fred Legner, a biological-control expert at the University of California, Riverside (UCR). He introduced *Gambusia* there but found that the mosquito population dropped at first, but then rose sharply. Legner believes that the mosquito fish feed on everything they can catch, including other mosquito predators. The fish also eat much of the zooplankton (tiny aquatic animals) that normally graze on algae. The algae then grow unchecked and ultimately choke out the fish population, including the *Gambusia*. Unfortunately, the water remains suitable for mosquito larvae.

As an alternative predator, Legner proposes the desert pupfish *Cyprinodon*, which gets its common name from its puppylike face. "All of the field data that we have seen indicates to us that the pupfish live

The mosquito fish, *Gambusia, below,* feeds voraciously on larvae, but it also eats other mosquito predators and organisms that control algae. The desert pupfish, *Cyprinodon, right,* eats the larvae, but not other predators or algae eaters.

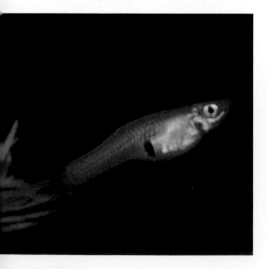

harmoniously with other organisms, rather than grazing out useful ones, as does *Gambusia*. The pupfish are doubly beneficial in that they also feed on algae...." he says.

Legner is even more enthusiastic about two other mosquito predators—planarians (flatworms), and hydras (tiny, tentacled animals). Both have been tested against insecticide-resistant *Aedes* and *Culex* mosquitoes in the area around Bakersfield, Calif.

Of the many species of hydra, Legner particularly endorses the ½-inch-long green hydra, *Chlorohydra viridissima*. These hydras eradicate mosquito larvae by stinging them with their tentacles. This paralyzes the larvae. The hydras may eat a few, but the bulk of the paralyzed larvae, which breathe through special organs that pierce the water's surface, sink to the bottom of the pond and die for lack of oxygen.

Legner cites a number of advantages that hydras have over other biological controls. They can be refrigerated in a semidormant form for months and can be spread easily either by hand or with a sprayer. Also, they live happily in tiny, shallow, breeding areas that could not support mosquito-eating fish.

In trials during July, 1973, Legner found that hydras reduced the *Aedes* mosquito population in irrigated pastures in California by more than 65 per cent. They wiped out nearly 80 per cent of the *Culex* mosquitoes in test plots during the winter of 1973. "As far as I and the Kern County Mosquito Abatement District are concerned, the hydras have great applicability to mosquito control and we're going to keep using them," Legner says.

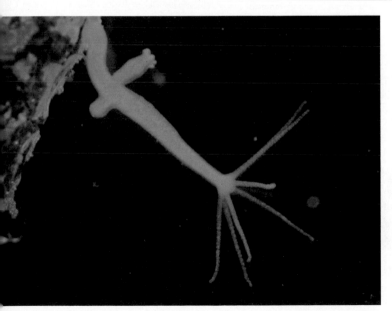

Hydra, *left,* paralyzes mosquito larvae with its stinging tentacles, eats some, and lets the rest sink to the bottom and suffocate. Planarian, *below,* covers eggs, larvae, or pupae with a sticky gum and then sucks out their body fluids.

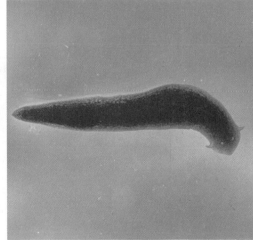

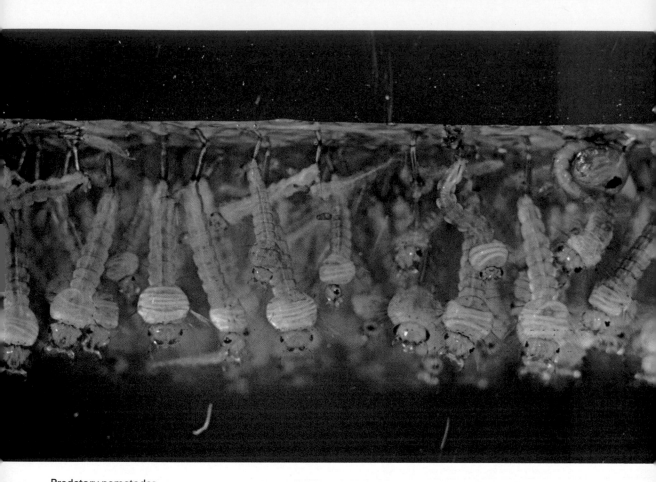

Predatory nematodes, or roundworms, curl up within the bodies of mosquito larvae hanging upside down from the surface of the water.

Legner will also keep using planarians, whose value as devastating mosquito predators was discovered quite by chance in the summer of 1973. Researchers at UCR were raising mosquito larvae by the hundreds of thousands in huge outdoor fiberglass tanks. Periodically, however, the test specimens were mysteriously wiped out. The scientists eventually were able to identify planarians as the culprits. Tests showed that the inch-long flatworms quickly destroyed *Culex* mosquitoes in the egg, larval, or pupal stages by covering them with a heavy, sticky gum. Weighted down by the substance, the mosquitoes sank to the bottom of the tanks. The flatworms followed them down and sucked out their body fluids. "In the field trials carried out in the Riverside area, planarians demonstrated their startling destructive capability," explains Legner. "Dropped by hand into a 1-square-meter test pond, 100 planarians destroyed 90 per cent of the mosquito larvae and eliminated all adults within a month."

Legner hopes to generate millions of planarians quickly and easily by using chemical techniques to speed up the rate at which they reproduce. He believes their durability makes them particularly desirable. Planarians can survive for long periods of time without any food by

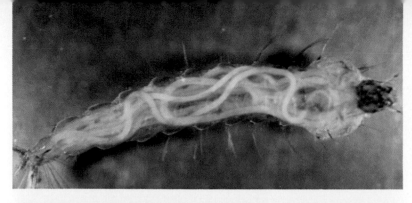

After a nematode feeds on the body fluids of a mosquito larva, *left,* it bores a hole in the body, through which it escapes, *below left.*

feeding on their own internal organs, and they can regenerate themselves even if cut up into many pieces.

Scientists are also testing other worms in small-scale field trials. Entomologist James J. Petersen of the USDA's mosquito control laboratory in Lake Charles, La., has found that the nematode, or roundworm, known as *Reesemermis nielseni* infects and kills mosquitoes. The tiny worm enters the mosquito larva, feeds on its body fluids, then bores an exit hole in it. The process is invariably lethal to the larva.

Petersen and his co-workers sprayed test ponds in Louisiana with nematodes, using a conventional backpack sprayer. The ponds ranged in size from about 2,000 to more than 32,000 square feet. "Within three days," says Petersen, "four-fifths of the *Anopheles* larvae were parasitized, and within a few weeks there was a comparable drop in the population." The nematodes performed equally well in tests in flooded rice fields in California.

Petersen's procedure for mass-producing the mosquito parasites is simple and efficient. He puts a box of sand containing nematode eggs in the bottom of a water-filled, glass aquarium. Mosquito larvae are then placed in the upper portion of the aquarium, separated from the

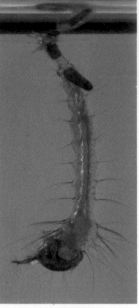
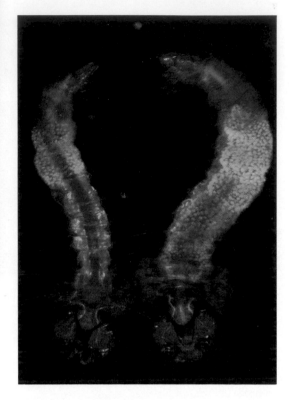

When normal mosquito larva, *above left,* is treated with *Bacillus thuringiensis,* a bacterium, it becomes infected with a fatal disease, *above right.* Viruses, seen as bumpy glowing areas, in mosquito larvae, *right,* also infect and kill them.

lower portion by a screen. When the nematodes hatch, they swim through the screen to the upper level and kill the mosquito larvae. After they emerge from the holes they bore in the mosquito larvae, they return, through the screen, to the lower level where they mate and lay eggs. Each female lays about 3,000 eggs. Petersen estimates that it costs only about 10 cents to produce a million parasites. For about 50 cents, he can produce enough nematodes to treat an acre of mosquito-breeding area.

But nematodes are not as hardy as mosquito larvae. For example, the worms cannot live in salt water or polluted water where mosquito larvae thrive. Consequently, Petersen and his co-workers are looking for hardier nematode breeds.

Perhaps the strongest weapon against mosquitoes, in the view of many researchers, is germ warfare. The idea is to infect mosquitoes with a lethal disease agent that is harmless to other species. This approach has worked successfully against other insects. The bacterium *Bacillus thuringiensis* has been produced commercially since the 1950s for use against cabbage loopers and other agricultural pests.

In 1974, insect pathologist Irvin M. Hall of UCR reported finding two strains of *B. thuringiensis* that, at concentrations as weak as 0.1 part per million, kill *Aedes* mosquito larvae. Hall screened more than 350 different strains of the bacterium from many different sources before he found the mosquito killers. Most of Hall's strains were supplied by Howard Dulmage, a bacteria cultivation expert working at the USDA's research laboratory in Brownsville, Tex. Dulmage looks for his new strains in sick insects, in soil samples, and sometimes in the open air. Once he has isolated and identified the bacteria, he mass-produces them in 15-quart laboratory fermenters. However, Dulmage is confident that should they be needed, within only a few months he could be producing the bacteria in commercial quantities in 30,000- to 50,000-gallon vats.

Another bacterium, *Bacillus sphaericus,* killed *Aedes, Culex,* and *Anopheles* mosquitoes in a series of laboratory tests in 1974. This bacterium was first isolated from sick mosquitoes that were collected in Delhi, India, by microbiologist Samuel Singer of Western Illinois University, who is associated with the WHO International Reference Center at Ohio State University. The center's director, entomologist John D. Briggs, says that the full potential of *B. sphaericus* will not become clear until field trials now underway in a malaria zone in northern Nigeria are completed. But Briggs reports that two American drug firms and a Japanese chemical company are already interested in developing the new agent as a commercial product.

Other deadly disease agents, including viruses and tiny animals called protozoans, are also promising. Together with worms, hydras, mosquito-eating fish, sterilization, and growth-stopping hormones— they are among the most promising biological weapons. But which is best? And why are so few in large-scale use?

To begin with, all biological controls appear slow and uncertain when compared to quick-acting chemical insecticides that can wipe out billions of insects in one swoop of a spray plane. And, unlike such insecticides, which work in almost all climates, biological controls are effective only under certain conditions. For example, a predator or parasite that thrives in rainy northern California might not survive in the drier regions of the South.

Many mosquito-control experts—faced with the continued threat of malaria and other mosquito-borne diseases—insist that they cannot yet afford to stop using DDT. When used properly, they say, it is still among the most economical, quick-acting, and effective mosquito killers available. A growing number of entomologists agree. But many of them argue for integrated control, a balanced blending of biological and chemical weaponry. The biological war against mosquitoes is still limited to small-scale probes and skirmishes. Most are successful, and some look promising for full-scale battle. But restoring natural checks and balances on mosquito populations, and discovering and applying new ones that do not upset nature's balance is a great challenge and a field still in its infancy. As UCR's Fred Legner puts it, "We're all pioneers at this point."

Technology Tunes To Nature

By Gerald Leach

Reviving discarded technologies and blending them with new life styles, a growing number of people are seeking to live in harmony with their environment

In the summer of 1973, three couples and their five children moved into an old farmhouse in the Welsh hills to launch a 10-year experiment in living. It was a brave move, one that marked a radical, new merger of social and scientific thinking.

Leaving comfortable city lives behind them, the group took over a run-down stone cottage, surrounded by 42 acres of hilly land supporting a hundred sheep, and located in a notoriously wet and sunless climate. They had no farming experience, only some unconventional blueprints and audacious convictions. They were determined to show that this unpromising farm would eventually provide a satisfying life for a community of 30 people.

According to plans, the community would be self-sufficient for all food, water, and energy. With much technical cunning—and luck— they could produce a tidy surplus to pay for extra goods and such services as health, transportation, and education. They would farm the land organically; tap the sun, wind, and streams for power; and recycle organic wastes for fertilizer and cooking gas. The farm, known for centuries as Eithin-y-gaer, they rechristened BRAD, for Biotechnic Research and Development.

In Scotland there are similar experimental communities called Laurieston Hall and Findhorn Community. Across the English Channel, in Les Assions, south of Lyons, France, ethnologist Phillipe Arreteau

**The Saving Cycle
Of Energy**

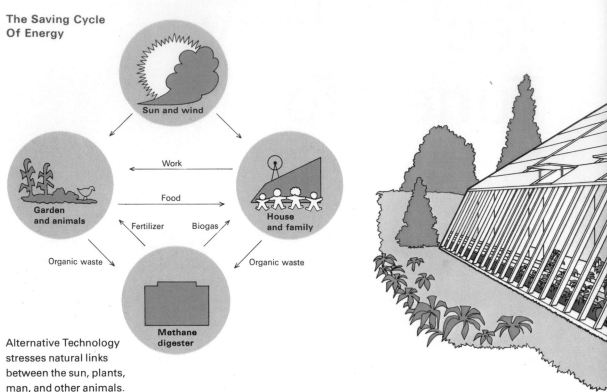

Alternative Technology
stresses natural links
between the sun, plants,
man, and other animals.

The author:
Gerald Leach is a
British science writer
and a Visiting Fellow
with the Science Policy
Research Unit of
Sussex University

runs a self-sufficient research center and teaches scores of Parisians eager to copy his methods. BRAD's French branch has started up in Normandy, as has Schoon Dorp (clean village) in Holland.

Across the Atlantic, on Cape Cod, a group called The New Alchemists has established a similar experimental community that has spawned two daughter groups in the western United States. Throughout the Western world, you can now find groups of people with aims similar to BRAD's—a few established in their new setting, a few just starting up, many planning to do so.

Is this a back-to-the-country movement by disgruntled, ecology-minded urbanites? Partly, yes. "Living in contact with the elements, the sun, the earth, the wind; taking care of animals; working with one's hands...eating food which has taste to it—these have truly become the rare luxuries of our age," Arreteau says.

But there is much more to it than tasty food. These pioneers share a conviction that the large-scale technologies of Western urban-industrial society are drowning people in boredom, isolation, and fruitless consumption, and wrecking the planet in the process.

Rejecting both our present system and the dropout, antiscience, hippie movement of the 1960s, these people are searching for a new middle way...for alternative technologies and life styles to match. "What we seek," says British science writer Robin Clarke, founder of BRAD, "is to put men before machines, people before governments, practice before theory, the country before the city, smallness before

A proposed Alternative Technology (AT) house could function without hookups to community utilities by tapping the wind for electricity, collecting and storing rain that falls on its roof, trapping solar heat in a greenhouse and a rooftop solar collector, storing heat for cloudy, cold days in insulated underground wet sand and earth reservoirs, and drawing gas for cooking from decaying organic wastes.

bigness, wholeness before reductionism, organic materials before synthetic ones, plants before animals, craftsmanship before expertise, and quality before quantity.''

It is a ragbag of a list, yet one can discern in it an overall theme. In essence, Alternative Technology (AT) is trying to re-create the freedom, togetherness, and rugged self-sufficiency of the best 19th-century American homesteading communities, only—and this aspect is crucial—with a good deal of carefully selected present-day know-how thrown in to match our wider horizons and higher living standards.

But what know-how? AT communities are committed to technologies that are small in scale, simple to build, inexpensive to operate, within their own control, and which neither use up nonrenewable resources nor harm the environment. They will meet their energy needs, for example, with homemade windmills and solar collectors rather than by taking electricity from a commercial power plant.

Because windmills and solar collectors are fitful, low-output energy sources, however, AT pioneers must display remarkable ingenuity just to stay warm in winter. And even then, they recognize that energy-saving life styles are just as necessary to self-sufficiency as are cleverly designed energy-producing systems. For example, members of BRAD-like communities may generate electricity with novel windmills, but they wash their clothes by hand and forego other modern conveniences such as dishwashers and food freezers until such time as they can invent more powerful energy systems and appliances that meet their criteria. In this way, these communities are experimental laboratories where technology for a new kind of life style is being developed.

What has AT actually achieved so far? Does it work? Unfortunately, it is too early to give an answer based on experience. Apart from a number of communes where there has been little technological invention, no AT groups aiming for complete self-sufficiency have been in operation long enough. Clarke estimates it will be 10 years before BRAD can be truly self-sufficient for 30 people.

But if you go by theory, AT can work. And perhaps the most likely scheme to prove it comes from a hard-nosed splinter group of professors and graduate students in a traditional university department, the Architectural School of Cambridge University in England. The scheme originated as the brainchild of Brenda Vale, a postdoctoral student who designed much of BRAD.

Vale's plans call for a self-sufficient, single-family house tailored to the climate in Cambridge, England, where there is little snow in the

Under the AT house, in an airtight tank called a methane digester, bacteria convert human, animal, and vegetable wastes into cooking gas. Warm waste water heats the decaying mixture. The floating tank, right, stores the gas and regulates its pressure.

Cooking with Yesterday's Waste

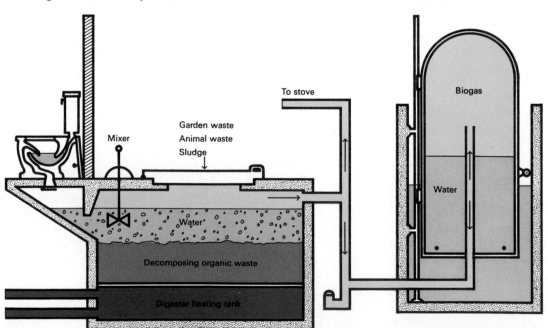

winter, but unfortunately, little sunshine either. The house would not need such community utilities as electricity, natural gas, heating oil, water, or sewage disposal. With three bedrooms, living room, kitchen, and bathroom on one 70- by 13-foot (21- by 4-meter) floor, and with additional space in the attic, the house has room for a family of four. Such a house was being built in 1974 at Brunel University, near London, for use as a student dormitory.

For family living, the Vale house would be erected on an acre of farmable land near a village or town where the adults can work and the children can go to school. Eventually, other AT houses, schools, and workshops may cluster around it to form a complete AT community, perhaps based on a small factory or craft industries. Or the community could concentrate on organic farming and gardening to produce and sell such products as cheese and quality vegetables.

Each family would grow 75 per cent of its yearly food needs on its acre of land. This would require intensive organic gardening of fruit, vegetables, and hay; two goats for milk; bees for honey; 20 hens for eggs and meat; rabbits; and a pig to turn table scraps into pork. The family would spend much of the day farming, but there would be enough time left over for the husband or wife to hold a part-time job.

The garden is much more than a source of food to the AT family whose motto is "Waste not, recycle, integrate, and interrelate." To begin with, none of the food nutrients and minerals leave the house and garden. After they are eaten, they eventually go back to the land as fertilizer. This food-to-sewage-to-fertilizer cycle provides more than organic soil enrichment—it provides the flame that cooks the food. Today's breakfast eggs boil by courtesy of eggs eaten months ago.

The recycling system that turns wastes into cooking gas and fertilizer is called a methane digester. Bacteria working in an airtight underground tank heated to about 80°F. (27°C.) digest human, animal, and vegetable wastes. From the wastes of the Vale house and garden, the digester would produce each day about 60 cubic feet (1.6 m^3) of biogas, a mixture of 65 per cent natural gas (methane) and 35 per cent carbon dioxide. Biogas burns in a slightly modified methane burner with a sufficiently hot flame for cooking.

Recycling wastes to produce cooking gas is both ecologically and economically sound. Cooking accounts for about 6 per cent of a typical household's energy budget. For clarity, all the entries in such a budget can be expressed in the standard electrical energy unit, the kilowatt-hour (kwh). The average British or American household with a gas stove uses about 2,300 kwh of natural gas for cooking each year. By comparison, a digester such as the Vale house's waste-digesting system produces at least 3,600 kwh of cooking gas each year.

And it produces fertilizer, too. When the sludge in the digester has given up its gas, it is removed, dried, and spread on the land. The sludge still contains all minerals and nutrients except for nitrogen, which can be restored to the soil by growing peas or other legumes.

Some AT houses may use digesters to meet most of their energy needs beyond cooking. A large methane digester fed by the wastes from five or six people and several farm animals, and the crop wastes from five acres or more of land, would generate about 40,000 kwh of gas a year. This is equal to the entire yearly energy demand of the average British house, and is about 10,000 kwh less than the typical energy-hungry American family uses. Because all the energy is in the form of gas, the AT family could either use gas lights or use some of the gas to run an electric generator to power electric lights and appliances.

But gardening has even more to offer than food and gas. Running the full length of the Vale house's south wall is a greenhouse where the occupants would grow flowers, fruit, and vegetables in the wintertime. But even more, this greenhouse would supply much of the hot air the family will need to keep warm during a typical Cambridge winter. In most homes, winter heating to a comfortable 68°F. (20°C.) contributes the largest single cost to the fuel bills. In the Vale house, excellent insulation cuts energy demand to just over 10,000 kwh for a typical heating season. And that energy, the sun provides free.

Basically, there is nothing at all complicated about using a greenhouse as a heating system. The greenhouse traps the sun's energy, warming the air inside to about 86°F. (30°C.). Thermostatically controlled fans blow this heated air into the house whenever the inside temperature drops below 68°F. On warm days, excess hot air is blown through ducts running under a 635-cubic-foot (18-m³) block of wet sand that is located within the house foundation. The sand serves as a heat store, accepting heat from the warm air on sunny days and warming cool air blown through the ducts and into the house at night or on cold, sunless days.

The Vale garden, greenhouse, and digester thus provide food, heat to cook it, a recycling system for the wastes, and even some heat to warm the occupants. But what about water?

Here the plans call for collecting rain water and carefully recycling it after it is used. Rain falling on the roof flows into a 2,520-gallon (9,550-liter) holding tank. Each day, 24 gallons (90 liters) of rain water and 75 gallons (285 liters) of waste water are fed through a sand filter tank that removes impurities. Drinking water is further purified by passing it through an activated charcoal filter. After use, waste laundry and bath water drains into a tank beneath the methane digester where it heats the digester as it cools. Before recycling, it mixes with other waste water in another tank in which chemicals precipitate large particles that would clog the sand filter.

Rooftop solar collectors heat the water. These devices can be made simply by covering large sheets of corrugated metal or plastic, painted black, with panels of clear glass or plastic. Tilted to face the sun and insulated to prevent heat loss, they trap heat as a greenhouse does. Water pumped to the roof trickles down the corrugations and warms to about 122°F. (50°C.), as hot as most people care to bathe with.

Heat from the Solar Furnace

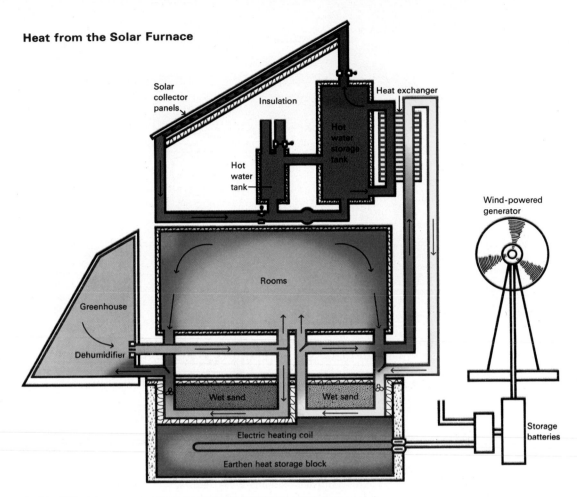

In this AT heating system, the sun's rays heat air in the greenhouse and water in a rooftop solar collector. Greenhouse air heats the rooms or a wet sand block that stores heat. Water from the collector heats more air for room heating or storage in a second sand block and an earthen block. A coil converts wind-generated electricity into heat when needed.

Solar collectors cover the entire 1,240-square-foot (115-m²) Vale house roof a far larger surface than is needed for heating the 63 gallons (240 liters) of hot water a family of four would use each day throughout the year. The additional heating capacity is needed to help warm the house during the winter.

Calculations for the Cambridge area show that during the mild autumn month of October, the greenhouse would supply 1,500 kwh of heat, while the rooftop solar collector would gather another 1,300 kwh. Only 900 kwh would be needed to heat the house to 68°F. and the water to 122°F., so the system produces 1,900 kwh more heat than is needed, plenty to cover heat lost during storage and recovery.

But blustery December is another story. Then, colder temperatures, shorter daylight hours, and a low angle for the sun across the sky are

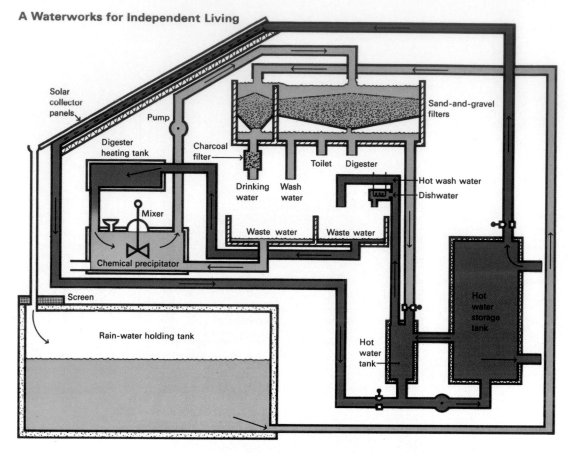

Solar
collector
panels

Pump

Digester
heating tank

Charcoal
filter

Sand-and-gravel
filters

Toilet   Digester

Hot wash water

Drinking
water

Wash
water

Dishwater

Mixer

Chemical precipitator

Waste water   Waste water

Hot
water
storage
tank

Screen

Rain-water holding tank

Hot
water
tank

Rain water that falls on the roof flows into a holding tank. Each day's ration is pumped up to a sand-and-gravel filter, where it mixes with waste water that has been chemically treated to precipitate out large particles. A portion of the filtered water flows into the solar heating system, where it heats by trickling through the rooftop collector, or by mixing with water from the hot water storage tank. An electric coil heats it further for dishwashing. Drinking water is filtered separately.

all factors that account for the greenhouse and solar collectors gathering 1,200 kwh less heat than is required. Similarly, the system falls short by at least 160 kwh in November and 900 kwh in January. In other months, as in October, more heat is supplied than is needed.

So what do the supposedly self-sufficient Vale house occupants do for hot water and heat during November, December, and January?

Mimicking squirrels storing acorns during the fall months for the hard times ahead, the Vale house occupants store heat when it is plentiful. To see how, recall the water trickling through the solar collectors on a sunny day. Part of the 122°F. water flows into a 63-gallon tank which takes care of daily hot water needs. The additional hot water is piped to a well-insulated, 800-gallon (3,000-liter) storage tank that acts as a kind of battery charger for the 63-gallon unit. On sunless days, when the solar collector system is turned off, the smaller tank is filled by water from the larger tank.

But the 800-gallon tank has an even more important charging role in heating the house. Throughout the summer, when far more heat can be collected than is needed for hot water, air is blown through a heat exchanger connected to the tank. The heated air passes through ducts running through an insulated 7,000-cubic-foot (200-m³) block of wet sand and earth buried beside the smaller greenhouse storage block under the house. By the end of each summer, the earthen block should be fully charged to its peak temperature. During the winter, the process can be reversed to extract heat when needed. Air blown through the ductwork to absorb heat from the massive earthen block goes either directly into the house or back through the heat exchanger to raise the water temperature in the large tank.

A thrifty system indeed—all your energy for space heating and hot water from the sun even in a notoriously cloudy climate. It sounds too good to be true. In fact, not all of the heat energy for the Vale house comes directly from the sun. To begin with, a small electric heater boosts kitchen hot water to a grease-cutting 140°F. (60°C.). More importantly, were the huge solar-collector heat-storage block allowed to cool much more than a few degrees at the beginning of the winter, it could not, because of its size, be fully recharged until the following summer. So electric heating coils buried in the block, using at least 1,000 kwh, maintain its peak temperature until about mid-December. After this time it can be allowed to cool completely, giving up its stored heat until February when the greenhouse and solar collectors once again produce excess heat. Were it not for this extra electric heat supply, the AT family would shiver in a cold house and shower with decidedly chilly water during the harsh winter months.

Where does the 1,000 kwh of electric energy needed to heat the coils come from? And what provides the electricity to boost the kitchen water temperature and, for that matter, to run the fans and pumps that circulate air and water through these systems? At present, electric power generation is the Achilles' heel of AT systems. BRAD, while planning to generate its own electricity, is prudently keeping its power lines connected to Britain's national power system for the time being. Another AT group has even more prudently settled on a Welsh farm that has a couple of streams that fall over a near-vertical 1,000-foot cliff. These waterfalls can provide the power to run a water wheel or low-speed turbine to produce electricity. Unfortunately, sites with steady-flowing streams are not easy to find.

Having squeezed all the energy they can from the sun, most AT groups turn next to the wind. Even with small-scale equipment, wind power is a surprisingly abundant energy source. Its great advantage is that winds are typically stronger in winter and during the day, just when power is most needed. Winds also tend to blow steadily, day and night, especially in winter; consequently, a wind generator can deliver

large daily totals of electricity to a storage system even though it may deliver it at a low rate. For example, throughout much of Britain a modest windmill with 8-foot (2.5-meter)-diameter blades that works at 40 per cent efficiency would deliver an average of at least 11 kwh of electricity a day from October to March.

The Vale house will use a standard 2-kilowatt windmill generator that delivers a 110-volt direct current (DC) output. In a typical year, such a windmill would generate 3,400 kwh of electricity, about 1,000 kwh more than calculations show is needed for lights, refrigerator, fans, pumps, TV, and other appliances in the Vale house. This excess energy goes to the coil that keeps the large solar-collector heat store peaked during November and December.

Even with this extra wind energy, the Vale house family must be miserly in its use of electricity. The plans call for only three fluorescent electric lights, and no freezer, clothes washer and dryer, or any of the other electric gadgets commonly found in a typical Western home.

And there are technical problems to overcome. Few DC appliances are manufactured today. So the family must either convert everything to run on DC, or install an expensive, regulated windmill that supplies 60-cycle alternating current (AC) power directly. A more serious problem is energy storage, without which a lull in the wind at night would plunge the house into darkness. The Vale house will use the standard solution: a set of automobile batteries, to store 30 kwh.

Experimental vegetable
plots at the New
Alchemy Institute on
Cape Cod share space
with experimental
fish farms. Geodesic
domes trap heat for
edible tropical fish
in the ponds inside.

These and similar problems do not discourage the resourceful, accommodating AT advocate, but they do raise doubts in the minds of traditional engineers who question the technical validity of some alternative technologies and schemes like the Vale house. For example, Sean Wellesley-Miller, professor of environmental controls at the Massachusetts Institute of Technology, believes that, "The Vale house system, as it stands, would not work." Although he sees nothing inherently wrong with the plan, he predicts that, "It will take a considerable amount of rethinking, redesigning, tuning, and testing before all, or even most, of the bugs are wrinkled out of the systems, and they begin performing close to expectations."

But even at the planning stage, he questions the double use of the greenhouse for growing out-of-season produce and also heating the Vale house. A former proponent of this concept, Wellesley-Miller found that few plants thrive at 86°F., the proposed greenhouse temperature. For example, lettuce grows poorly, and tomatoes grow only half as well at 86°F. as at 68°F. On the other hand, cucumbers thrive, and the clever AT advocate might be able to adapt both his taste and his techniques to edible tropical plants.

Even if nutritious, heat-resistant plants can be grown, the plan has generally ignored certain engineering realities, according to Wellesley-Miller. "The greenhouse, the solar collectors, and their similar heat-storage systems are assumed to work at near-maximum theoretical efficiency," he stresses. "Practice will be quite another matter." He points to heat exchangers as an example. Realistically, air leaving the greenhouse at a temperature of 86°F. could heat the wet-sand storage block to only about 76°F. Run in reverse, the system would deliver air at only about 68°F. At this low temperature, large volumes of air must be circulated almost constantly to provide heat, and a larger storage block would be needed than the one specified in the plans.

Similar problems exist with the solar collector and its heat-storage system, which has as many as four heat-exchange steps (water-to-air, air-to-sand, sand-to-air, and air-to-water). A heat reservoir larger than the 7,000-cubic-foot sand-earth block seems out of the question, so the solar collector operating temperature must be raised, which practically means that more surface area is needed in order to collect the same amount of heat.

"But wait a minute," counters a hypothetical AT planner. "AT is truly experimental, and if one part of a system falls short of expecta-

A New Alchemist feeds marigold blossoms to the tasty *Tilapia*.

tions, another can be substituted. What AT attempts to show is how devices that many conventional engineers have abandoned as inadequate can be combined in novel ways to create workable systems."

For example, rather than raise the solar collector temperature to make up for heat lost in the exchangers, they might eliminate the air-to-water heat transfer step by removing the buried electrical coils from the heat-storage block. To supply extra heat to the system in winter, they might install in the 800-gallon, hot-water-storage tank hot condenser coils from a heat pump, a device often described as a refrigerator in reverse. Driven by wind, water, or electric power that turns its shaft, a heat pump concentrates heat energy from a large source such as the soil, a stream, or a lake, and channels it into needed heat energy at much higher, house- and water-heating temperatures. Furthermore, it transfers much more energy as heat than it consumes as mechanical energy to drive the pump. Despite these advantages, many attempts to use heat pumps have been commercial disasters. This is largely because the amount of heat that can be transferred decreases as the temperature difference between the opposite ends of the heat pump increases. For example, in heating water to 160°F. by extracting heat from winter soil at 32°F., a heat pump theoretically transfers five times as much energy as is required to drive the pump. In cost terms, a gas- or oil-fired boiler does much better.

Βut try using this heat pump as an AT practitioner would in winter, using tepid water from a solar collector instead of soil as the heat source. Now, working between temperatures of 80° and 122°F., the pump theoretically can transfer nearly 14 times more heat energy than the electric energy needed to drive it–though in practice this ratio would drop to three or four. Even so, using wind-generated electricity to drive a heat pump would provide three or four times as much heat as converting that same electricity directly into heat in coils.

Nor is a tropical vegetation ecology for the greenhouse beyond the innovative reach of AT enthusiasts. Some years ago, John Todd, a Ph.D. ethologist and founder of the U.S. New Alchemists group, developed the Backyard Fish Dome. His aquaculture concept calls for farming the tropical fish *Tilapia*. In the proper, warm conditions, fantastic fish yields are possible–44 tons of fish an acre per year has been recorded in Thailand. To provide Thai conditions in Wyoming or Wales, the New Alchemists enclose their *Tilapia* pond in a sun-trap geodesic dome made simply and cheaply from plastic sheets and wooden struts. In spring and fall, the dome keeps pond temperature well above the 60°F., below which the fish begin to die, and well into the 70s, where they grow to their full half-pound size in about six months. The *Tilapia* can feed solely on masses of algae that grow abundantly because sacks of manure are hung in the water to fertilize it. The New Alchemists also add such animal protein as earthworms and insects to the fishes' diet to greatly enhance their growth rate and resistance to disease. This practice provides a way of getting rid of

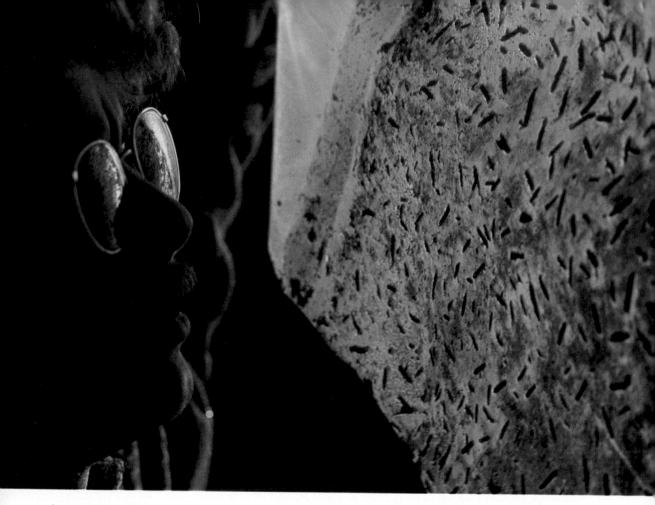

A researcher at the New Alchemy Institute counts midges, tiny insects grown on treated sewage as *Tilapia* food.

waste meat—as food for the insects. Other elaborations are possible, with ducks feeding on surplus insects, *Tilapia*, and greens from a vegetable garden, while the bottom sludge, rich in fish and duck droppings, is dredged from the pond and applied to the vegetable patch.

But, even if AT is acceptable on a technological basis, there are sharp questions about its basic social and political aims. What do Alternative Technologists intend doing about the cities—an acre of land and a solar array for each family in a brownstone apartment? Even in suburbia, where land is more open, zoning and building codes would have to be revised, to say nothing of the cost of converting existing power, water, and sewerage systems to their alternatives.

"And how many people want to be tied to their homes to feed the animals, water the plants, and stir sludge in the methane digester?" asks Wellesley-Miller. "It is one thing to live in harmony with nature's natural tempo; it is another thing to be its slave." But freedom from these chores requires automation, and hence the kind of advanced technology that most AT advocates reject.

In response, AT enthusiasts point out that most families spend from one-fifth to one-fourth of their income for food, so why not use the time spent earning this money to grow your own if you enjoy the work?

For those who do not enjoy the work, a moderate form of AT might be attractive. It provides some self-sufficiency and may even be an inescapable result of a deepening energy crisis.

Finally, how much does AT cost? In Wellesley-Miller's view, AT is both expensive to build and time-consuming to operate. "Built by a contractor," he estimates, "a house like Vale's would cost two or three times as much as a conventional home the same size. Even though its energy would then be essentially free, its initial cost places it beyond the reach of all but the skilled do-it-yourselfer." A case in point is its windmill which sells in the U.S. for $2,700. By the time the cost of the mounting tower and storage batteries are added, the total runs close to $4,500. Energy from the sun and wind may be free, but the equipment to harness it can be costly.

"In a more favorable climate than Wales—for example the Boston, Mass., to Washington, D.C., area in the U.S.," says Wellesley-Miller, "solar hot-water heating is practical and economical today, in large part because of the higher cost of electricity and natural gas resulting from the 1973-1974 energy crisis." Solar house heating, using a solar collector and a basement hot-water storage tank capable of storing three days worth of heat, could meet 80 per cent of the winter heating load in this same area. A conventional gas or oil heater would take up the slack. In fact, just such a system was built in Maryland in 1959 by Washington patent attorney Harry Thomason. His system is similar to the Vale plan except for the heat storage and exchanger which consists of a 1,500-gallon hot-water tank surrounded by tons of small stones, among which the air passes. It stores only a 4-day supply of heat, but Thomason reports that his fuel bill for the auxiliary oil burner was less than $10 each winter.

Such 80 per cent self-sufficient systems raise the crucial question of the scale best suited for AT. Wellesley-Miller believes that a self-contained community utility and food-production system would be much more efficient and economical than attempting to make individual homesteads self-sufficient. Such a community system would integrate several hundred homes with separate intensive horticulture, aquaculture, and animal husbandry units; waste treatment stations; power generation stations; and light industry. Just such communities have been envisioned by one alternative presented in the Ford Foundation's Energy Policy Project preliminary report delivered in March, 1974. Picturing an America in the year 2000 where the philosophy "more is better" has been replaced by "enough is best," one of the report's projections would have much of the population living in AT-style communities.

For the present, AT remains no more than an embryonic, if vigorous, alternative. Its strongest appeal is not to governments and societies, but to individuals. When challenged, many Alternative Technologists reply simply: "I want to live like that. I think it will be healthful, challenging, and fun. If you want to join us, then welcome."

Can Coal Make a Comeback?

By Ralph E. Lapp

The United States must dig into its earth and its technical tool kit to make coal flow in its pipelines

Many Americans played numbers games in the winter of 1973 and 1974. They played the "Even-Odd License Number" game at gasoline stations, then watched the gas pump's spinning dials as pennies per gallon went up. At home, their heating bills also went up, even though they turned their thermostats down.

The basic cause of this is also told by numbers—the mind-boggling statistics of energy use in the United States. In 1973, Americans burned up 25 trillion cubic feet of natural gas, 6.3 billion barrels of oil, and 600 million tons of coal. These fuels accounted for 94 per cent of the nation's energy. Nuclear power and falling water provided the rest. And this energy use was growing. United States consumption increased 4.8 per cent over the previous year.

The United States, which consumes more than one-third of the world's energy output, produces almost all of its own energy. In 1973, the nation imported about 16 per cent of its energy, but only a fraction came from the Middle Eastern oil producers. Most industrial nations in Europe and Asia are not so fortunate. They, along with many of the developing nations of the third world, depend heavily on imported petroleum from the Middle East. When the Arab nations imposed the oil embargo in November, 1973, and later raised oil prices, Europe shivered and Asia scrambled for fuel. The United States had merely to tighten its belt. Why, then, and how, did the Energy Crisis suddenly burst on the American scene? Some spoke of conspiracies and others muttered about domestic bungling and international blackmail, but there were more fundamental causes.

The events of late 1973 and early 1974 in the United States might better have been called the Energy Inconvenience. The embargoed fuels were all fluid, and what the United States actually experienced was a shortage of pumpable fuel. Over the years, its millions of vehicles, machines, furnaces, and other energy-consuming devices have turned the United States into a greedy megamachine. A constant flow of pumpable fuel—gasoline, oil, and natural gas—is required to keep the megamachine going, and Americans, so accustomed to an abundance of all things, could hardly imagine they would ever run short of anything. But domestic production of oil and natural gas leveled off in the late 1960s, and the United States imported more and more petroleum to keep its fuel lines full.

The Arab nations, first by turning off the valves and then by hiking the price tag on a barrel of oil, did the United States a service. They triggered an early warning of what growing dependence on imported energy might bring. They may finally have forced the United States to do what it should have done years before: Plan its energy use and needs in relation to present and future supply.

It is a reasonable, though conservative, estimate that American energy demands will increase at a rate of about 3.5 per cent a year. At that rate, the U.S. will require some 50 per cent more energy in 1985 than it did in 1973, which poses a difficult question: How can it build and fuel the increasing number of energy-consuming machines needed to maintain its economic progress?

There is no easy answer. Although the nation still has adequate domestic fuel resources, they are simply not the type best suited to the megamachine's millions of moving parts because these resources are in a solid form. Truly staggering amounts of energy are locked up in U.S. coal deposits. But coal is bulky and expensive to ship, and much of it is high in sulfur and other impurities. Despite extensive research, scientists have not yet found a truly reliable way to cleanse the stack gases of coal-burning electric generators. But if coal could be converted to a gas or liquid that would be cleaner, and that could be pumped through existing pipelines, the onetime king of American energy might return to the throne.

Although the black rock had been known and used for thousands of years, two developments of the middle 1700s, both British, first gave

The author:
Ralph E. Lapp is a nuclear physicist and a consultant on energy problems. His latest book, *The Logarithmic Century*, and many articles deal with problems of growth and the energy supply.

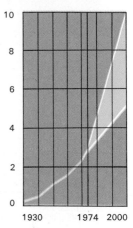

U. S. Energy Consumption (1930–2000)

In billion tons of coal

U.S. Coal Production (1930–2000)

In billion tons

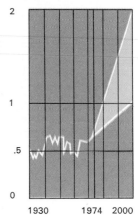

coal its crown. When coke (made from coal) replaced charcoal (made from wood) in the manufacture of iron, the British iron industry expanded quickly. At about the same time, coal-fired steam engines brought sweeping changes to other industries. Powered by coal, the Industrial Revolution spread from Great Britain to Europe and North America, bringing great material progress and social change with it. For 200 years, coal fueled the industrial development of the world. In many countries, it still does.

At peak U.S. production in 1947, more than 500,000 miners dug 700 million tons. But then the nation turned more and more to cheap, convenient, relatively cleaner oil and gas, and coal production declined by 1974 to about 550 million tons a year, dug or stripped by 140,000 miners. The U.S. Geological Survey estimates that there are still more than 3 trillion tons of coal in the United States, ranging from the well-worked veins of Pennsylvania anthracite (hard coal) to huge,

Countless coal cars full of sized and graded coal wind their way from Harlan County, Ky., to the steel mills and power plants of America. The range of future coal production is closely linked to the increasing national energy demand, *above.*

223

virtually untouched beds of low-sulfur bituminous (soft coal) in the Upper Missouri River Basin in Montana and Wyoming.

These estimates indicate that the nation has enough coal to fill its projected energy needs for hundreds of years. Utilizing this enormous resource, however, will be difficult. To rapidly expand an industry that has been in eclipse for 20 years or more will require very large infusions of money and trained manpower. The thorny environmental questions involved in strip mining, such as water use (particularly in the dry western states) and pollution, must be solved. And, finally, much research is needed to develop new technologies that can convert coal into gas or liquid forms.

Formed from the remains of ancient living things, coal, oil, and gas are often called fossil fuels. The dense, decaying vegetation of ancient swamps, acted on by bacteria, crushed and heated by thick overlaying sediments of mud, sand, and still more vegetation, first formed peat. Over millions of years, further pressure and heat eventually produced coal. Oil and gas have a somewhat different history. A slow, steady rain of dead organic material from tiny sea animals and plants, worked on by sea-bottom bacteria and covered by other sediments, was transformed into the hydrocarbons of oil and gas. While most coal deposits are hundreds of millions of years old, many peat deposits are younger and oil has been found in rocks only a few million years old. The processes may still be going on, but so slowly they could never keep pace with human consumption.

Despite its different history, coal is not very much different in composition from oil or natural gas. It is about 80 to 85 per cent carbon, 4 to 5 per cent hydrogen, and the rest is a mixture of other elements, such as sulfur. Oil is about 85 per cent carbon, 13 per cent hydrogen, and 2 per cent other elements. Methane, the major constituent of natural gas, is 75 per cent carbon and 25 per cent hydrogen. The basic chemical difference between the solid, liquid, and gaseous fuels is in hydrogen content. This suggests that adding some hydrogen to coal might produce a liquid and adding more hydrogen, a synthetic substitute for pipeline gas.

Coal gas lit the streets and homes of many American and European cities in the 1800s. One form, "town gas," was used in the United States until about 30 years ago. Much of it was produced simply by heating coal in an oven until it began to break down chemically, releasing the gas. Such coal gases, composed primarily of hydrogen, carbon monoxide, and methane, in various ratios, ranged in heating value from about 450 to 550 British thermal units (B.T.U.) per cubic foot. This early gasification industry died when the transcontinental gas pipelines were built after World War II and the nation began to use natural gas, which was cheaper, more convenient, and had greater heating value—over 1,000 B.T.U. per cubic foot.

The world's largest mobile land machine, the walking dragline, *opposite page,* takes a 220-cubic-yard bite of surface material to expose coal bed.

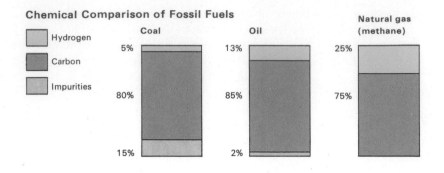

Chemical Comparison of Fossil Fuels

Hydrogen

Carbon

Impurities

Coal

5%
80%
15%

Oil

13%
85%
2%

Natural gas
(methane)

25%
75%

Raising the hydrogen content and eliminating impurities are the major requirements in making coal into fuel oil or natural gas.

The chemical similarity of coal and oil was not lost on the leaders of Nazi Germany prior to World War II. Anticipating that Germany's oil supplies might be cut off, Adolf Hitler ordered a number of coal liquefaction plants built. They used various processes to produce synthetic fuel for German tanks and airplanes in World War II. For example, in the Bergius process, which had been developed in 1913, hydrogen is added directly to a coal-tar mixture which is subjected to temperatures of 700° to 900°F. (350° to 500°C.) and pressures of several hundred atmospheres. The Fischer-Tropsch process, developed about 1925, used "synthesis gas," a mixture of carbon monoxide and hydrogen made by burning coal incompletely in the presence of oxygen and steam. This gas is passed over a catalyst under high pressure and temperature to produce various chemicals, including liquid fuels. Complex, expensive, and clumsy as they were, these processes helped to fuel the war effort of an oil-poor Germany.

Several German processes are still in use. One, the Lurgi process, developed in 1936, has had considerable commercial success. Fifty-six Lurgi plants have been built in Australia, Germany, Pakistan, and South Africa. The Sasolburg synthetic gas plant near Johannesburg, largest in the world, has 13 Lurgi gasifiers. The Lurgi process produces a medium-B.T.U. synthesis gas. South Africans use it in combination with the catalytic conversion step of the Fischer-Tropsch process to produce liquid fuels and chemicals.

The El Paso Natural Gas Company has designed a Lurgi-type gasification plant, to be built on Navaho Indian land in northwestern New Mexico. Coal will be strip-mined from an 800-million-ton coal reserve in the area to provide a flow of 9 million tons per year to the plant. If there are no delays in construction, gas could begin to flow in El Paso's pipeline by the late 1970s.

Laboratories in the United States are studying a variety of coal gasification processes, and some of these are now being tested in pilot plants. Although they differ greatly in detail, these schemes are similar in general outline. Coal is heated in an enclosed vessel under great pressure to react with varying proportions of air, pure oxygen or some other gas, and steam. This produces a low- to medium-B.T.U. gas, which is then purified, or scrubbed, to remove tars, dust, sulfur, and other impurities. Some of the impurities, such as sulfur, can be recovered and used. This gas may have only from one-third to one-half the heating value of pipeline quality gas and it would not be economic to pump it great distances. However, industry can use the gas in many ways. For instance, it could fuel a gas-fired, steam-electric power plant located near the gasification plant.

To manufacture a high-B.T.U. gas of pipeline quality, the hydrogen content of the synthesis gas must often be increased. Then the gas is passed over a nickel-based catalyst, which helps the carbon and hydrogen atoms combine to form a synthetic methane.

Whatever processes finally emerge, gasification plants will probably not be cheap, and many will be needed. The El Paso plant will cost more than $600 million to build. It will produce about 0.1 trillion cubic feet of gas annually. The Federal Power Commission estimates that gas demand in 1985 will be 40 trillion cubic feet. The commission also estimates that only from 19 to 27 trillion cubic feet a year may be naturally available from U.S. gas reserves in the 1980s. The nation is clearly running the risk of an enormous gas gap in the near future, and it will be difficult to close it.

The high cost of building gasification plants has focused some interest on the possibility of on-site production. In this process, oxygen is pumped into an underground mine and the coal is burned there. The mixture of hydrogen, carbon monoxide, and methane that this produces could then be drawn off by pipe. A test of on-site gasification by the U.S. Bureau of Mines is underway in a coal mine near Hanna, Wyo. A certain amount of methane occurs naturally in coal beds. In past years, mining companies have merely drawn the gas off in order to prevent mine fires and explosions. The Bureau of Mines is currently studying ways of harnessing this resource for commercial use.

One reason coal conversion research has been concentrated on gasification instead of liquefaction is that domestic natural gas supplies are more uncertain than oil supplies. Pipeline companies are naturally interested in developing coal gasification techniques to supply a substitute product for their business. Furthermore, as long as both domestic and foreign oil were cheaper than synthetic oil, there was no incentive to develop means for producing such oil. But when the price of foreign oil soared above $10 per barrel, U.S. companies began to look with new favor upon synthesizing oil.

A ton of fairly good quality coal could yield three barrels or more of oil. However, the technology needed to convert coal has not yet been developed. Many proposed processes must still go through pilot plant and demonstration tests before their feasibility can be assessed. Some of the newest processes include catalytic hydrogenation of a coal-oil mixture under high pressure. Such a process, designed by Hydrocarbon Research, Inc., would work at 3,000 pounds per square inch. The product is a light crude oil that can be refined to gasoline and furnace oils by conventional methods. Exxon Corporation is pursuing another process. Called "donor solvent extraction," it uses a chemical solvent

From Coal Pile to Pipeline: The HYGAS Process

The HYGAS Process, being developed by the Institute of Gas Technology in Chicago, is one of more than a dozen gasification techniques now being tested. Now in the pilot-plant stage, HYGAS must also go through demonstration-plant tests before commercial production of pipeline gas can begin, sometime in the 1980s.

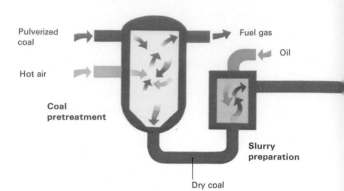

Pulverized coal

Hot air

Coal pretreatment

Fuel gas

Oil

Slurry preparation

Dry coal

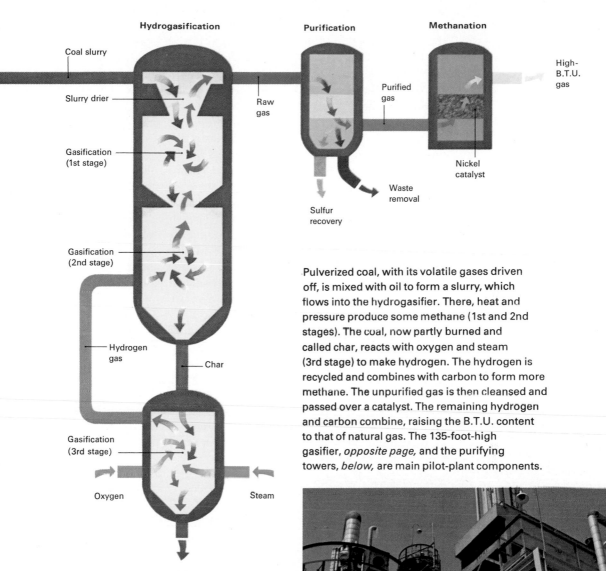

Hydrogasification

Coal slurry

Slurry drier

Gasification
(1st stage)

Gasification
(2nd stage)

Raw
gas

Hydrogen
gas

Char

Gasification
(3rd stage)

Oxygen

Steam

Ash

Purification

Purified
gas

Sulfur
recovery

Waste
removal

Methanation

High-
B.T.U.
gas

Nickel
catalyst

Pulverized coal, with its volatile gases driven off, is mixed with oil to form a slurry, which flows into the hydrogasifier. There, heat and pressure produce some methane (1st and 2nd stages). The coal, now partly burned and called char, reacts with oxygen and steam (3rd stage) to make hydrogen. The hydrogen is recycled and combines with carbon to form more methane. The unpurified gas is then cleansed and passed over a catalyst. The remaining hydrogen and carbon combine, raising the B.T.U. content to that of natural gas. The 135-foot-high gasifier, *opposite page,* and the purifying towers, *below,* are main pilot-plant components.

that breaks the coal down and adds hydrogen to make synthetic crude oil. FMC Corporation's COED process uses pyrolysis—decomposing the coal by heat—to form petroleum. Coal tars and gases are distilled off, leaving a char residue. Then the coal tars are hydrogenated, using hydrogen from the coal gas, to form crude oil. Pyrolysis-produced petroleum, however, requires additional processing to upgrade its quality. A pilot COED plant, sponsored by the U.S. Office of Coal Research, has been in operation in Princeton, N.J., since 1970.

Like gasification plants, liquefaction units will be expensive. Private financing of large plants is unlikely unless the U.S. government provides price supports for the synthetic oil to ensure a reasonable return on investments. Even with such support there is little prospect of any substantial flow of oil from coal before 1980.

And even if the financial and technological difficulties of gasification, liquefaction, and increased coal mining are solved, some very complex problems and choices remain. It would require nearly 5 billion tons of coal a year to produce the 25 trillion cubic feet of gas and 6.3 billion barrels of oil the nation now uses. Clearly, some priorities of use will have to be established, because there are practical and environmental limits to how much coal can be mined in a year.

The coal deposits of Wyoming and Montana provide an instructive example. They contain an estimated 100 billion tons of accessible low-sulfur coal. But the coal lies in agricultural, range, and resort country that is thinly populated, with little industry and relatively small power requirements. The region also has relatively little water, and large quantities of water are needed to process coal. Montana's water problem is so critical that in March, 1974, the state declared a three-year moratorium on all new applications for water use, until a water survey and resource plan can be developed.

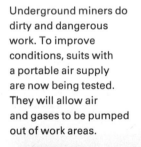

Underground miners do dirty and dangerous work. To improve conditions, suits with a portable air supply are now being tested. They will allow air and gases to be pumped out of work areas.

Other questions will also have to be studied: How will strip mining affect agriculture in these states? How quickly can land be restored in the dry climate of this area? What happens to the coal industry in particularly dry years (about one in four) when there is barely enough water to maintain farms and ranches? In other words, what are the rights of these two states in the face of a growing energy demand in other parts of the country?

Much public attention has been focused on the energy potential of less rich fossil deposits, the oil shales and tar sands. Oil shale deposits under parts of Utah and Colorado hold at least 300 billion barrels of oil. They yield an average of 30 gallons (about three-fourths of a barrel) of oil per ton. U.S. oil firms have paid record prices for oil shale leases in the expectation that the synthesis of oil from the shale will eventually be technically feasible and profitable.

In one likely technique for recovering oil from shale, the mined rock will be crushed and fed into a retort, a large vessel. Exposed then to temperatures of from 800° to 1000°F. (425° to 550°C.), the rock forms oil, combustible gas, and carbonaceous residues such as char or coke. Oil produced by retorting shale is thick and sticky and hard to move through pipelines. It is also high in nitrogen and sulfur, and has to be hydrogenated before it can be processed in a refinery. About 150,000 tons of crushed shale would be required to make 100,000 barrels of oil.

Simply handling the materials would be an enormous problem, since producing 1 billion barrels of oil from shale would mean mining and processing 1.4 billion tons of rock and disposing of five-sixths of it. Many environmentalists strongly oppose processing oil shale on the grounds that it will consume prohibitively large quantities of water

Soil stripped off in mining is hard to replace in dry areas like Four Corners, New Mexico, *top*. Even crown vetch, often used to restore mined eastern land, cannot grow in this desertlike atmosphere.

and that the enormous amount of spent shale waste left over will pose too great an environmental risk.

The Canadian tar sands lie along the Athabasca River in Alberta province. They contain huge deposits of bitumen, a black tar-oil mixed with sand. This sticky material was once used by Indians to patch their canoes. Much of the tar sand lies from 150 to 200 feet (45 to 60 meters) beneath the surface, and giant machines would be needed to dig it out. About 180,000 tons of the sand must be processed to produce 100,000 barrels of oil. If the expense, the difficult weather conditions, and a scarcity of labor can be overcome, geologists estimate that 80 billion barrels of oil may be recoverable. But again, the environmental difficulties are great; water must be used to separate the oil from the sands, and 300,000 tons of waste and water will accumulate for every 100,000 barrels of oil produced. This polluted water would have to be cleansed. Still, a plant at Fort McMurray, Alta., is already producing 45,000 barrels of crude oil a day.

Although much energy is wasted in the United States, the megamachine is so immense and represents such a capital investment that it cannot be changed quickly. Consider, for example, the 100-million passenger cars in the United States. Compared to mass public transportation, the private automobile is an extremely inefficient method of moving the population. Yet, much of the nation's economic well-being is geared to Detroit's automotive output, and a sharp cutback in production, even though it would certainly save gasoline, would be an invitation to economic recession. Cars must be kept moving, homes heated, and industrial production maintained.

Thousands of everyday items are made from the chemical components of coal, oil, and gas. When these fossil treasures are exhausted, many familiar and useful things will also vanish.

For the present, then, the problem is one of finding enough fuel to meet existing needs. Until the end of the century, it appears that the nation must turn again to its coal and other solid fossil fuels, adjusting its megamachine to use them, or altering the fuel to suit the machine.

At the same time, nonfossil energy sources such as nuclear and solar power must be developed. This is particularly important because fossil fuels—coal, oil, and gas—can be used up. This legacy of sunshine and life laid down millions of years ago and trapped in ocean sediments and luxuriant swamps cannot be renewed. In 75 years, we have burned our way through 38 billion tons of coal and 120 billion barrels of oil. Yet the molecules in these fuels are so useful in other ways—for making drugs, dyes, fertilizers, lubricants, petrochemicals, and plastics —that it is a chemical crime to burn them just to release heat. But burn them we must until workable alternatives are developed.

The shortage of such pumpable fuels as gas and oil and the limits on other fossil fuels have profound implications for industrialized societies and for developing countries. Growth must be planned in conformity with available resources. Having depleted the planet's most readily available source of energy, man must now learn how to exploit the energy of the atom, the sun, and the earth's heat. Meanwhile, grimy, tough coal, once the king of world energy, must briefly reign again.

Science File

Science Year contributors report on the year's major developments in their respective fields. The articles in this section are arranged alphabetically by subject matter.

Agriculture

A significant breakthrough occurred in 1973 with grain sorghum, the fourth largest food crop in the world and the basic cereal grain in many parts of Asia and Africa. Two new strains of sorghum that are high in protein were identified by John D. Axtell and Rameshwar Singh of Purdue University. The new strains contain 30 to 40 per cent more protein than other varieties, which should bring new hope to the 300 million protein-deficient people in the world. They also contain twice as much lysine, a substance that increases digestibility. The tendency to store more protein and lysine is carried in the genes of the plants, and can be crossbred into other varieties of sorghum all over the world.

There were also noteworthy improvements in rice, the number-one world food crop. A variety of rice plant that discourages birds from eating the growing grain was developed by scientists at the International Rice Research Institute at Los Baños in the Philippines. The new variety has sharp pointed flag leaves that protrude well above the point at which the grain forms. Another variety, IR-26, is resistant to brown plant hoppers and most other insects and diseases found in tropical Asia.

New crop varieties. Many new crop varieties with colorful and descriptive names were introduced in 1973 and 1974. These included: Tangi, a high-quality, high-yielding strawberry; Magnifico, a superior globe artichoke with rose-colored leaves; Self-Blanche, a cauliflower in which the leaves naturally fold over the head so they do not have to be tied by hand; Sonnette, a new disease-resistant bell pepper; Vermillion and Caro-Red tomatoes; and Tamu-Triple, the first pickling cucumber formed by crossing three plants.

Other new varieties include: Cherokee and Comanche erect blackberries, adapted for mechanical harvesting; Spartan Sleeper, an onion that will not sprout in storage; Vogue, a large, shiny, dark red cherry; and Spartlett, a new pear with high blush, that ripens 12 days ahead of the common Bartlett variety.

New planting methods. Many crops were planted without tillage during 1973 and 1974. That is, they were planted

Chemical engineer William Albrecht tests a sample of a new fireplace log made of peanut shells and wax against a traditional wood chip and wax log, *below*. The new material burns brighter and longer, and puts peanut wastes to good use. Pressed logs, *right*, stand in front of their respective ingredients.

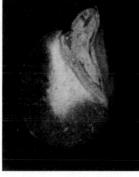

Purdue University plant researchers Dallas Aswalt, Rameshwar Singh, and John D. Axtell, left to right, hold a high-lysine sorghum they developed. Cross sections of the new seed, *right,* and a normal one, *below right,* show that the high lysine seed has a floury endosperm (white) characteristic that provides it with a higher protein content.

Agriculture

Continued

directly on land that was not plowed, disked, harrowed, or cultivated. A herbicide was used to kill weeds and sod before the seeds were drilled into the soil. The technique is of worldwide significance because it conserves the soil, water, and energy. In the United States, an estimated 5.5 million acres of crops were planted in this way in 1974. This was an increase of about 12 per cent over the amount of acreage planted by this technique in 1973.

Mechanization. Substitution of machines for labor continued. Clarence M. Hansen and Richard Ledebuhr, of the Michigan Agricultural Experiment Station at East Lansing, designed a foolproof electronic sensing device that rejects processed cherries which have not had their pits removed. Theodore H. Short, an agricultural engineer at Ohio State University, developed a machine that harvests greenhouse lettuce.

The sweet-cherry harvest in Michigan in 1973 and 1974 was completely mechanized. A chemical (Ethephon) was sprayed on the trees a few days before the harvest to loosen the cherries. Then machines dislodged the cherries by shaking

the trees, reportedly with little tree injury and no damage to the fruit.

Nitrogen fixation. Ralph W. F. Hardy and U. D. Havelka of the E.I. du Pont de Nemours Experiment Station laboratories in Wilmington, Del., achieved a nearly sixfold increase in nitrogen fixation with field-grown soybeans. Nitrogen fixation is the process by which bacteria that live in knotlike growths along a plant's roots turn atmospheric nitrogen into a chemical form of nitrogen that can be used by the plant.

The scientists found that increased photosynthesis, which they achieved by raising the carbon dioxide levels around the leaves, produced more carbohydrates in the plants, which in turn increased the amount of nitrogen that the bacteria processed. The carbon dioxide around the leaves was raised from a normal of about 300 parts per million to 1,000. They used special open-top plastic structures that trapped some of the added carbon dioxide so it could be measured by infrared gas analyzers. Since soybeans do not generally respond to nitrogen fertilizers, this discovery sets the stage for

Agriculture

Continued

finding ways of increasing photosynthetic accumulation and thus also increasing soybean yield.

Chemical ripeners for sugar cane achieved a gain of 1 ton per acre – 10 per cent over the yield of sugar in 1973. Tested by Louis G. Nickell and David T. Takahashi of the Hawaiian Sugar Planter's Association, the ripeners were applied in liquid form to the sugar cane leaves and to the roots through subsurface irrigation systems. One ripener, named Racuza, showed a maximum effectiveness at concentrations of from $1/4$ to 1 pound of chemical per acre. Most other compounds were active in a range of from 3 to 6 pounds per acre. Scientists do not yet know how the ripeners act.

Fruit. In 1973, George Nyland of the University of California Agricultural Experiment Station at Davis found a cure for a pear disease that has devastated pear orchards since 1959. The disease is caused by a mycoplasma, a small bacterialike organism, and has killed 1.2 million trees, and severely damaged many of those that survived. Nyland found that injections of the antibiotic Terramycin

into the trunks of the pear trees cured them. When properly used, the drug leaves no residue to affect the fruit, and helps to combat other diseases.

New hope for preventing spring frost damage to fruit came from the work of researchers at the Utah Agricultural Experiment Station at Logan. They developed a system for delaying the flowering of the fruit trees. Sprinklers, which extended above the tops of the fruit trees, were set to turn on whenever springtime temperatures rose to 45°F. (7°C.). The sprinklers operated for 2 minutes, then shut off for 2 minutes, until temperatures again dropped below 45°F. The evaporative cooling effects of the sprinkling delayed the flowering of peaches, cherries, and apples from two to three weeks, assuring their opening at a time when the danger of frost was past.

The same scientists also increased the color of Red Delicious apples by a similar water spray, or misting, technique prior to the time of harvest where the apples' color development would have been retarded by high temperatures. They sprinkled the orchards during the hottest part

Untreated feed corn, *left,* developed mold seven days after germination, while corn treated with 5 per cent ammonia did not in experiments at a U.S. Department of Agriculture laboratory.

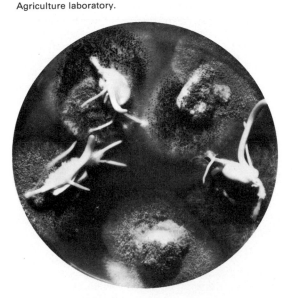 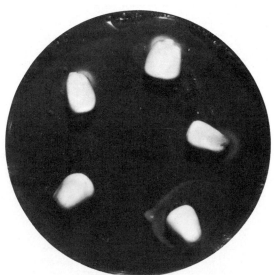

Agriculture
Continued

of the day, dropping fruit temperatures by 20°F.

Cotton. Using narrower rows, cotton farmers in Texas increased the number of plants in their fields from 40,000 to 200,000 per acre. This method of planting, only possible with the introduction of modern varieties, reduced production costs by $20 per acre because of earlier maturity, higher yields, and reduced water and tillage requirements. Cotton farmers also used a new method of handling seed. The seed cotton is mechanically compacted into modules weighing from 10 to 13 pounds per cubic foot, rather than being put loosely into seed bags. This greatly reduces labor, transportation, and storage costs.

Cottonseed flour as a by-product of cotton production for fiber also increased in importance. The first commercial cottonseed flour mill was dedicated at Lubbock, Tex., in August, 1973. It processes a newly developed, high-protein, gossypol-free cottonseed. Gossypol is a compound located in the pigment glands of ordinary cottonseed that adds undesirable flavor to ordinary cottonseed

flour. The new cottonseed flour contains up to 70 per cent protein, nearly seven times that of wheat flour. It is added to other types of flour during milling to boost their protein content.

New protein sources. Nitrogen combined with corn silage became a major factor in the production of usable protein and in combating the rising costs of protein supplements for beef- and dairy-cattle food. Over 400,000 tons of urea and 40,000 tons of ammonium solutions, both of which contain nitrogen, were fed to beef cattle and dairy cows in 1973.

It was added to silage to form ammonium salts of organic acids, which microorganisms in the animals' stomachs convert to protein residues used by the livestock. More than 50 per cent of the supplemental crude protein fed to beef cattle and 30 per cent of that fed to dairy cattle was provided by urea. Livestock producers believe such nitrogen additions can furnish all the protein supplement needed for beef cattle in typical rations based on corn and corn silage, and over half of the nitrogen that is required for dairy cows. [Sylvan H. Wittwer]

Anthropology

An autopsy on the mummified remains of a Chinese woman buried 2,100 years ago revealed a surprising amount of information about her physical condition at the time of her death. The tomb was excavated in 1972, but the results of the autopsy were not released until September, 1973. The silk-wrapped body of the 50-year-old woman, thought to be Lady Ch'eng, consort to Emperor Ching, was found by Chinese archaeologists in a tomb near Changsha in central China. It was in an airtight coffin, the innermost of seven boxes surrounded by five tons of charcoal and a thick layer of white clay.

A study of the body, which still retained some of its original fluids, revealed that Lady Ch'eng had blood type A, and that she had borne children, broken her right forearm, suffered from tuberculosis and gallstones, and eaten melon shortly before her death. One of her coronary arteries was almost completely closed by atherosclerosis, and doctors felt that this caused her death.

Oldest American. The results of a new dating process, announced in May, 1974, indicate that humans lived in southern California at least 50,000 years ago. Jeffrey L. Bada of the Scripps Institution of Oceanography at La Jolla, Calif., analyzed a human skull found in 1929 by archaeologists from the San Diego Museum. It was found between Del Mar and Solana close to the mouth of the San Dieguito River. Using the new dating technique, called aspartic acid racemization, Bada dated the skull at 48,000 years, making it the oldest human remnant yet identified in the Americas.

No land bridge existed between Siberia and Alaska at that time, and it is believed that this is the only way man could have come to the New World from Asia. Such a land bridge probably existed between 20,000 and 35,000 years ago, which anthropologists have assumed is the time man migrated from Asia. But now, with the discovery of the 48,000-year-old skull, man's antiquity in the New World has been pushed back to 70,000 to 80,000 years ago, when a land bridge may also have existed, or even 140,000 years ago, when a land bridge was a certainty.

The new dating technique utilizes the fact that human bones contain amino

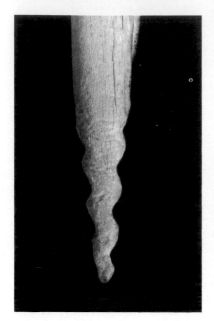

Although bone, *below,* appears to have been fashioned into a prehistoric tool, it actually was gnawed and left by a deer, *right.* Bones such as this have sometimes confused anthropologists.

Anthropology

Continued

acids that, in crystalline form, rotate to light waves passed through the crystals to the left. When the organism dies, the amino acids gradually change their geometry to a mirror-image configuration, in which light is rotated to the right. The age of a fossil can be determined by measuring the amount of left-handed and right-handed amino acids in it.

African finds. Manlike fossils were discovered in 1973 at Hadar in the central Afars region of Ethiopia by C. Donald Johanson of Case Western Reserve University in Cleveland. The site is more than 500 miles (800 kilometers) north and east of the Omo region, where similar fossils have been found. The discovery, therefore, greatly extends the known range of these manlike creatures. The fossils include several leg bones thought to be from the same individual, and a fragmentary temporal bone from the skull of another individual. Johanson believes that the leg bones are from a small creature and the skull is from a larger, robust australopithecine. Both probably walked upright. Found with the manlike fossils were the remains of pigs, rhinoceroses,

elephants, and hippopotamuses, all dating from more than 3 million years ago.

Australopithecine remains found many years ago in five South African cave sites have proven difficult to date. In 1973, Tom C. Partridge of Johannesburg, South Africa, applied geomorphological techniques, based upon rates of cyclic erosion, and they produced surprising dates. Previously the relative positions of the sites from early to late were generally listed as Taung, Sterkfontein, Makapansgat, Swartkrans, and Kromdraai. The Makapansgat cave apparently was formed and occupied first 3.67 million years ago. Sterkfontein followed (3.26 million years ago), and then Swartkrans (2.57 million). Taung, rather than being the oldest site, is the most recent, less than a million years old. Kromdraai has not been dated. The new dates of the South African sites can be roughly correlated with sites in East Africa—Makapansgat and Sterkfontein with the Shungura beds of the Omo region, Swartkrans with the East Rudolf finds, and Taung with Olduvai Gorge. The late date of the Taung skull fragments suggests that it was an

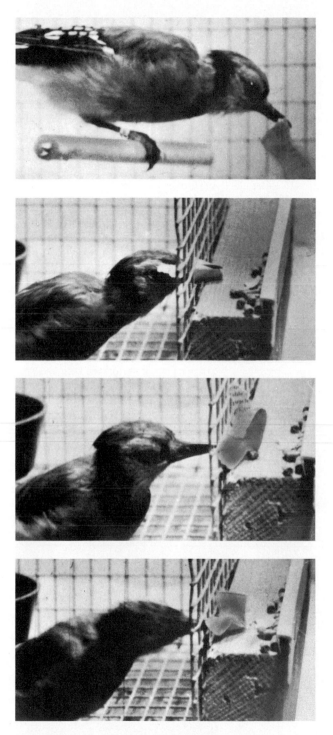

A Northern blue jay uses a bit of paper that it has torn from a large newspaper to rake food pellets nearer so that they are within its reach. Making and using tools, once thought to be an exclusive characteristic of man, has since been observed in many animals, including birds.

Australopithecus robustus, rather than being an *A. africanus.*

Reconstruction. Among the various apelike fossils related to early man is *Ramapithecus,* known from fossils in India (*R. punjabicus*) and fossils in Kenya (*R. wickeri*). One known feature of the ramapithecines that seemed to argue well for manlike status was a dental arch based on reconstructions that more closely resembled the curved dental arch of man than the parallel-sided dental arch of the apes. Based largely on a fragment of jawbone from Kenya, the only specimen that included the midline jaw area, Alan Walker of the University of Nairobi and Peter Andrews of the National Museums of Kenya produced another reconstruction in 1973. The new one contains a parallel-sided dental arch reminiscent of the apes, but the unusually broad, flat face sets it apart from the dryopithecine apes, the extinct species that lived approximately 25 million years ago.

The Broken Hill Fossils, recovered in 1921 near Kabwe, Zambia, and the Saldanha skull, found in 1953 at Elandsfontein, South Africa, were thought to be of relatively recent age (30,000 to 40,000 years old for Broken Hill), although their structure is quite primitive. The specimens have been used by one anthropologist to suggest that the evolution of African prehumans to humans occurred very late in time compared with other continental groups. A restudy of these fossils and related artifacts from these sites, however, suggests a much earlier date. The study was based on comparisons with artifacts from other sites and more accurate radiocarbon dates. It was published in 1973 by Richard G. Klein, University of Chicago. According to Klein, the Saldanha and Broken Hill fossils date from the latter part of the Middle Pleistocene, which is at least 125,000 years ago, and may be much older.

East Rudolf. The East Rudolf Research Project, directed by Richard E. F. Leakey of the National Museums of Kenya, found the fossil remains of another 20 manlike creatures in 1973, bringing to 107 the total collected by the team in six years. Among the new finds was a skull heavily encrusted with a hard matrix that must be carefully removed before the entire shape can be determined. However, it appears to be a new type of hominid.   [Charles F. Merbs]

Archaeology

Old World. A 3,300-year-old song, that is probably the most ancient known, was sung again in March, 1974, at the University of California, Berkeley. The song, which sounds like a modern hymn or a lullaby, was written in the Hurrian language in about 1400 B.C. It was found in an excavation close to the city of Ras Shamra, once the ancient city of Ugarit, on the Syrian coast. Both the lyric and the music were preserved on clay tablets excavated by French archaeologists in 1954.

Anne D. Kilmer, professor of Assyriology at Berkeley, spent 15 years deciphering these tablets. She believes the song was written in a major scale and composed in double notes, with the two tones sounded at the same time. She says that numbers in the cuneiform text refer to the repetition of certain notes. This interpretation results in a harmonious matching of the syllables of the text with the notes of the music. Kilmer's conclusions suggest that the seven-tone diatonic scale, familiar in the music of the West, is some 1,400 years older than had been supposed, and originated in the Middle East rather than in Greece.

Her interpretation was based on a tablet about mathematics that discusses a stringed musical instrument, and on information from another tablet describing methods of tuning a harp found at Ur, in southern Mesopotamia.

The text of the song is not yet fully understood, but words in it known to mean *love* and *heart* suggest its character. Kilmer's interpretation of the music is not unchallenged. A different version, prepared by musicologist David Wulfstan of Oxford University in England, was first performed in 1970. Further studies should confirm which of the two interpretations is correct.

The song was sung at Berkeley by Richard L. Crocker, professor of music history, who accompanied himself on a 10-string lyre, a replica of an instrument known from Ur and dated to about 2600 B.C. The original lyre, discovered almost 50 years ago, was reconstructed on the basis of the impression it left in the soil and from the positions in the soil of the remaining silver and mother-of-pearl decorations that had once ornamented its frame. The wood decayed long ago.

Performance of world's oldest known song took place at Berkeley, Calif., in March, 1974. It was written about 1400 B.C., in what is now Syria. The song was played by Richard Crocker on a replica of an ancient lyre.

Bowl, *left,* depicting warriors, and head of Greek goddess Demeter were found in ancient burial site uncovered by archaeologists in the Russian Ukraine. These and other gold and silver articles found at the site were made by the Scythians in the 4th century B.C.

Archaeology
Continued

Physicist Robert R. Brown, an amateur harpsichord builder, made the Berkeley replica. The frame is of red birch and the sounding board of spruce, types of wood thought to have been available in ancient Ugarit. Gut was used for the strings. Although Ur, in present-day southern Iraq, and Ras Shamra, on the Syrian coast, are far apart, and the song is from tablets dated much later than the lyre, archaeologists assume that the two sites were culturally similar.

York studies. Peter Addyman, director of the York (England) Archaeological Trust, is coordinating research projects and retrieval techniques to build a detailed picture of the life of the people of York from its foundation by the Romans in A.D. 71. His approach has already yielded new information about Roman diets, Viking leather working, and the life span among various medieval peoples. Rising underground water at York has preserved many remains.

Three sites have been excavated during the past 18 months. The first, a Roman sewer about 150 feet long that was dug during the 3rd century A.D., had served the military bath house. In one section of the sewer, entomologists found the remains of a type of ant that flourishes only in warm, damp conditions, suggesting that this part of the sewer ran under the warm room of the bath house. The concentrated remains of sewer flies in two side channels of the main sewer, plus round holes in the stones roofing these channels, suggest that these were toilets. Analysis of the sludge in the side channels yielded grape, raspberry, and blackberry seeds, showing that the soldiers did not lack for fruit in their diet.

A second site revealed the flimsy huts of Viking leather workers. Large quantities of animal hair suggested that fur processing took place there, and remains of maggots in a section of one hut suggested that skins were scraped there. Chicken manure, presumably used to rot down skins, had covered the floor. Botanical remains also indicated the presence of heather, perhaps used as a dye, and of a ferment of elderberries, that must have been used to cure skins.

The third site is a medieval burial ground where Addyman has found

Archaeology

skeletal evidence of disease and malnutrition. Skeletons of richer and more prominent persons, buried within a church, indicated these persons were both larger and healthier than the general population buried in the churchyard.

Vindolanda. A singular discovery was reported in April, 1974, from an excavation at Vindolanda, a fort and civilian town at Chesterholm on Hadrian's Wall in Northumberland, in northeastern England. The pre-Hadrianic fort, which dates to the first century A.D., was discovered during the summer of 1973. The excavators found it from 8 to 14 feet below the town. They also found a timber structure, probably the quarters of the commanding officer. It had been preserved by water-logged clay.

The most significant find from this timber building was some writing tablets covered by a thin layer of wax and containing writing made by a stylus. Other tablets made of thin slivers of lime wood had writing in ink. Such tablets have never before been found. Those deciphered record requests for beer, new shoes, and underwear. [Judith Rodden]

New World. Robert H. McGhee of the National Museum of Man in Ottawa, Canada, uncovered a series of Eskimo sites in 1973. The sites, from different time periods, are on the Grinnell Peninsula, on Devon Island in the Canadian Arctic. Excavations of two of five houses at one location revealed tools similar to those used by the Greenland Inugsuk culture of A.D. 1500.

Another location had the remains of 20 houses believed to date between 2000 and 1500 B.C. Tools were also found there. Five other nearby sites had artifacts of a slightly later date, four of them between 1000 and 500 B.C.

Rene Levesque of the University of Sherbrook in Quebec, Canada, excavated two small sand and rock mounds on the straits of Belle Isle, Quebec. A slab-lined burial chamber in one mound was colored with red ocher and contained some stone tools. Charred wood from this site was dated at from 1400 to 1200 B.C., making this one of the earliest radiocarbon-dated mound sites in Canada.

North American finds. A University of Tennessee field party uncovered a settle-

Hand axe and other tools from Cobleskill, N.Y., are 70,000 years old, says Bruce Raemsch, archaeologist from Hartwick College. The controversial date was based on age of soil in which the tool was found, *right*.

Archaeology

Continued

ment radiocarbon dated between 7000 and 6000 B.C. on Rose Island, in Monroe County, Tennessee, in 1973. The party was under the direction of Jefferson Chapman of the University of North Carolina. Stone tools were found there, including spear points, flake knives, hammerstones, and digging stones.

Richard I. Yarnell of the University of North Carolina found remains of acorns and hickory nuts, which were probably important in the diet of the people who lived in the village. Charcoal fragments also suggested that an oak and hickory forest grew in the area at the time.

Richard W. Jeffries of the University of Georgia uncovered a group of small burial mounds in Dade County, Georgia. The materials he recovered from this site include seven copper and two silver Panpipes (musical instruments), stone and clay smoking pipes, mica designs and squares, shark's teeth, a copper breastplate, and 10 earrings. The pottery was similar to early pottery previously found in Georgia. The site is also considered an important link between the prehistoric Hopewell Indians of southern Ohio and Indian societies in northwest Florida. Radiocarbon dates indicate that these Georgia burials took place from about A.D. 100 to 200.

Central America. The range of Mexican influence in early Mesoamerican, or Central American, civilizations was extended to an area south of Trujillo, Honduras. Paul F. Healy of Harvard University directed excavations in the Cuyamel limestone caves of the area, and found pottery at the site that was clearly Mexican in design.

In western Mexico, Philip C. Weigand of the State University of New York at Stony Brook and Joseph Mountjoy of the University of North Carolina studied two large urban sites, called Teuchitlan and Providencia, near lake areas in the state of Jalisco. Each site had a ceremonial center with a circular stepped pyramid and a ball court. The scientists also identified irrigation ditches and terraces, as well as specialized workshop zones.

The problem of when cotton was domesticated in what are now Peru and Mexico has long puzzled archaeologists. At one time, some scholars believed domesticated cotton from this part of the world was a mixture of both New and Old World types of cotton, developed in rela-tively recent times. But a study in 1973 by Stanley G. Stephens of the North Carolina State University Department of Genetics and M. Edward Moseley of Harvard's Peabody Museum showed that this is incorrect. They reported genetic studies showing that seeds, fiber samples, and boll parts from four coastal excavations north of Lima, Peru, belong to the species *Gossypium barbadense* L., the same wild species now found near Manta, Ecuador. The excavations date from 2500 to 1750 B.C., suggesting that the initial domestication of cotton in this area probably occurred at about this time.

West Indies. Irving Rouse of Yale University, working in the summer of 1973 and in January, 1974, on Antigua, one of the Leeward Islands in the West Indies, discovered a site with a sequence of three different stages of occupation. He estimated that the three occupations occurred between A.D. 1 and 1200. Each occupation stage contained ceramics and other materials, and the later stages were of far greater complexity than were the earlier ones.

South America. Gary S. Vescelius, who directed the Cornell University excavations in the Peruvian highlands, found that the shrines around Cuzco, capital of the Incas, and the design of the central temple were closely linked in design to the Inca calendar. His studies of Inca records, early Spanish chronicles, and the calendar itself also resulted in his proposing radical revisions in the chronology of Inca history prior to the conquest by the Spanish conquistadors.

Vescelius believes that the Inca calendar originated at least 1,000 years before the Inca empire reached its peak (about A.D. 1500). He cites evidence for this in the inscription on the famous Sun Gate at Tihuanaco in the Bolivian Andes, dating from about A.D. 500. He says that two figures of trumpeters over this gate stand for the summer and winter solstices.

Dennis E. Pulestone of the University of Minnesota discovered a preagricultural Stone Age site in northern Belize, British Honduras. Field work in 1973 identified the remains of ancient hearths and a number of stone tools, including crude stone scrapers. Future work will probably determine whether this site was part of a more complex prehistoric society or represents an early, undeveloped Stone Age society. [James B. Griffin]

Astronomy

Planetary Astronomy. Pioneer 10 made its closest approach to Jupiter, about 81,000 miles (130,000 kilometers), on Dec. 4, 1973, after a flight of 21 months. Its primary objectives were to probe the asteroid belt between Mars and Jupiter and the intense radiation belts that surround Jupiter, two regions of space that could be major hazards to spacecraft. The future of planetary exploration beyond Mars depended on a successful mission. Remarkably, the spacecraft emerged from its adventure essentially unscathed.

Jupiter's radiation. Astronomers detected the first signs of an intense radiation field around Jupiter in 1955 when they found strong radio waves coming from the planet. Pioneer 10 carried six experiments to measure the particles and fields near Jupiter.

A helium vector magnetometer found that Jupiter's magnetic field is a dipole, like that of earth, with its magnetic axis inclined to the axis of rotation by about 15°. However, the positive magnetic pole points toward the south pole of rotation, unlike the earth, where the positive magnetic pole points north.

The center of Jupiter's magnetic field is offset from the center of the planet by about 10,000 miles (16,000 kilometers). At its center, Jupiter's dipole is 17,500 times stronger than the earth's. Because of Jupiter's much larger radius, however, the field at the planet's surface is only about 10 times that at the earth's surface. Because the magnetic center is displaced from the center of the planet, the field at the surface varies widely, ranging in strength between 2.3 and 11.7 gauss. Earth's surface field varies between 0.3 and 0.7 gauss.

Jupiter's magnetic field shields it from the solar wind and forms a large magnetosphere, a region that traps and holds high-energy charged particles. These particles produce the strong radio emission detected on earth. Pioneer 10 carried five particle detectors—a plasma analyzer, a Geiger tube telescope, a charged particle detector, a cosmic ray detector, and a trapped-radiation detector. Together, these detectors measured the fluxes, or flows, and energies of essentially all the electrons and ions in the magnetosphere surrounding Jupiter.

Pioneer's charged particle detector first detected radiation from Jupiter about 15.5 million miles (25 million kilometers) away, when it registered bursts of energetic electrons escaping from the planet's magnetosphere. About 5 million miles (8 million kilometers) from Jupiter, Pioneer detected a major change in the solar wind as the spacecraft passed through an interplanetary shock wave, or bowshock, caused by the planet. Pioneer crossed the boundary of the magnetosphere when the spacecraft was about 930,000 miles (1.5 million kilometers) from the sunward side of the planet.

Between the bowshock and the boundary of the magnetosphere, the properties of the plasma, or ionized gas, differed from any that have been observed before. The region has been dubbed the magnetodisk because the magnetic field is stretched out in a rough raylike pattern and the energetic particles tend to accumulate in a thin disk at the planet's magnetic equator.

Other results. In addition to the radiation experiments, Pioneer 10 carried equipment to determine the planet's hydrogen to helium ratio, measure the output of energy from the interior of the planet, and study the thermal structure of the atmosphere. An ultraviolet photometer measured the intensity of sunlight scattered by hydrogen and helium atoms in the planet's upper atmosphere. From this experiment, astronomers at the University of Southern California deduced a value of 0.18 for the ratio of helium to hydrogen. This is close to the ratio found in the sun, and shows that Jupiter, unlike the terrestrial planets, did not lose the lighter elements after it formed.

A combination of two experiments measured the production of energy in the planet's interior. The infrared radiometer measured Jupiter's total radiation output. The imaging photopolarimeter, which also provided some remarkable close-up color pictures of Jupiter, measured the net energy input from the sun. Preliminary analysis indicates that Jupiter radiates from 2 to 2.5 times as much energy as it receives from the sun.

The detailed nature of the change and disappearance of the radio signal from Pioneer 10 as the spacecraft passed behind Jupiter served to examine the temperature of the atmospheric layers. This technique, known as radio occultation, provided the major surprise of the mission. Results showed temperatures

Astronomy

Continued

Mariner 10 carried 170 pounds of cameras, electron spectrometers, magnetometers, and other measuring equipment to analyze the secrets of Mercury and Venus.

that are roughly twice as high as those predicted from ground-based studies. This promises to become a major topic of controversy, in view of the demonstrated accuracy of radio occultation in determining temperatures on Mars and Venus.

Studies of Io. Io is the second closest satellite to Jupiter and is well within the planet's magnetosphere, as measured by Pioneer 10. Several of the energetic particle experiments showed changes in their particle flux measurements when the spacecraft crossed Io's orbit.

Pioneer 10 passed close to and behind the satellite, as seen from the earth. The subsequent radio occultation showed that Io has an ionosphere with a peak electron density of roughly 6×10^4 electrons per cubic centimeter at about 62 miles (100 kilometers) above its surface. Io's gravity measurably deflected the orbit of the spacecraft as it passed. J. D. Anderson of the Jet Propulsion Laboratory in Pasadena, Calif., used this to deduce a value of 3.5 grams per cubic centimeter for the mean density of Io. This is about 20 per cent higher than previous estimates and falls between the densities of Mars and the moon.

Astronomers have so far identified two gases in Io's thin neutral atmosphere. The ultraviolet photometer on Pioneer 10 detected a strong signal from atomic hydrogen. Robert Brown of Harvard University discovered strong, but short-lived, emissions from sodium atoms with a ground-based telescope. Both the hydrogen and sodium atoms are constantly escaping from Io's gravity to form a giant doughnut-shaped ring of atoms in orbit about Jupiter. The atoms appear to be released at the surface of the satellite through intense particle bombardment from the Jovian radiation belts.

New molecules on Jupiter. In early 1974, Steven T. Ridgway of Kitt Peak National Observatory in Tucson, Ariz., using ground-based observations, announced the discovery of three new molecules on Jupiter—ethane (C_2H_6), acetylene (C_2H_2), and phosphine (PH_3). This increases the known atmospheric constituents on the planet to seven.

Mariner 10 and Venus. Mariner 10 flew by Venus on Feb. 5, 1974, on its way to Mercury. Its pictures of Venus, taken in ultraviolet light, show an upper atmosphere in rapid and complex motion, with circulation quite different from that on

the earth. The upper part of the atmosphere moves around Venus at about 325 feet (100 meters) a second, at least 50 times faster than the surface rotates. Similar strong winds are found on earth in jet streams high in the atmosphere, but these are confined to relatively small regions. On Venus, however, the entire upper atmosphere moves at high speed, circling the planet every four days.

The cloud patterns near the subsolar point, the point directly opposite the sun, and downwind of it are quite different from elsewhere on the planet, presumably as a result of strong local heating. Away from the subsolar region, the clouds are drawn out into long streaks that swirl from the equator to higher latitudes and give the impression of streamlined flow. They may be the Venusian equivalent of jet streams. At the south pole, which can be clearly seen in the pictures, the cloud patterns spiral downward in a vortex, apparently caused as the cooled atmosphere descends to lower levels to return to the equator.

Mercury encounter. Mariner 10 passed Mercury on March 29, 1974. Television pictures show a heavily cratered surface similar to that of the moon. This surprised astronomers who had believed that Mercury evolved quite differently from the moon and that evidence for this would show up in the character of surface geological formations. The pictures are putting stringent limits on astronomers who are developing theories of the formation and early evolution of the terrestrial planets.

The surface appearance of Mercury is about the only major similarity with the moon. The extreme ultraviolet spectrometer detected a thin helium atmosphere on Mercury. The magnetometer experiment detected a weak planetary magnetic field, which is surprising because a planetary magnetic field is generally associated with rapid rotation, and Mercury rotates very slowly.

Other experiments found substantial flows of charged particles near Mercury that seem to be associated with trapped radiation in the planet's magnetic field. The infrared radiometer found that the temperature on the dark side of Mercury falls to about −300°F. (−185°C.), as would be expected if the microphysical properties of the surface are similar to those of the moon. [Michael J.S. Belton]

Views in Collision

Proponents of two highly divergent views on the solar system squared off in a sometimes tense, sometimes humorous encounter in San Francisco in February, 1974. Focus of the debate was the Russian-born psychiatrist, Immanuel Velikovsky, who created a storm of protest among scientists when his best-selling *Worlds in Collision* was published in 1950.

From his studies of historical and archaeological records, Velikovsky has concluded that Venus was born as a comet ejected from Jupiter; that it nearly collided with the earth about 1500 B.C.; that it perturbed or changed the original orbit of Mars so much that Mars also nearly collided with the earth about 775 B.C.; and that both Mars and Venus then settled into their present orbits. Astronomers flatly deny the possibility of such remarkable activity among the planets within historical times. Nevertheless, public interest in Velikovsky's writings persists, mostly because of several apparently correct astronomical predictions that he made based upon his theories.

Without conceding that Velikovsky's theories are any more acceptable today than they were in 1950, the American Association for the Advancement of Science (AAAS) provided a forum for both Velikovsky and those with opposing views at its annual meeting in February. First to challenge Velikovsky was Peter Huber, a statistician with a professional knowledge of ancient cuneiform languages. Huber said that ancient tablets give convincing evidence that Venus was already in its present orbit before 1500 B.C., and added that Velikovsky had been misled by inadequate translations of Mesopotamian texts. J. Deral Mulholland, a University of Texas astronomer and an expert on celestial mechanics, pointed to "fatal flaws" in Velikovsky's treatment of planetary motions. He said the present arrangement of almost circular orbits lying in nearly the same plane argues against the possibility that any serious upheaval could have occurred within mankind's memory.

Velikovsky counterattacked vigorously, emphasizing his "advance claims." He had correctly predicted the high temperatures on Venus, he said, arguing that "Venus, due to its recent birth and dramatic, though short, history, must be very hot under the clouds, nearly incandescent, and giving off heat." Skimming over his claim that the Venusian atmosphere was largely composed of hydrocarbons, he stressed a claim that burning hydrocarbons had created the massive carbon dioxide atmosphere now observed. He ended by saying: "Nobody can cool off Venus, and nobody can change a single sentence in my books."

In a detailed and witty rebuttal, astronomer Carl Sagan of Cornell University criticized the vagueness and qualitative nature of Velikovsky's predictions. "Where Velikovsky is original, he is likely to be wrong; where he is right, the idea has been pre-empted by other workers."

Sagan added that Velikovsky can also be apparently right for the wrong reasons. For example, if Venus is hot because of its violent birth out of the planet Jupiter and is now cooling off, it should be giving off energy and its temperature should be decreasing, but neither is the case. The correct explanation for the high surface temperature—a phenomenon known as the greenhouse effect—was given by Yale astronomy professor Rupert Wildt, 10 years before Velikovsky proposed his theory. Wildt showed that sunlight can penetrate the atmosphere and warm the surface, but the carbon dioxide layers absorb the infrared rays reradiated by the planet; as in a greenhouse, the solar energy is trapped, driving up the temperature. Sagan added that if Velikovsky were correct, then Mars, with an equally erratic history, should also be hot, which is not the case.

Velikovsky accused Sagan of changing his mind about the surface temperature of Venus. Sagan replied, "I do not consider that a serious flaw. I think it is precisely the ability to change one's mind that is the method by which science advances. . . . The idea that texts are canonical and need no revision in the light of 25 years of subsequent study—that I find more strange."

Whether the AAAS will sponsor a future tilt with some other unorthodox theory is an open question. Organizers of the Velikovsky symposium hoped to publish the proceedings to allow a wider public to form its own judgment. However, because Velikovsky objected unless he received unlimited space for rebuttals (a condition unacceptable to the organizers), the fate of the proposed volume is uncertain. In any event, debates on such controversial topics seem likely to remain infrequent.   [Owen Gingerich]

Immanuel Velikovsky

Astronomy

Continued

Stellar Astronomy. Astronomers in 1973 and 1974 investigated gamma-ray bursts from outside the solar system, studied data on the sun from Skylab, and increased their understanding of quasars. But they also raised doubts about the one previous good case for a planet circling another sun and discredited the observations of an illustrious predecessor.

Interstellar gamma rays. In June, 1973, Ray W. Klebesadel, Ian B. Strong, and Roy A. Olson of Los Alamos Scientific Laboratory in New Mexico reported bursts of gamma rays coming from distant space. The gamma-ray bursts tell us that enormous amounts of energy are being released in just a few seconds, but astronomers have not discovered their source. See ASTRONOMY, HIGH ENERGY.

The National Aeronautics and Space Administration's Small Astronomy Satellite-2 mapped other gamma rays that are continuously emitted from the direction of the supernova (exploded star) remnant Vela X. A team led by David J. Thompson of the Goddard Space Flight Center in Greenbelt, Md., reported the results of these observations in early 1974. They concluded that if the observed gamma rays are created by collisions between cosmic ray particles and atoms of the interstellar gas, the total energy of the cosmic rays ejected from the supernova must have been about 3×10^{50} ergs. This is more energy than the sun produces in 2 billion years at its present rate.

The sun's core could be rotating more rapidly than its outer regions, according to calculations published in November, 1973. Pierre Demarque and other astronomers at Yale University made the computations while trying to explain the puzzling lack of solar neutrinos. According to present theory, there should be an observable stream of neutrinos flowing from the sun's core, but none have been found. The new calculations indicate that if the sun has a fast-turning core, it would produce fewer neutrinos than a slowly rotating one. The subject is important because all our models for the evolution of stars in our Galaxy are based on our understanding of our own sun.

Solar bright points. A solar experiment conducted with Skylab's Apollo Telescope Mount produced new in-

A picture obtained with a new television sensor attached to the 200-inch telescope at Mount Palomar, shows fine details in a cluster of galaxies, *below right.* Standard photographic exposure, *below,* looks much sharper, but it contains less information.

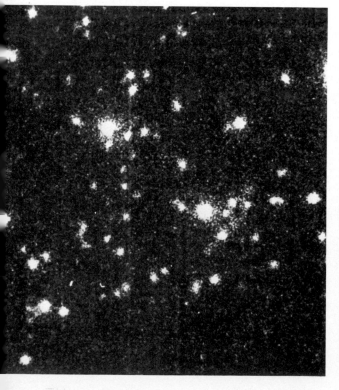

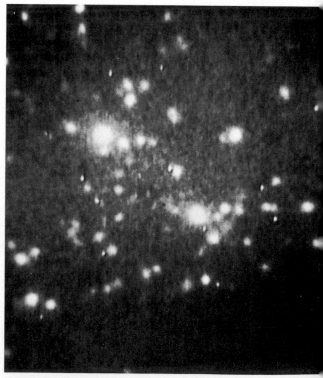

Astronomy

Continued

The 158-inch Mayall telescope, the world's second largest optical telescope, was dedicated at Kitt Peak National Observatory, near Tucson, in June, 1973.

formation about bright X-ray emission points on the sun. The astronauts used an X-ray telescope developed by Giuseppe S. Vaiana of American Science and Engineering, Cambridge, Mass., to make a systematic series of photos in late 1973.

The Skylab data showed that about 1,500 bright points occur each day, with equal frequency at all latitudes on the sun—unlike sunspots, which occupy restricted zones. The X-ray points last for up to 40 hours, with an average lifetime of 8 hours. They may mark regions of emerging magnetic flux, or places where magnetic fields from lower regions are breaking through the visible surface. The total amount of magnetic flux emerging at the bright points appears to exceed that from the active regions where sunspots and flares occur. See RESEARCH IN ORBIT.

Quasar studies. In 1974, J. Beverly Oke of Hale Observatories in southern California reported on his investigations of the ultraviolet radiation from the quasars OQ 172 and OH 471. In 1973, the two quasars were found to have the greatest red shifts yet known. The shift occurs because wave lengths of light from a distant object grow longer and shift to the red side of the spectrum as the object moves away. Due to the large red shifts, ultraviolet radiation from OQ 172 and OH 471 reaches the earth as visible radiation and thus can penetrate the atmosphere. Oke concluded that the hydrogen emission lines in the spectra of the two objects are best explained if a quasar consists of a small bright object that ionizes a larger volume of surrounding gas. The gas may exist in the form of nebular clouds or filaments, or perhaps a disk.

An elusive planet. A study published in October, 1973, cast doubts on the existence of a planet formerly believed to orbit Barnard's Star. Barnard's Star, discovered in 1916 by Edward Emerson Barnard, is the second closest star to our sun, only 5.9 light-years away. Only the triple star, Alpha Centauri, is closer. The apparent angular motion of Barnard's Star across the sky—10.3 arc seconds per year—is the greatest found for any star. This means that in only two centuries Barnard's Star moves more than the apparent diameter of the full moon across the background of distant stars.

In 1969, Peter van de Kamp of Swarthmore College in Pennsylvania climaxed a long series of observations by concluding that Barnard's Star did not proceed along a smooth line. Rather, a tiny wiggle with a period of 25 years seemed to be superimposed on the general movement. This suggested that the star was not alone in space, but had a companion. The wiggle would occur as the star revolved around the center of mass of the star and its companion at the same time as it moved through the Galaxy.

Calculations indicated that the star's companion must have a relatively low mass, only 50 per cent greater than that of Jupiter. This was far too small for a star and appeared to be our first solid evidence that a planet was orbiting another star.

But a study published in October, 1973, by George Gatewood of Allegheny Observatory in Pittsburgh and Heinrich Eichhorn of the University of South Florida failed to confirm Van de Kamp's observations. Gatewood and Eichhorn studied 241 photographs of the motion of Barnard's Star taken from 1916 to 1971 and found no wiggle.

Other studies. A critical review of observations of the Hyades star cluster resulted in a slight, but significant, revaluing of the distances from the sun to other stars. Distance estimates have been based largely on the distance from earth to the Hyades, which include most of the stars in the V-shaped head of the constellation Taurus the Bull. William F. van Altena of Yerkes Observatory in Williams Bay, Wis., combined data on parallaxes, binary star orbits, spectra, and photometric measurements on members of the Hyades to obtain an improved distance of 143 light-years to the star cluster. Previously, astronomers thought the cluster was 133 light-years away. As a consequence of the correction, most other objects in the Galaxy and beyond are 8 per cent farther away than previously believed and 16 per cent brighter.

Robert R. Newton of Johns Hopkins University's Applied Physics Laboratory in Maryland criticized parts of the work of the ancient astronomer Claudius Ptolemy in December, 1973. Newton investigated Ptolemy's solar and lunar observations described in the *Almagest*, a 13-volume astronomical compilation prepared about A.D. 142. He said Ptolemy's data were so greatly in error that, beyond any doubt, "these observations were fudged." [Stephen P. Maran]

Astronomy

Continued

A map of the radio
emission from galaxy
NGC 1265 shows the
strange tadpole shape
that it shares with
several similar galaxies.
Typically, the "head"
of one of these galaxies
coincides with a visible
galaxy—superimposed
on this map. The tail is
a stream of radiation
as much as 1 million
light-years in length.

High Energy Astronomy. The discovery of brief bursts of extraterrestrial gamma rays by Ray Klebesadel, Ian Strong, and Roy Olson of the Los Alamos Scientific Laboratory in New Mexico was one of the most exciting events in 1973. For several years, Vela satellites have been monitoring the earth and nearby space for evidence of gamma rays from nuclear explosions. Gamma rays are high-frequency electromagnetic radiations, similar to Xrays, but with a shorter wave length. Pairs of Vela satellites have been placed in an orbit 75,000 miles from the earth. The two members of each pair are on opposite sides of the earth. Each can record the intensity and time of arrival of gamma rays at energies ranging from 0.2 to 1.5 million electron volts.

Inspecting the records for a three-year period, Klebesadel and his colleagues found 16 brief bursts of gamma rays that had been detected simultaneously by both members of a satellite pair.

The bursts last from 0.1 second to as much as 30 seconds. Records from other satellites that have also detected the bursts show that the burst energies range down to typical X-ray energies as low as 10,000 electron volts.

Origin of bursts. Astronomers first thought that the gamma rays came from the sun, but a simple test ruled this out. The two members of a satellite pair are about 150,000 miles apart. Like all electromagnetic waves, gamma rays travel at the speed of light, about 190,000 miles per second. If they came from the sun, they would take almost a second to move from one satellite to another, with the satellite nearest the sun registering the burst first. This is not the case.

Astronomers used the observed arrival times at each satellite to estimate the direction from which each burst came. So far, the bursts seem equally likely to come from any direction in space.

A significant clue to the source of the bursts is that they come from all directions. For example, neither the most luminous stars in our Galaxy nor the bright X-ray stars could be responsible because they are all located near the plane of the Milky Way. Gamma-ray bursts from them would not come equally from all directions.

Astronomy

However, nearby faint stars and very distant galaxies have about the right distribution. If the nearby stars are the source, the bursts might well be a very energetic version of solar flares.

Other theories. Stirling Colgate of the New Mexico Institute of Mining and Technology predicted in 1968 that gamma rays might result from supernova explosions in distant galaxies. When a star explodes, a very strong shock wave moves out from its center. When this shock reaches the star's outer layer, the temperature becomes so high that the star may emit gamma rays. Although the theory looks promising, there is one problem. Astronomers have seen several supernovae in distant galaxies during the last few years, but none seems to have generated a gamma burst.

Martin Harwit and Edwin Salpeter of Cornell University, Ithaca, N.Y., have proposed another alternative to this. They note that our own solar system has a belt of comets far beyond the orbit of Pluto, where a passing star occasionally perturbs one of the comets, sending it close to the sun. In rare cases, a comet may fall into the sun and perish in a bright flash of light. If a similar comet cloud were to orbit a nearby neutron star, Harwit and Salpeter suggest that the very intense gravity near the star would break up an incoming comet. The resulting impact of material falling onto the star could be sufficiently violent to generate a brief burst of gamma rays.

Unusual quasars. For several years, astronomers have known an object called BL Lacertae as a mysterious source of radio, infrared, and optical radiation. At first, they thought it was a variable star in the Milky Way Galaxy. But it has a very blue color and its energy output is violently variable at all wave lengths like a quasar. However, all previously known quasars had strong emission line spectra and BL Lacertae had no emission lines. As a result, astronomers could not establish its true nature.

As they discovered several more objects of this type, it became increasingly important to solve the mystery. In early 1974, J. Beverly Oke and James Gunn of the Hale Observatories in California reported on their study of the faint luminous glow around BL Lacertae that appeared on long-exposure photographs. They reasoned that if BL Lacertae was a quasar, the glow might come from a surrounding galaxy. To investigate this, they blotted out the light of BL Lacertae itself with a small disk at the focus of the 200-inch telescope on Mount Palomar and obtained a spectrum of the surrounding glow. This spectrum looks like that of a giant elliptical galaxy.

Oke and Gunn derived a red shift of about 7 per cent from the spectrum. The red shift occurs when a source of light is receding from the viewer and the waves of energy it emits are lengthened and shifted to the red side of the spectrum. If BL Lacertae's red shift is caused by the expansion of the universe, it would be about 1 billion light-years away, making it one of the nearest quasars.

Black hole? Just when several astronomers seemed to have confirmed the existence of a black hole in the X-ray source Cygnus X-1, other astronomers suggested an alternative interpretation of the data that leaves everything still in doubt. The long-sought black holes are the most compact form of matter. In a black hole, gravity becomes so strong that even light cannot escape. This makes it impossible to see a black hole directly, but matter falling into it could become quite hot and radiate X rays before being completely swallowed up.

In Cygnus X-1, a luminous star is visible at the same position as the X-ray source. However, the star's temperature is much too low for it to be the source of the X rays. These must come from a more compact companion, so compact that its gravity can contain the hot gas that emits the X rays. Recent studies show that the mass of the luminous star is about 25 times that of the sun. The mass of its companion is estimated at about six times that of the sun. Since this is at least twice as large as the maximum mass allowed for a neutron star or white dwarf, it seemed that the companion must be a black hole.

However, John Bahcall and his associates at the Institute of Advanced Studies, Princeton, N.J., propose that Cygnus X-1 might be a triple star system. If so, the second star could be a rather normal star six times the mass of the sun. It would be so much fainter than the luminous star that it would be invisible. This would leave the mass of the third star, the X-ray source, undetermined. And it might be a neutron star or white dwarf, after all.   [Lodewyk Woltjer]

Astronomy

Cosmology. The first large red shift at radio wave lengths was measured in 1974 by Robert Brown and Morton Roberts of the National Radio Astronomy Observatory in Charlottesville, W. Va. Previously, the red shifts of distant galaxies and quasars have all been measured from spectrograms taken in the visible part of the spectrum by large optical telescopes, by comparing the wave lengths of emission or absorption lines with the values measured in the laboratory.

Each chemical element emits radiation at a characteristic set of wave lengths when heated, forming bright lines on a spectrum. Absorption lines are dark lines that occur when a cloud of gas intervenes between the observer and a source of energy. The gas blocks the energy at wave lengths corresponding to its own chemical composition, and dark lines appear on the spectrum, revealing the composition of the intervening gas.

A red shift occurs when light and radio waves from a receding source are lengthened so that the absorption and emission lines are shifted from their normal place in the energy spectrum. The usual inter-pretation of the red shift relates it to velocity in an expanding universe; the greater the red shift, the faster an object is moving. Also, since the Hubble Law relates velocity to distance, the size of the red shift also indicates how far away an object is.

In studying the radio spectrum of the quasar 3C-286, Brown and Roberts found an absorption line, which they identified as the line normally produced by hydrogen gas at a wave length of 21 centimeters (cm). But the line they found had a wave length of 36 cm, indicating that the hydrogen that produced it has a red shift of 0.7. This is 80 percent of the red shift of the quasar itself, which is 0.85.

The astronomers concluded that the radio absorption line is produced by a cool cloud of hydrogen gas between the quasar and the earth that absorbs part of the radio waves emitted by the hot quasar. The most likely place to find such a cloud would be in a spiral galaxy. But with the large red shift of 0.7, and with the bright quasar in the background, such a galaxy would be completely invisible. However, if the hydrogen cloud is located in a spiral

"It just doesn't seem right for you to contemplate the universe and eat a baloney sandwich at the same time."

Astronomy

Continued

galaxy, it would be the most distant galaxy yet measured.

Radio sources. Studies of very small scale changes in the structure of radio sources continued in 1974. These studies use two or more radio antennas, thousands of miles apart, as an interferometer to examine the structure of a radio source on a scale of 0.001 second of arc—equivalent to viewing a quarter at a distance of 2,000 miles. The signals received by the radio telescopes are recorded on tape recorders synchronized by atomic clocks. The proper combination of such signals provides pictures of the radio emission with a resolution in one direction comparable to that obtained from a single radio telescope thousands of miles in diameter.

Past observations made at different times show structural changes in quasars that have been interpreted as two components moving apart. However, at the distances implied by the red shifts, they would be moving apart at several times the speed of light, violating the most fundamental laws of physics. Either the quasars are much closer than their red shifts indicate, or astronomers must come up with some other explanation.

One alternative is the so-called Christmas-tree model proposed by William Dent of the University of Massachusetts. He suggests that a quasar has several components, each of which is fixed in space, but which become brighter or fainter between observations. The general effect is like a Christmas tree with blinking lights, and this may give the illusion of rapid motion.

In early 1974, a group of radio astronomers reported on a series of observations they made of the quasar radio sources 3C-279 and 3C-273, using radio antennas in California, Massachusetts, and West Virginia as an interferometer. Their studies suggest that the detailed structure of radio sources may be more complicated than any of the simple models proposed so far. They found that although many of their observations can be explained either by a simple Christmas-tree model or by a faster-than-light expansion model, other observations require a more complex structure for the sources. [Jerome Kristian]

Biochemistry

Reports of experiments probing the roles of a biochemical that may be a key substance in controlling a vast number of metabolic processes in living cells interested biochemists in 1973 and 1974. The substance is called cyclic GMP.

A closely related compound, cyclic AMP, has already proved to be one of the most important substances in the body. It stimulates or inhibits many enzymes, thereby playing a significant role in a host of reactions necessary to life.

Scientists formerly found it difficult to determine the level of cyclic GMP in cells because it is present in such small quantities, only one-tenth to one-fiftieth the amount of cyclic AMP. But relatively new, extremely sensitive techniques of detecting cyclic GMP, such as one using antibodies tagged with an easily detected, radioactive substance, have changed that. Scientists now have found that, like cyclic AMP, cyclic GMP is very widely distributed in nature. They believe that the substance may also be as important as cyclic AMP in metabolism.

Studies on the biological effects of cyclic GMP are still hampered because the compound is not easily taken up by cells growing in laboratory cultures. In the case of cyclic AMP, biochemists had the advantage of having available certain synthetic forms of the compound with enhanced abilities to enter such laboratory-grown cells. Similar forms of cyclic GMP are not yet available.

Despite this problem in working with cyclic GMP, scientists have learned enough about it to become aware of its importance. Nelson Goldberg of the University of Minnesota, who has been working with cyclic GMP for several years, thinks that it counteracts the effects of cyclic AMP. He and others have found many examples. In May, 1973, for instance, Gordon Tomkins and his associates at the University of California, San Francisco, added cyclic AMP to proliferating mouse cells and found that it slowed the production of protein and ribonucleic acid (RNA). Then the scientists added cyclic GMP, and the cells began to synthesize the materials at a normal rate again.

Goldberg's research team reported in 1973 that cyclic GMP levels in cells in-

Biochemistry

Continued

crease when hormones that reverse the action of cyclic AMP are added. This suggests that hormones trigger cyclic GMP production to reverse the effects of cyclic AMP.

Role of calcium. Jack Mongar and his co-workers at University College in London and Bastien Gomperts of University College Hospital Medical School, also in London, reported in October, 1973, on experiments that probed the roles of calcium in cells. Scientists have long known that the release of calcium from storage vessels in muscle cells causes the muscles to contract, but Mongar and Gomperts proved other roles for calcium.

All animal cells store some of their chemical compounds in small packages that release them only when the proper stimulus acts on the cell surface. Scientists have suspected that calcium was the link between the outside and inside of cells in such instances. One problem with proving it is that cells grown in the laboratory normally are permeable to only a small amount of the calcium in the growth medium. But Mongar and Gomperts used certain compounds called "iono-

phores" that allow calcium ions to enter cells freely.

When the scientists added an ionophore to allow calcium to enter rat cells, histamine, a packaged compound they were monitoring, was released. This suggests that calcium releases these compounds, and, in turn is released by stimulation at the cell surface.

Like histamine, which plays a role in allergies, many of the packaged compounds are of great importance to our health. They include hormones and substances that are active in the transmission of impulses in the nervous system.

3-D structure of tRNA. In March, 1974, Alexander Rich and his research group at the Massachusetts Institute of Technology, using new data accurate to a resolution of 3.0 angstroms (about 0.00000001 inch), described a refined 3-dimensional structure for a transfer ribonucleic acid (tRNA) molecule. It has long been thought that knowledge of the 3-dimensional structure of tRNA would be important in learning more about translation, the mechanism by which cells correctly make all the proteins necessary

A plastic model of a transfer ribonucleic acid molecule was constructed after the 3-dimensional structure of the molecule was described in 1974.

Biochemistry

Continued

to maintain life. The tRNA in cells carries amino acids to sites where they are linked together to form a protein.

There are about 60 different kinds of tRNA molecules. Each one is made up of about 80 chemical bases, mostly adenine (A), cytosine (C), guanine (G), and uracil (U). The sequence of the bases in many tRNAs is known. The bases at different parts of the molecule come close enough to each other to form weak bonds, called hydrogen bonds. Thus, tRNA is a complex folded structure.

To determine this structure, Rich and his co-workers formed crystals of the tRNA molecule, beamed X rays at them, and analyzed how the X rays scattered upon impact. With this technique, known as X-ray crystallography, the scientists obtained thousands of pictures. Analysis of more than 4,500 of them enabled the scientists to "see" the tRNA molecule at the 3-angstrom resolution.

The molecular structure has basically the cloverleaf shape that was proposed several years ago on the basis of physical and chemical studies and the base sequence of the molecule. However, some new details were uncovered. Most important, in three dimensions, the molecule appears L-shaped. The anticodon loop, which binds to a complementary portion of a molecule called messenger RNA (mRNA) during protein synthesis, projects out at one end of the molecule. At the other end of the tRNA molecule, 82 angstroms away and fully exposed, is the site to which an amino acid is attached before it is passed on to a growing chain of amino acids that form the protein. This part of the molecule appears to be flexible, which may be necessary to place the amino acid in the growing protein.

Gene control. Deoxyribonucleic acid (DNA), of which genes are composed, contains all the information necessary for the synthesis of cell proteins. However, protein is not constantly made from all DNA regions during a cell's lifetime. Some genes are repressed, or turned off, and no protein is made from them because that protein is not required by that particular type of cell at that time.

Repression is often accomplished by proteins called repressors. A repressor binds to a specific region of DNA, called the operator region, near the genes to be controlled. Somehow, the binding of the repressor prevents an mRNA copy of the genes from being made. This copy is necessary for protein production.

Knowledge of what is involved in the binding of the repressor protein to a specific DNA region might help scientists understand repression, the control of which might help cure several diseases characterized by the production of too little of a genetic product. Walter Gilbert and Allan Maxam of Harvard University have taken a step toward such understanding. In December, 1973, they reported that they had determined the sequence of bases that form an operator region of the DNA in the bacterium *Escherichia coli.* Known as the lac operator, it is the region involved in regulating lactose metabolism.

The first problem was to isolate pure lac operator DNA. The scientists took advantage of the fact that when the repressor binds to the lac operator DNA, the repressor protects it from the enzyme deoxyribonuclease, which destroys DNA. Gilbert and Maxam mixed bacterial DNA and the repressor and then added the nuclease. The only DNA remaining after this treatment was the region protected by the repressor, the lac operator, which was then isolated. This DNA fragment is 27 base pairs long. Because the ability of the repressor to bind to the operator must, to some extent, depend upon the sequence of the bases, knowledge of this sequence would be revealing.

There is no known way to directly sequence DNA, but there are ways to directly determine the sequence of bases in RNA. So, Gilbert and Maxam used a technique that makes complementary RNA copies from DNA to make a copy of the operator DNA. Then, by determining the sequence of RNA bases, they determined the corresponding DNA sequence for 24 of the 27 base pairs.

The sequence has many interesting features, one of which is a two-fold symmetry of some of the base combinations about the center of this region. Scientists are intrigued by the function of these symmetrical, or palindromic, sequences. They are believed to be rare in DNA and may be characteristic of all operator and other recognition regions. Researchers must now determine how this DNA sequence fits with the known structure of the lac repressor, a large protein molecule that has four subunits with a two-fold symmetry.   [Julian Davies]

Books of Science

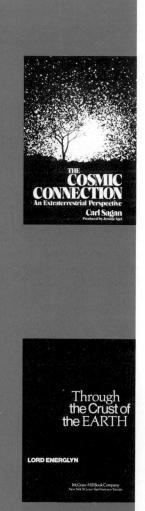

Here are 39 outstanding new science books suitable for general readers. The director of libraries of the Smithsonian Institution selected them from books published in 1973 and 1974.

Archaeology. *Before Civilization: The Radiocarbon Revolution and Prehistoric Europe* by Colin Renfrew. The author, using knowledge derived from radio-carbon-dating techniques, indicates that cultures existed in prehistoric Europe long before the better-known advanced civilizations of the Mediterranean were established. He raises some new questions about the diffusion of culture. (Knopf, 1973. 292 pp. illus. $8.95)

Hunters of the Whale: An Adventure in Northwest Coast Archaeology by Ruth Kirk. In describing the techniques used to unearth a rich deposit of Indian artifacts in the Northwest, and by verbally reconstructing an old culture, the author reveals how an archaeologist works. In so doing she unfolds a fascinating tale of whaling in prehistoric times. (Morrow, 1974. 160 pp. illus. $5.95)

Riddle of the Pyramids by Kurt Mendelssohn. The author describes the construction and appearance of the Egyptian pyramids and discusses various theories about why they were built. (Praeger, 1974. 224 pp. illus. $12.95)

Astronomy. *Black Holes: The End of the Universe* by John Taylor. This is the story of the discovery of, and a description of, stars that have used up their fuel and are collapsing inward, becoming so dense that their gravity permits no light to be emitted from them. It describes the strange things that could happen to a space traveler caught in the "pull" of a black hole. (Random House, 1973. 174 pp. $5.95)

Comets, Meteorites and Men, by Peter Lancaster Brown, is an introduction to the physical nature of comets and meteorites and the role each played in ancient astrology and legend. Much information in this book was derived from recent space exploration. It also features famous and unusual comets and meteorites. (Taplinger, 1974. 255 pp. illus. $9.50)

The Cosmic Connection: An Extraterrestrial Perspective by Carl Sagan. A noted astronomer examines the many issues involved in the quest for extraterrestrial life. He comments on the findings of current planetary explorations, and raises questions concerning both the value and the danger of possible contacts with other forms of life in space. The author also shows how the astronomer learns to differentiate the characteristics of individual planets and stars. (Doubleday, 1973. 274 pp. illus. $7.95)

Mars and the Mind of Man by Ray Bradbury, Arthur C. Clarke, Bruce Murray, Carl Sagan, and Walter Sullivan. Hypotheses and notions about man, both before and after the Mariner 9 flight to the region of Mars, are examined by a group of notable scientists and writers. They also suggest other potentially useful space probes. (Harper & Row, 1973. 143 pp. illus. $7.95)

Whispers from Space by John Macvey. The author describes various experiments and coding systems that could be used, via radio astronomy, to establish the existence of, and to communicate with, other life in the universe. (Macmillan, 1973. 250 pp. illus. $8.95)

Biology. *The Animal in Man* by Lorus Milne and Margery Milne. This book describes the need for love, status, territory, and sex among animals, and relates their behavioral patterns to those of man. The authors also raise questions pertaining to predetermination of man's actions. (McGraw-Hill, 1973. 250 pp. $7.95)

The Brain Revolution: The Frontiers of Mind Research by Marilyn Ferguson. This review of our current knowledge of the brain ranges from basic facts about neurology to speculation on parapsychological phenomena. It tells how the brain works and how it is affected by alcohol, electronic stimulation, and drugs and other chemicals. (Taplinger, 1973. 380 pp. $9.95)

Children of the Universe: The Tale of Our Existence by Hoimar von Ditfurth. The author integrates fundamental knowledge of the natural world, derived from geophysics, biology, atomic physics, and space science, into a flowing account about creation, from universe to earth to life and finally, to man. The result is an unusual account about the continuity of, and relationships between, all elements of nature. The author also tells how major scientific theories contributed to an understanding of natural phenomena. (Atheneum, 1974. 301 pp. illus. $10.95)

Evolution for Everyone by Paul Gastonguay. The author explains the processes of change that have occurred in the stars, the earth's crust, plants, animals,

Books of Science

Continued

man, and his tools and products. In so doing, he explains how knowledge about man is derived from fossil skulls. (Bobbs-Merrill, 1974. 213 pp. illus. $6.95)

Botany. *International Book of Trees: A Guide and Tribute to the Trees of Our Forests and Gardens* by Hugh Johnson skillfully combines text and illustrations to provide a superb and valuable reference work on the trees of the world. Johnson describes how a tree grows and can be nurtured; he surveys a large variety of tree families, and provides essential information about them that includes diseases and pests to which they are prey. (Simon & Schuster, 1973. 288 pp. illus. $29.95)

Climatology. *Man Changes the Weather* by Ben Bova covers the changes caused in the weather by processes such as agriculture, forest fires, pollution, jet planes, rainmakers, and even urban construction projects. The author describes the atmosphere as an energy bank. (Addison-Wesley, 1973. 159 pp. illus. $4.95)

Conservation. *Conservation: The Challenge of Reclaiming Our Plundered Land* by C. William Harrison. This is a simple but poignant story of man's destruction and pollution of the American environment and the potential role conservation can play in restoring it. It describes the interrelationships of the pollution processes as well as the cumulative effects of pollution and the misuse of resources. (Messner, 1973. 191 pp. illus. $5.95)

Rampage: The Story of Disastrous Floods, Broken Dams, and Human Fallibility by Peter Briggs. The author makes a case for increased federal flood control efforts by describing the devastation that results from dam failures, flooding, and coastal hurricanes and other storms. (McKay, 1973. 224 pp. illus. $6.95)

Ecology. *Environment and Man* by Richard Wagner covers a wide array of contemporary environmental problems such as pollution, population control, urban planning, the energy crisis, and endangered wildlife species. (Norton, 1974. 528 pp. illus. $7.95)

Where the Place Called Morning Lies: A Personal View of the American Government by Frank Graham, Jr. The author tells how the advent of technology and industry in Maine has eroded the quality of the state's environment. (Viking Press, 1973. 238 pp. $7.95)

Food. *Food in History* by Reay Tannahill. This is a comprehensive story of food and man's eating habits through the ages. It demonstrates how the quest for food influenced society and the development of man, and describes the foods of various eras. (Stein & Day, 1973. 448 pp. illus. $15)

Geology. *Through the Crust of the Earth* by Lord Energlyn. The author describes how volcanoes, underground caves, and veins of ore and minerals were formed. He examines the role the earth plays as a source of energy. (McGraw-Hill, 1973. 127 pp. illus. $10.95)

History of Science. *The Ascent of Man* by J. Bronowski is an informal history of science developed from a British Broadcasting Company television series. It encompasses a wide range of events and provides evidence of man's attempt to understand and use nature. (Little, Brown, 1973. 448 pp. illus. $15)

Inventors and Inventions of the Ancient World by Gordon C. Baldwin. Drawing upon archaeological evidence, the author speculates on how early man invented and used many tools to improve his skills in agriculture, hunting, and other activities. (Four Winds Press, 1973. 251 pp. illus. $6.50)

Lost Discoveries: The Forgotten Science of the Ancient World by Colin Ronan recounts both the scientific and the technical achievements of the ancient world as garnered from the study of tombs, clay tablets, and other artifacts. It ranges all the way from Roman taximeters to sophisticated astronomical and mathematical concepts. (McGraw-Hill, 1973. 126 pp. illus. $10.95)

Instrumentation. *The Changing Tools of Science* by Irving Adler explains in simple terms the principles of basic scientific instruments and how they are used. The coverage ranges from simple balances and pendulums to sophisticated radio telescopes, television cameras, and holography. (John Day, 1973. 158 pp. illus. $4.65)

Closing the Loop: The Story of Feedback by Stanley Angrist. The author explains the phenomenon of feedback and its use to control scientific, biological, and social processes. (T. Y. Crowell, 1973. 85 pp. illus. $4.95)

Measurement. *Thinking Metric* by Thomas F. Gilbert and Marilyn B. Gilbert. This is a self-teaching book on the metric system of measurement. It includes a section that deals with the United

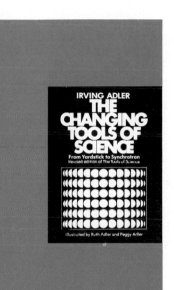

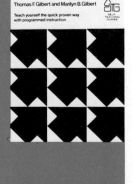

Books of Science

Continued

States proposed conversion from its present system to metric units. (Wiley, 1973. 143 pp. $2.95)

Medicine. *Fever: The Hunt for a New Killer Virus* by John Fuller. The story of the identification of a new and deadly disease, Lassa fever, its carrier, and its cure. The author also describes the process by which virus mutations and adaptations take place. (Reader's Digest Press, 1974, 297 pp. $8.95)

Natural History. *Desert: The American Southwest* by Ruth Kirk. A nature writer and photographer portrays the climate, plant, and animal life of Arizona, Utah, New Mexico, and California desert areas, and the ways in which life has adapted to this harsh environment. (Houghton-Mifflin, 1973. 361 pp. illus. $8.95)

Earthwatch: Notes on a Restless Planet by Daniel Shepard and Jean Shepard. This book describes many recent natural events that range in scope from volcanic eruptions, earthquakes, ice falls, and insect infestations to discoveries of lost tribes. It is based on reports from the Smithsonian Institution's Center for Short-Lived Phenomena. (Doubleday, 1973. 238 pp. illus. $8.95)

Humboldt and the Cosmos by Douglas Botting is the biography of the great naturalist who is listed as one of the 10 great contributors to the world's knowledge of America. He studied many aspects of biology and earth sciences and is credited with establishing the modern science of botanical geography. This is a Notable Book Award winner for 1973. (Harper & Row, 1973. 295 pp. $15)

Nature Atlas of America by Roland Clement. This book is more than a traditional atlas; it is a factual and concise survey of the plants, animals, and geology of North America. (Hammond, 1973. illus. $17.95)

Oceanography. *Arms of the Sea: Our Vital Estuaries* by Elizabeth Shepherd. Where sea and land meet there is a transition zone, with its own forms of life and ecology. The author describes this zone and discusses the problems caused by dredging, reclaiming, and filling in marshes and tidal flats with dirt and refuse. (Lothrop, Lee & Shepard, 1973. 160 pp. illus. $4.95)

Into the Ocean World by Ritchie Ward. This book recounts the work of the great marine biologists as they explored the seas of the world to find what lives in them and how ocean life is sustained. It was largely through their work, the author makes clear, that the science of oceanography was born. (Knopf, 1974. 323 pp. illus. $8.95.)

Physics. *Explorers of the Atom* by Roy Gallant. This is a brief account of the key roles played by researchers, beginning with the ancient Greek philosopher Democritus and extending into modern times, in expanding our understanding of the atom and its uses. The author also describes the techniques involved in looking inside the atom. (Doubleday, 1974. 79 pp. illus. $4.95)

Technology. *How It Works: The Fascinating Inner World of Everyday Gadgets and Mechanisms* by Rudolf Graf and George Walen. The book offers simple descriptions about the workings of common devices in the home, office, and factory. (Harper, 1974. 184 pp. illus. $10)

Zoology. *Golden Shadows, Flying Hooves* by George Schaller. This Notable Book Award winner is a popularized version of the author's previous observations on the mammals of the Serengeti Plain in Africa. He describes the behavioral patterns and complex life habits of lions, hyenas, leopards, wild dogs, and other mammals, and he comments on man's role in the African ecosystem. (Knopf, 1973. 287 pp. illus. $8.95)

Marine Mammals and Man: The Navy's Porpoises and Sea Lions by Forrest G. Wood. This is a nontechnical account of the U.S. Navy's work with porpoises, whales, and sea lions. It describes the capture, care, and training of these animals and their experimental use in performing various jobs. (Luce, 1973. 264 pp. illus. $7.95)

The View From Hawk Mountain by Harwood Michael. This is an experienced birdwatcher's commentary on hawks and other birds that he observed near a sanctuary in Pennsylvania. It is spiced with comments on the problems that arise from diminishing nesting areas. (Scribner's, 1973. 191 pp. illus. $6.95)

Walking Catfish and Other Aliens by Charles E. Roth. This is the story of creatures that are not native to the United States, how they immigrated, and their trials in adapting to a new land. They include rats, burros, horses, walking catfish, carp, gypsy moths, fire ants, and man himself. (Addisonian, 1973. 176 pp. illus. $4.95)

[Russel Shank]

Botany

Flowers of the crowfoot, or buttercup, family (Ranunculaceae) are generally described as having an indefinite or irregular number of sepals, petals, stamens, and carpels. This conclusion is not surprising, because most botanists think that many species in the family are ancestral relics of many of the more advanced flowering-plant families. Numerical irregularity in such primitive forms is expected.

Sir Edward Salisbury, a fellow of the Royal Society in London, demonstrated in May, 1973, that there is apparently a genetically determined numerical relationship among these parts. The British scientist found that flowers of the more specialized species and some subspecies within the family showed increasing numerical stability.

Oxygen and plant output. Bruno Quebedeaux and Ralph W. F. Hardy of Du Pont's Central Research Department in Wilmington, Del., reported in June, 1973, that below-normal concentrations of oxygen drastically reduce reproduction in certain plants. However, it results in greater vegetative growth of C_3 plants, so-called because the first identifiable product of their method of fixing carbon from carbon dioxide in photosynthesis is a three-carbon compound. It had little effect on the growth of C_4 plants, which have a more efficient carbon-fixing mechanism and produce an initial four-carbon compound.

For example, a 5 per cent oxygen level, much less than the atmosphere's normal 21 per cent oxygen level, prevented soybeans, a C_3 plant, from producing any seed, even though there was a 74 per cent increase in the plant's dry weight. Sorghum, a C_4 plant, produced no seed in a 5 per cent oxygen atmosphere, but there was no significant change in the plant's dry weight.

The scientists suggested that plants growing at high elevations, where oxygen levels are lower than normal, may produce less seed and fruit, but that they should be able to produce greater root or leaf yields.

Symbiotic evolution. At the University of California, Irvine, J. A. Hijner and Joseph Arditti showed in September, 1973, that orchids and a fungus that lives in the orchids' roots exchange vitamins,

"I want a plant I don't have to talk to."

Botany
Continued

or at least the chemical components of vitamins. The scientists suggested that such intimate root-fungus vitamin relationships may form the basis for a coevolution in which changes in one organism made possible related changes in the other. Their work confirmed the importance of the fungus to the orchid and demonstrated for the first time the importance of the orchid to the fungus.

Cell research. K. K. Nag and Herbert E. Street of the University of Leicester in England found that carrot cells grown under sterile laboratory conditions can be frozen, stored, then thawed and used. Carrot cells have long been isolated and grown in the laboratory for experiments in plant physiology. But like all living things, they often show genetic mutations over long periods of continuous growth, which reduce their usefulness in ongoing experiments.

Nag and Street froze growing cells in a medium containing 5 per cent dimethyl sulfoxide (DMSO). A highly effective cell penetrant, DMSO acts as a protective agent against freeze damage. Their best results, measured by cells recovered after thawing, occurred when cultures in DMSO were cooled at a constant rate of 3.25° F. (1.8° C.) per minute, stored for seven days at a temperature of −320° F. (−196° C.), and then thawed rapidly at the rate of 250° F. (120° C.) per minute. Between 65 and 68 per cent of the cells survived. Thus, the work may lead to the establishment of tissue banks of valuable experimental plant cells.

In November, 1973, Robert Cleland of the University of Washington suggested how auxin, a naturally occurring growth substance, causes cell elongation, which is essential to plant growth. Auxin affects the inner, main portion of the cell, but elongation requires an effect in the surrounding cell wall.

Using oat plants, Cleland found that the acidity of the cells increased immediately after he administered auxin. This rise, expressed as a drop on the acid-base pH scale from a pH of 6.0 to 5.0, occurs in a matter of minutes. Cleland says the increase in acidity is sufficient to account for cell elongation as described in the acid-growth theory. This theory proposes that auxin causes plant cells to increase acidity by excreting hydrogen ions, which induces cell-wall loosening and elongation.

Ancient cells. James W. Schopf and Thomas R. Fairchild of the University of California at Los Angeles reported in 1973 that fossil plant cells found in rocks in Boorthana, South Australia, showed the first clear evidence of eucaryotic, or nucleated, cells in the Precambrian Era, which began about 4½ billion years ago. The well-preserved fossils apparently include bacteria and threadlike single-celled blue-green algae, which do not have a nucleus, and several types of red and green algae, which are nucleated. The specimens, about a billion years old, should shed light on blue-green algal evolution, the diversification of microscopic organisms made up of nucleus-containing cells, and possibly on the emergence of the important evolutionary process of sexuality at a time when larger, multicelled forms of life were beginning to appear.

Cell diversification. Lois Nagy, working at the University of Arizona in Tucson, reported in February, 1974, the first known cell diversification within a single organism in Precambrian time. She found many examples of an organism in South African rocks dated at 2.2 billion years old. The fossil, apparently a blue-green alga, has segmented filaments interrupted by occasional large spherical or elongated cell-like structures. These resembled certain cells of various living species of blue-green algae in the genus *Raphidiopsis*.

Plant anatomy. The Casparian strip is a thickening of the cell wall in the root cells that form the boundary between outer cells and the inner fluid-conducting cells. Plant anatomists have long suspected that it prevents certain materials from passing from the outer root cells to the internal stream of fluid which flows upward toward the leaves. Gerry Nagahashi, William W. Thomson, and Robert T. Leonard of the University of California, Riverside, partially confirmed this theory in February, 1974.

They immersed the roots of 4-day-old corn plants in a solution containing lanthanum, an element which shows up well when it is viewed with an electron microscope. Microscopic examination showed lanthanum in the outer root cells and in the boundary cells. But they found that no lanthanum had crossed the Casparian strip to the inner cells of the young corn seedlings.   [Norton H. Nickerson]

Chemical Technology

A broad variety of new products, processes, and techniques developed in 1973 and 1974 attested to continuing efforts at applying chemical technology to many practical uses. However, energy-conservation efforts highlighted the work of chemical innovators.

Waste and energy. To conserve energy resources, researchers turned increasingly to ways of converting garbage and other solid wastes into methane (natural gas) and oil. Such reclamation processes can simultaneously solve two of the most serious problems in 1974, waste disposal and fuel shortages.

Organic solid wastes can be converted into gases containing methane by treating them with hydrogen gas, with bacteria, or with heat. Also, gas "wells" can be drilled in existing trash landfills, where natural decay produces methane.

One typical process for obtaining methane from municipal waste was proposed by Allis-Chalmers Corporation and Waste Management, Incorporated, of Oak Brook, Ill., in March, 1974. Magnetic and air separators remove metals, plastics, and other nonorganic materials from shredded solid refuse. The remainder is treated with growth-supporting nutrients and digested by bacteria for several days at 130° to 140°F. (50.5° to 60°C.), releasing about 3 cubic feet of methane for each pound of raw refuse.

Municipal sewage-treatment facilities normally produce methane-rich gases. Nevertheless, these gases are generally burned as waste. But engineers are now trying to use the gas. For example, a Los Angeles plant produces 4 million cubic feet of methane-rich gas per day, which is piped and burned as fuel in a nearby electric power plant.

In late 1973, the Wallace-Atkins Oil Corporation of Houston developed a method for turning garbage into oil, gas, and charcoal. Bacteria react with garbage in one container to form a fuel cell, which operates similar to a battery. A chemical reaction takes place, releasing electricity. The electricity produced in this cell then breaks water down into its component parts of hydrogen and oxygen. In another container, bacteria decompose garbage into hydrogen and methane. The methane is collected, and the hydrogen

Supral 150, a new aluminum alloy, can be molded as easily as plastic into a wide variety of objects and ornamental designs.

Ion Probe
Ends Flap
Over Map

The Vinland Map shows the world as mapmakers knew it in about 1440, with one startling exception—the large island in the upper left, labeled *Vinlanda Insula* (the island of Vinland). The circled numbers show where the investigators took the 29 ink samples that exposed the map as a fake.

In 1965, scholars from Yale University and the British Museum announced the discovery of the Vinland Map, believed to be the earliest map showing North America. They said the map had been drawn about 1440, some 50 years before Columbus discovered America.

The announcement aroused controversy among experts, and delighted people who thought it proved that Leif Ericson found the New World before Columbus. For a decade historians argued, but no one could prove the map either a genuine 15th-century document or a fraud. Yale University Library, which owns it, concluded that chemical analysis of the ink would prove its authenticity.

No one contested that the wormholed parchment on which the map is drawn is old. The ink also looks old; most of it is pale yellowish-brown, and not more than 5 per cent of it is still covered with black, the rest having flaked off. Initial tests showed that the ink did not absorb ultraviolet light like an iron gallotannate, the conventional medieval ink. The chemical identity of the map's ink thus became very important.

Yale officials discussed the map in 1968 with Walter C. McCrone Associates of Chicago, a laboratory specializing in ultramicroanalysis. The problem was to identify the organic compounds in the ink. These tests would require scraping a sample of the ink from the map. But the methods then available for organic analysis were too insensitive to test the amount of ink that could be spared. Three years later, however, the ion microprobe, a new and much more sensitive analytical device, became available. The ion microprobe is a type of mass spectrometer. It bombards samples weighing less than a billionth of a gram with a narrow beam of ions, breaking them into fragments, whose masses it then measures. Ideally, the structure of the sample can be deduced from the fragments.

In 1972, 29 such minute samples of the ink were taken from the map with a specially sharpened needle. The ion microprobe confirmed that the ink is not iron gallotannate nor any of many other medieval and modern inks with which it was compared. Scientists were unable to identify the ink.

Analysis showed several inorganic elements in the ink particles. These were examined more closely with an electron microprobe, an excellent tool for studying inorganic substances. The electron probe revealed that several ink particles contained high percentages of titanium, an element not discovered until 1790. Micro X-ray diffraction, a refinement of conventional X-ray diffraction, which identifies crystalline substances by the pattern of X rays reflected from them, showed anatase to be present, a crystalline form of titanium dioxide (TiO_2).

Anatase occurs naturally as a yellow-brown to black mineral. But a 15th-century scribe could not have obtained some, ground it fine, and added it to his ink. Ground anatase particles are much larger than the particles found in the ink. The transmission electron microscope, which is needed to resolve these particles, found that they have the characteristics of precipitated TiO_2 pigments, a highly sophisticated product of 20th-century technology. How could a 15th-century map contain precipitated TiO_2 pigments, which were not available before 1910?

Perhaps a restorer touched up the map with modern materials. Further analysis showed that this was not the case. All lines and legends are drawn with the same ink.

Anatase is used in making paper. Could the map have been pressed against modern paper and anatase transferred to the map surface? Scanning electron micrographs of fractured ink particles showed the anatase pigment embedded in the ink, not just on the map surface. Also, anatase was not found in the parchment.

The ion microprobe showed the thin black layer covering some of the yellow-brown lines to be soot, which must have been mixed with a liquid and drawn over the ink. Most of it then flaked away or was rubbed off to make the map look old.

There can be no doubt that Yale's Vinland Map is the work of a clever forger. The yellow-brown ink was applied first to simulate the faded appearance of old ink. The black ink was used to make the lines more visible and to simulate old ink lines.

There is, of course, considerable other evidence of the Norsemen's presence in North America hundreds of years before Columbus. But there is still no cartographic proof. Leif Ericson and his colleagues were evidently better sailors than mapmakers.   [Lucy B. McCrone]

from both containers is then applied to still more garbage in a process that produces oil, charcoal, and more gas.

More recycling. In March, 1974, the Niigata Engineering Company of Tokyo announced they had developed a process that may cure disposal headaches caused by plastic wastes. The process begins by crushing solid wastes containing plastics and removing all metals. The remaining plastics are further crushed, then combined and mixed with dried sewage sludge. The mixture is melted, kneaded, and molded into plastic shapes. The properties of the reclaimed materials fall somewhere between those of cedarwood and concrete. It can be used for all types of products, from bricks to furniture.

A process for recovering copper from mixed scrap metal was judged the best new idea in materials recovery at a competition held in London in September, 1973. Vandervell Products, Limited, Maidenhead, England, developed the new technique to solve the problem of separating copper from bronzed steel scrap.

The scrap is put into a steel cage that is immersed in a bath of molten lead saturated with copper and heated to about 1830°F. (1000°C.). The cage keeps the relatively light scrap from floating to the top of the lead. The hot lead dissolves the copper and tin that make up the bronze. But the steel remains solid at that temperature. So, when the cage is withdrawn, it contains only the steel.

To recover the copper, the bath is cooled to about 1742°F. (950°C.), at which point the copper solidifies and floats to the surface. Of course, the copper contains much tin and some lead when it is removed. But adding a small amount of pure copper to this mixture makes it suitable for use in bearings.

Water-recycling schemes have often been foiled by the high cost of treating waste water, particularly when it is necessary to transport the cleansed water to distant locations where water is scarce. In late 1973, developers at the Irvine Ranch Water District in Irvine, Calif., came up with a novel system, called Pressure Pipe Treatment, for overcoming both these problems. They built a 6½-mile-long pipe in which the water is both treated and transported.

First, the solids from screened raw sewage are treated with bacteria and oxygen. Then the sludge is recombined with the

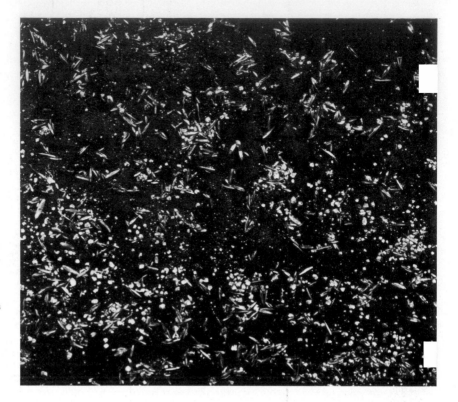

Sheets of water-soluble plastic containing seeds and fertilizer can speed up erosion-control and land-reclamation projects because their contents cannot wash away.

Chemical Technology

Continued

liquid portion of the sewage for the trip through the pipeline. Oxygen, air, or both, is injected at the start of the pipeline and at several points along its length to further break down and purify the waste components. One big advantage of the system is that it can get 15 times more oxygen to the sewage than can the typical open-air secondary sewage treatment. This is largely because oxygen is much more soluble in water under pressure, and the water must be pressured in order to move it through the pipeline.

Water taken directly from the end of the pipeline contains only microscopic sludge particles and would be suitable for irrigating forests or crops, such as animal feed, that are not intended for human consumption. But generally the particles are removed mechanically, and the water may be given further treatment, depending on how it will be used. Some of the particles may be recycled through the system. The rest is used for fertilizer.

Heat pipes, unique devices that transfer heat without using moving mechanical parts, such as blower fans, have taken on an expanded role in industry. Two lead-

ing manufacturers of heat pipes — Q-Dot Corporation of Dallas and Isothermics, Incorporated, of Clifton, N.J. — reported in September, 1973, that fuel cost and supply problems prompted increased inquiries from industrial customers.

A heat pipe is simply a cylindrical chamber, or pipe, sealed at both ends. Its inner walls are lined with a wicklike structure — several layers of wire mesh, for instance. The wick is filled with any fluid that transfers heat, such as liquid metal, Freon gas, or water.

When heat is applied to one end of the heat pipe, liquid evaporates from the wick. This produces local high pressure that drives the evaporated liquid along the center of the pipe to the other end, where it condenses and gives up heat. Capillary action of the wick, sometimes aided by gravity, pumps the liquid back to the hot end to restart the cycle.

In practical applications, a barrier can be placed around the outside of the pipe, totally separating two atmospheres outside the chamber. The barrier might be a floor or a wall through which the heat pipe runs. In this situation, hot gas could

266

be circulated around one end of the pipe. The gas would be cooled and the heat it gave up transferred to the other end of the pipe. This end, now hot, would warm the air or gas surrounding it. Hot waste gases from smokestacks could be used in this way to heat buildings.

One projected use for heat pipes involves the trans-Alaska pipeline and would require 100,000 pipes. Part of each pipe would be aboveground and part below to take heat generated by the pipeline from the ground so that the permafrost (permanently frozen ground) in which the pipe is to be laid remains frozen and stable.

In this operation, Freon or ammonia—liquids with low boiling points—would boil underground. The vapor would travel up the pipe, and condense in the part aboveground. Since this part of the pipe would be exposed to the Arctic cold, the heat would be carried away by the winter winds, ensuring that the ground remains frozen.

Magnetic liquids, curiosities 10 years ago, are finding practical applications. These liquids are created by adding tiny magnetic particles to a suitable liquid to form a colloidal, or nonsettling, suspension. Because they are so small, the particles do not settle out in gravitational or magnetic fields. Thus, when a magnetic field is applied, the entire liquid acts as a uniform magnetic material.

Magnetic fluids have many practical uses. They make good lubricating materials, because through the application of an outside magnetic force, they can be held longer in friction areas, prolonging the life of equipment.

The Avco Corporation's Systems Division in Lowell, Mass., has manipulated the physical properties of magnetic fluids by varying the magnetic field surrounding them. For example, they have artificially changed the fluids' densities. This determines which materials will float and which will sink in a fluid. Through such manipulation, two nonmagnetic metals or alloys put in the fluid can be separated. One will sink and one will float. Avco opened an experimental plant in 1974 to test the use of magnetic fluids in reclaiming nonmagnetic metals from junked autos.

Antistatic fibers. Polyester and nylon fibers that conduct electricity were introduced as a new product in 1974 by ICI Fibers, a division of Britain's Imperial Chemical Industries. The fibers, made by imbedding particles of carbon into the surface of a polymer filament, are used in manufacturing antistatic materials for such items as carpeting or industrial filter fabrics. Since the antistatic materials eliminate sparks, this is a significant contribution to industrial safety.

Agricultural applications. In July, 1973, Oceanography International Corporation in College Station, Tex., announced they had developed a microwave device that kills weeds and insect pests. The machine, called a Zapper, sends microwave energy into the ground between rows of crops to a depth of 2 feet and can cover up to 75 acres a day. It causes none of the toxic soil residues or pollutant run-off that comes from chemical herbicides and pesticides.

University of Minnesota scientists discovered a way to deal with thermal pollution and simultaneously improve agricultural production. They circulate spent cooling water from nuclear plants—which is heated to about 85° to 100°F.—through pipe buried about a foot in the ground. This transfers to the soil much of the heat in the water which might harm fish and cause excessive plant growth if discharged into lakes or rivers. It can also boost agricultural output. The added warmth in the soil provided by the piped hot water produces the greatest dividends in early spring and late autumn, sometimes allowing two crops per season.

Plastic pencils were scheduled for marketing in July, 1974. Companies in the United States, Japan, and West Germany have devised a substitute for the wooden pencil with its core of graphite lead. The plastic pencils have a shell of polystyrene or other polymers and "lead" made of a plastic and graphite mixture.

Optical fibers. Bell Telephone Laboratories announced in June, 1974, that their researchers had succeeded in creating highly efficient light-carrying glass fibers. These hair-thin strands, made of fused silica inside a borosilicate coating, are virtually free of impurities. They are capable of retaining two-thirds of the original light entering them over a distance of one mile. This is three times more efficient than previous fibers. This low light makes the fibers potential pathways for communication by light. See COMMUNICATIONS. [Frederick C. Price]

Chemistry

Chemical Dynamics. Experimenters put together molecular beam and laser techniques in 1974 to create a method for studying molecules formed in reactions resulting from single collisions. It promises unprecedented sensitivity and selectivity in characterizing the vibrations and rotations of these molecular products. With the details now accessible in such experiments, the chemical physicist can look forward to much more incisive tests of theories of reaction dynamics.

Richard N. Zare and his students at Columbia University developed the method, called laser-induced fluorescence. They formed the reactant molecules into two beams and crossed them in a vacuum chamber. Then they irradiated the reaction zone at the intersection of the beams with laser light from an organic dye laser. The laser frequency could be tuned over a band of energy. At certain energies the laser frequency was just right for the product molecule to absorb energy by changing to an excited electronic state. Subsequently, a molecule in this state returns to the unexcited state by emitting radiation. Experimenters can compare the intensities of the radiation arising from different vibrational and rotational excited states to determine the percentage of product molecules that had been in each.

Zare's group studied the reaction of beams of barium atoms with oxygen molecules, which produces atomic oxygen and the product molecule barium oxide: $Ba + O_2 \rightarrow O + BaO$. Laser-induced fluorescence revealed hundreds of vibrational-rotational states for the BaO molecules. The distribution of molecules in these states indicated that the reaction involves a sticky collision complex, which lasts long enough for energy to shuffle among the bonds before the products emerge. As few as 50,000 BaO molecules per cubic centimeter could be detected in a specified vibration-rotation state. This sensitivity is comparable to detecting certain colored Ping-pong balls among hundreds of other colored balls when the average distance between balls of the same color is about 2 miles.

Laser light is essential in order to achieve such sensitivity. It is almost a million times brighter than other laboratory energy sources. The laser light is also polarized, so the direction of its electric field can be varied. Thus, laser-induced fluorescence can also reveal the direction of translation and rotation of the product molecules as they emerge from the reactive collision.

The first tunable laser that operates over the energy range characterizing many rotational and vibrational states was announced in early 1974. See PHYSICS, ATOMIC AND MOLECULAR.

Breaking pairs of bonds. Most elementary chemical reaction steps involve breaking one old bond and making a new one. However, chemists have long been fascinated by theoretical questions about reactions which involve making and breaking two or more pairs of bonds in a single collision. In May, 1974, David L. King and David A. Dixon at Harvard University obtained some notable results on such reactions. They found in a molecular beam study that the reaction of chlorine molecules with bromine molecules, $Cl_2 + Br_2 \rightarrow 2BrCl$, is undetectable even at quite high collision energies.

This result confirmed recent theoretical and experimental work on similar four-center reactions — reactions involving electron clouds centered on four atoms. The theory predicts that concerted rearrangement of the electron clouds is strongly inhibited in such cases.

The same theory allows a six-center process in which the concerted making and breaking of three pairs of bonds is much less inhibited. Dixon and King found that a three-molecule reaction involving two molecules of chlorine with one of bromine indeed occurs readily at low collision energies.

In related work, King found that four-center reactions can occur if one or more of the participating bonds has a strongly ionic charge distribution so that there is almost no electron sharing in the bond. An example is the reaction $Cs^+ Br^- + I^+ Cl^- \rightarrow Cs^+ Cl^- + I^+ Br^-$, involving the strongly ionic cesium bromide and cesium chloride salt molecules and similar ones in which iodine and cesium are interchanged. Such reactions occur readily at low collision energies to form a sticky collision complex which vibrates and rotates many times before breaking up to form the products. At higher collision energies, however, the complex breaks up before the energy is shared by all the possible bonds. The Harvard group's results show that, for suitable electronic structures, reactions involving two or

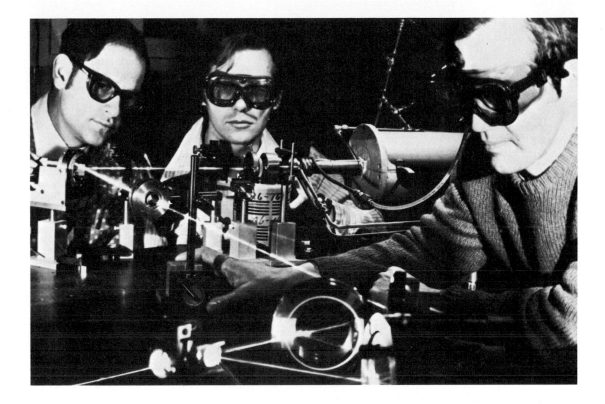

Chemistry

Continued

Physicists tune a laser they developed to generate coherent light in the far ultraviolet. The laser is well suited to aid in the study of chemical bonds.

three pairs of bonds can proceed much more readily than many reactions involving only one pair of bonds.

Surface catalysis. In June, 1973, Gabor A. Somorjai and his students at the University of California, Berkeley, demonstrated a promising new approach to understanding catalysis. Many reactions are made possible or speeded up in the presence of a catalyst, a substance which remains essentially unchanged. But until recently, most basic research has yielded contradictory results about catalysis of reactions at metal surfaces. A major handicap has been the lack of a technique to identify the active sites where catalysis occurs on the surface.

Somorjai's group directed a mixed beam of hydrogen (H_2) and deuterium (D_2) molecules onto a single-crystal platinum surface, which was kept clean by placing it in an ultrahigh vacuum. Some reacting molecules simply rebounded at various angles from the surface, while others formed the product molecule hydrogen deuteride (HD) on the catalyst surface. The researchers used a mass spectrometer to observe the relative abundance of H_2, D_2, and HD for various rebound angles and metal surface temperatures.

Monitoring the surface geometry of the crystal was a key aspect of the experiment. By diffracting low-energy electrons from the surface, Somorjai was able to select two different crystal faces. One face that the researchers chose to study was flat—all the surface atoms lay in a common plane. The other was terraced, with an ordered series of steps one atom high, separated by plateaus nine atoms wide. No HD product formed at the flat crystal face, but a large yield (about 10 per cent) formed at the terraced face. The rebound of H_2 and D_2 from the flat face showed that the molecules were simply reflecting from the surface like light from a mirror. By contrast, the scattering from the terraced face showed a broad range of angles, indicating large energy transfer. Somorjai measured time lags of a few milliseconds for the lifetimes of HD molecules on the terraced surface. His results provide clear evidence that the terrace steps are the active sites for catalysis.   [Dudley Herschbach]

Chemistry
Continued

Structural Chemistry. Crystal structures were determined for several proteins that play important roles in plant and animal biological processes. Called the iron-sulfur proteins, they participate in plant photosynthesis and nitrogen fixation—the restoration of nitrogen to soil by the action of nitrogenase, a protein found in the root nodules of legumes such as clover. The exact biological functions are not yet known for some of these iron-sulfur proteins, but chemists predict rapid progress now that they understand the structures. Moreover, they have synthesized inorganic complexes of iron and sulfur which mimic the iron-sulfur bond geometry in some of these proteins.

In these relatively small proteins (molecular weight as low as 6,000) an iron ion is bonded to one or more sulfur atoms which may be part of a larger complex. However, in this class of proteins the iron does not bond to a porphyrin ring as it does in such other biologically important proteins as hemoglobin and myoglobin that transport and store oxygen.

Rubredoxin structure. The simplest iron-sulfur proteins are rubredoxins, molecules that help move electrons throughout biological processes. They were first isolated from the bacterium *Clostridium pasteurianum* in 1965, and have since been found in a number of anaerobic bacteria. Rubredoxins contain one atom of iron (Fe) for every four sulfur atoms (S). Each S atom is located at one end of a long amino acid molecule called cysteine.

Lyle H. Jensen and his colleagues at the University of Washington in Seattle recently determined the structure of a rubredoxin molecule through X-ray crystallography experiments. They pinpointed the location of the molecule's nonhydrogen atoms to within 1.5 angstroms (A) (about 1/250,000,000 inch). They found that the four S atoms bond to the Fe atom to form a distorted tetrahedron of FeS_4 which has no structural counterpart in inorganic systems. The tetrahedral distortions—possibly caused by the cysteine amino acid side chains—may be responsible for the unusual oxidation-reduction (redox) properties of the molecules—the ease with which they give up (oxidation) or accept (reduction) electrons.

IBM mathematician David Sayre refines a map, based on X-ray crystallography data, of the structure of a bacterial protein called rubredoxin.

Chemistry

Continued

HiPIP's Active Core

- **Cys** Cysteine
- ● Iron
- ● Sulfur
- ● Inorganic sulfur

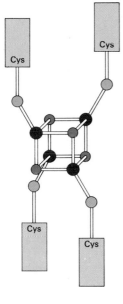

A cubical core is the active site in the high-potential iron protein, HiPIP, an iron-sulfur protein that resists oxidation by air.

In a second class of iron-sulfur proteins, iron bonds to otherwise unbound inorganic sulfur (S*) as well as to cysteine-bound sulfur (S) in the ratio Fe:S*:S of 2:2:4. Examples include the green-plant ferredoxins and animal putidaredoxins, both of which are involved in a number of metabolic processes. Although their active sites (the Fe-S*-S arrangement) have not been established by X-ray crystallography methods, spectroscopic evidence indicates that the two inorganic sulfur ions form a bridge between dissimilar FeS_2 units.

In August, 1973, Richard H. Holm and his associates at Massachusetts Institute of Technology prepared nonprotein analogues of the $Fe_2S*_2(SR)_4$ type, in which R is an organic group. Holm believes that these analogues closely resemble the active sites, or cores, of the Fe:S*:S (2:2:4) iron-sulfur proteins. He hopes that the proteins' redox properties can be understood by modifying and studying the inorganic analogues.

HiPIP. A third class of iron-sulfur proteins contains Fe:S*:S in a ratio of 4:4:4, as typified by high-potential iron protein (HiPIP). It has a high redox potential, and so, unlike the other iron-sulfur proteins, HiPIP resists oxidation when exposed to air. Joseph Kraut and his co-workers at the University of California, San Diego, identified HiPIP's active site as a central cubical $Fe_4S*_4S_4$ core, in which Fe and S* are located at alternate corners of a cube and an S group is bound to each of the four Fe atoms.

Holm also synthesized some inorganic models for this active site, and structural investigation of one such compound revealed the same $Fe_4S*_4S_4$ arrangement. Because Holm's inorganic analogues are more easily oxidized than is HiPIP, Kraut believes that the arrangement of certain complex ring structures along the sides of the core of the molecules play an important role in determining how easily the molecules transfer electrons.

A fourth class of iron-sulfur proteins is characterized by a Fe:S*:S ratio of 8:8:8. These proteins—the bacterial ferredoxins, for example—play key roles in metabolism based on fermentation and perhaps in nitrogen fixation. Jensen's X-ray crystallography group determined the structure of one such protein in June, 1973. They found that two $Fe_4S*_4S_4$ cores, separated by about 12 A, form the active site.

Many protein chemists believe that the cubical core may be the largest that will ever be found in the iron-sulfur proteins. If true, this information will prove valuable in determining the structure of larger iron-sulfur proteins such as the nitrogenase proteins responsible for nitrogen fixation.

Fertile possibilities. Such a breakthrough could revolutionize the manufacture of synthetic fertilizer. Nitrogen, an essential element for plant growth, can be resupplied to the soil by planting clover or similar legumes and then plowing these plants into the soil. But this traditional method of crop rotation has been largely supplanted by the use of synthetic fertilizers containing nitrogen in the form of ammonia. Consequently, most industrial and many developing countries depend on complex industrial processes run at high pressures and temperatures for making ammonia. They begin with hydrogen gas, usually obtained from natural gas, now in short supply because of the energy crisis.

Dr. Raymond Ewell, an authority on world fertilizer use, estimates that about $8 billion per year will have to be spent on new fertilizer plants, and $12 billion a year by 1980, just to stay even with the growing demand.

If it can be imitated on a large scale, biological conversion of water and nitrogen gas (or nitrogen oxides) into ammonia would ease this financial burden. But before this can be done, chemists must determine the roles of the large iron-sulfur proteins.

The group of iron-porphyrin complexes—heme proteins including the familiar hemoglobin and myoglobin—were investigated in much the same way. Biochemists study these proteins because of their important functions—for example, the transport of molecular oxygen in man. Extensive studies were carried out before it was dreamed possible that the proteins' molecular structures would someday be known. Yet, through the work of many scientists, especially Nobel prize winners Max Perutz and John Kendrew at the Medical Research Council in Cambridge, England, the structures of both hemoglobin and myoglobin are now known in fair detail. This information has considerably furthered our understanding of how these important biological molecules function. [James A. Ibers]

Chemistry

Continued

Chemical Synthesis. During 1973, three research groups synthesized simple models that closely resemble the active core structures of hemoglobin and myoglobin, important protein molecules that carry and store oxygen in the blood. These breakthroughs will allow chemists to study the core structures, called heme groups, without complications by the molecule's long protein chains found in nature. They might ultimately be able to synthesize hemoglobin substitutes for medical use.

The hemoglobin oxygen-binding core that researchers imitated contains tightly bound iron ions (Fe^{+2}) at the center of a heme group, a circular structure. Hemoglobin contains four such heme groups per molecule and myoglobin contains one. In both molecules, four of the six Fe^{+2} bonds are formed with nitrogen atoms in the porphyrin ring. The fifth bond forms with an imidazole group ($C_3H_4N_2$), which in turn is attached to a large protein chain. The sixth Fe^{+2} bond is formed either with an easily removed water or oxygen (O_2) molecule.

Imitating hemoglobin. Previous attempts to imitate the ability of hemoglobin and myoglobin to take up and give back O_2 in solution failed because the Fe^{+2} ion in the models was irreversibly changed to Fe^{+3}. But in August, 1973, Teddy Traylor and his co-workers at the University of California at San Diego reported synthesizing a myoglobin molecule model. It contains a simple porphyrin ring attached to a seven-atom side chain ending in an imidazole group. This arrangement keeps the imidazole group close to the bound Fe^{+2}, preventing its rapid, irreversible oxidation to Fe^{+3} by oxygen in the air. Oxygen could replace water at the sixth bonding position of the Fe^{+2} ion, and could be removed and replaced at will — an indication that this synthetic heme group was indeed imitating the ability of myoglobin to transport molecular oxygen.

Jack Baldwin and Joel Hoff of Massachusetts Institute of Technology synthesized a different type of Fe^{+2} complex in which the naturally occurring porphyrin rings were replaced by other molecules. They prevented the irreversible oxidation of complexed Fe^{+2} to Fe^{+3} by providing so much bulk that two such molecules could not approach each other in the presence of oxygen. Reacting a dilute solution of his complex with O_2 at −108° F. (−78° C.) in the presence of pyridine (which replaces imidazole), Baldwin produced a cherry-red solution containing exactly one molecule of O_2 per molecule of Fe^{+2} complex. He then showed that the oxygen binding was reversible by exposing this solution to low pressures. The O_2 was removed and the heme model regenerated.

"Picket-fence" model. James Collman's group at Stanford University created a similar model that absorbs molecular oxygen reversibly at room temperature. They prepared an unusual "picket-fence" porphyrin to replace the natural heme porphyrin. The term "picket fence" describes the bulky amide groups that stick out at right angles from one side of the porphyrin ring and prevent the close approach of two hemelike molecules, thus slowing oxidation of the reversible Fe^{+2} complex to its irreversible Fe^{+3} counterpart. Imidazole bonds to the fifth coordination position of the Fe^{+2} on the less-crowded side of the porphyrin ring, as it does in hemoglobin and myoglobin. By exposing a benzene solution of 1-methylimidazole and Fe^{+2} "picket-fence" porphyrin to O_2, Collman found that one O_2 molecule formed a coordinate bond with each Fe^{+2} complex. This compound can be separated as a red crystalline solid and studied by X-ray diffraction to confirm the exact nature of the reversible O_2:Fe^{+2} bond.

The work of Traylor, Baldwin, and Collman clearly shows that hemelike oxygen carriers must have bulky groups in the vicinity of the Fe^{+2} center to prevent irreversible oxidation to Fe^{+3} when oxygen is taken up. Also, imidazole, or a similar nitrogen base, must be attached to the Fe^{+2} before O_2 will form a coordinate bond with it. Apparently, the protein chains in hemoglobin and myoglobin provide both of these necessary functions simultaneously. In addition, the hydrophobic proteins create a pocket for the heme molecule which allows O_2 molecules to enter and exit freely, but prevents solvents from interacting with Fe^{+2}.

Xenon bonded to nitrogen. In June, 1974, Darryl D. DesMarteau and Robert D. LeBlond of Kansas State University reported synthesizing the first compound ever made in which the noble atom xenon bonded with nitrogen. The compound, fluoro [imidobis (sulfuryl fluoride)] - xe-

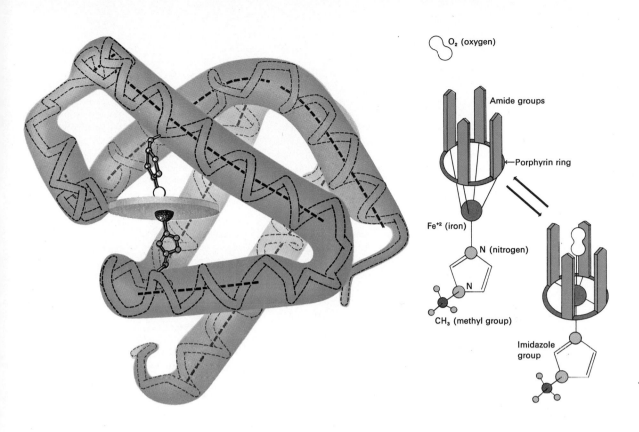

O₂ (oxygen)

Amide groups

Porphyrin ring

Fe⁺² (iron)

N (nitrogen)

N

CH₃ (methyl group)

Imidazole group

Chemistry

Continued

Imitating Nature

Chemists synthesized simple molecules in 1973 that can store and release molecular oxygen, as can the active heme core in myoglobin, *above,* a muscle protein. In the "picket-fence" model, *above right,* bulky amide groups prevent the close approach of two such molecules, thus preventing the iron's irreversible oxidation.

non, or FXeN(SO₂F)₂, is a white crystalline solid at room temperature.

It is made in a four-day process with the last step taking place at a temperature of 32° F. (0° C.) to prevent decomposition of the compound into xenon and fluorine compounds. The researchers reported yields of 90 per cent for their synthesis.

Prior to 1962, chemists believed that xenon and other noble gases such as argon or krypton would not form chemical bonds with any element because their outer electron shells were completely filled. That year, Neil Bartlett of the University of British Columbia synthesized a compound in which xenon bonded to fluorine, and since then numerous other compounds of the noble gases have been made. However, prior to DesMarteau's work, xenon compounds that were stable at above-freezing temperatures involved bonds with either fluorine or oxygen, not nitrogen.

The claim that a xenon-nitrogen bond was actually formed is largely based on an analysis of the compound's nuclear magnetic resonance (NMR) spectrum. The NMR spectrum is the pattern of radio-

frequency energy that the compound's fluorine atoms absorbed when in solution and placed between the poles of a strong magnet. The technique is widely used by chemists because it can be tuned to select one type of atomic nuclei, and the pattern it produces reflects their environments in the molecule.

DesMarteau's and LeBlond's NMR spectrum revealed two identifying peaks—one for the two identical fluorine atoms that were bonded to sulfur, and one half as large for the fluorine atom bound to xenon. Interactions among the three fluorine nuclei further split these two broad peaks into narrower ones. The chemists inferred from the splitting that a xenon-nitrogen bond was present.

DesMarteau believes that his finding may breathe new life into the field of xenon chemistry. Just 13 years old, the field has lagged because most of the xenon bonds with fluorine and oxygen have been discovered. Now that xenon has been shown to bond with nitrogen, researchers will be looking for other xenon bonds with carbon as well as with other atoms. [M. Frederick Hawthorne]

Communications The United States inched toward a domestic satellite communication system with the launching of Westar I in April, 1974. The Western Union satellite, stationed in orbit above the Galapagos Islands, was scheduled to begin telegraph service in August.

Expanded domestic system. The American Telephone and Telegraph Company (AT&T) and General Telephone and Electronics Satellite Corporation proposed in April, 1974, a joint operation of their domestic satellite communication system, scheduled to begin operating in 1976. Existing satellite systems are for international communication. Domestic communications rely on wire, cable, and microwave transmissions. The new satellite system will be better able to handle the expanding number of telephone calls and other transmissions. The system would consist of seven earth stations served by two satellites and a backup satellite.

Earth-to-satellite transmissions would operate at the 4-gigahertz (GHz) band and satellite-to-earth transmissions at 6 GHz. (A gigahertz is a billion cycles per second.) But because the 4- and 6-GHz bands are widely used for the already crowded microwave radio systems on earth, they are not ideally suited for large-scale domestic service.

So AT&T researchers are already preparing for the next generation of communication satellites that will operate on higher frequencies. The satellites being readied for 1976 will carry transmitters that will beam test signals to earth at 20 and 30 GHz. Scientists will use the signals, called beacons, to study transmissions at higher frequencies.

Not only do higher-frequency bands have more space for transmissions, but the area on the earth affected by the satellite's antenna at these frequencies can be quite small, no larger than one metropolitan area. This will allow the same frequency to be used in different cities without interference between them.

A problem is that rain and clouds affect transmissions at the higher frequencies in a way that scientists do not completely understand. Researchers will use the experimental beacons to find ways of overcoming this phenomenon. Scientists at

Bell Laboratories' new electronic blackboard transmits writing over a telephone line to a television screen, and costs far less than closed-circuit TV.

Communications

Continued

RCA engineer Paul J. Smalser displays the home-television antenna he patented in 1973. The flying-saucer design was hailed as the first major change in antennas since the early days of television broadcasting.

Bell Laboratories are building an antenna to receive the signals from the 20- and 30-GHz beacons at Crawford Hill, N.J.

Other space transmissions. An extraordinary feat of interspace communication took place in December, 1973, when the Pioneer 10 spacecraft passed within 81,000 miles of Jupiter, which was more than 500 million miles from the earth. Pioneer 10 transmitted pictures of Jupiter and such environmental information as the chemical composition of Jupiter's atmosphere and measurements of its magnetic field. It took 46 minutes for the microwave signals sent from Pioneer 10 to reach the receiving antennas on earth. See SPACE EXPLORATION.

An ambitious experiment in public-service broadcasting began in April, when the National Aeronautics and Space Administration (NASA) launched the Applications Technology Satellite (ATS). For about a year, the ATS will provide a variety of educational radio and television broadcasts to remote U.S. regions, ranging from Appalachia to Alaska. Then, NASA controllers will change its orbit to a permanent position over East Africa to beam programs to India.

Terrestrial systems. In late 1973, AT&T installed a new coaxial cable, the L5, between Pittsburgh and St. Louis that has three times the capacity of its forerunner, the L4 cable. The L5 can carry more than 100,000 simultaneous telephone calls through one cable containing 22 coaxials. A coaxial is a copper tube with a copper rod held in its center by insulating material.

Another new AT&T cable, the T2, went into operation in Texas. Like its predecessor, the T1, it uses a digital mode of operation. In digital communications, human speech is converted to a stream of 0's and 1's. These symbols are transmitted over wires, processed through digital computers, and converted back to speech.

The T2 system consists of a pair of specially insulated wires that can transmit 6.3 million bits of digital information per second. A bit is one 0 or 1. The system has four times the capacity of the T1 system, which is the mainstay of telephone networks in densely populated areas.

The Bell System conducted laboratory experiments with digital switching in 1973. In this type of call switching there is no permanent electronic connection between callers. Instead, streams of digital bits representing the information sent by many callers are fed into a switcher, a huge special-purpose computer. There the bits are sorted out and the correct streams are sent on to their destinations. This new time-division switching machine is the largest toll-call switcher ever made. It will handle more than 100,000 telephone lines.

Optical communications. Researchers continued to make very great advances in optical communications, transmitting signals on a beam of light through a fiber made of glass or quartz. Bell scientists announced in June, 1974, that they had perfected a highly transparent silicate fiber. Light guided by this fiber would lose only about one-third of its intensity traveling 1 mile. By comparison, light loses this much passing through an ordinary windowpane—a small fraction of an inch. See CHEMICAL TECHNOLOGY.

With methods now available for making low-loss fibers, scientists and engineers began concentrating on other problems which must be solved before optical communications can become a reality. These include how to control dispersion in a fiber, which causes a narrow pulse of light to lengthen as it travels along the fiber. This could cause a stream of light pulses traveling closely behind each other to overlap and scramble the information they carry.

Most fibers for optical communication have a cylindrical core and a surrounding layer, or cladding. The biggest dispersion problem in these fibers is the fact that the different components of the light pulse, called rays, strike at different angles where the core and cladding meet. The larger the angle, the longer the distance and time of travel. Therefore, the rays that strike at large angles fall behind, and the pulse lengthens. Even though all the light rays started in unison, they would quickly get out of step.

One solution is to scramble the angles by deliberately making the core material "bumpy" or the core-cladding interface rough, so that a ray of light bounces against the interface at many different angles during its travel. This helps ensure that all rays will travel about the same distance, arriving at their destination at about the same time—like mixing slow and fast lanes of highway traffic so that both lanes move at about the same average speed.   [Solomon J. Buchsbaum]

Drugs

The Supreme Court of the United States, on June 18, 1973, handed down decisions on five "drug effectiveness" cases that both strengthened and expanded the regulatory powers of the Food and Drug Administration (FDA). The unanimous decisions by seven justices—two did not participate—have been held by some legal authorities to constitute virtually a new drug law.

Specifically, the court held that the FDA can review all marketed drugs for their therapeutic effectiveness by class and apply the findings to all agents within that class. This includes the "me-too" drugs, those with similar characteristics. The court also endorsed the FDA's mass review for effectiveness of the nearly half a million drugs that are sold over the counter in the United States.

Perhaps the most far-reaching ruling was that the FDA has primary jurisdiction for administering the food and drug laws, and that its decisions have administrative finality. Recourse to court judgments in medical and scientific matters is not appropriate, the court affirmed, unless the administrative decision is found to be arbitrary, capricious, or unreasonable.

Only in time will we know the extent of the impact of these decisions, but clearly they will significantly affect the development and regulation of drugs in the United States.

Vitamin preparations. The FDA has acted to restrict the amount of vitamins A and D available for self-treatment without a prescription. Americans spend about $500 million a year for vitamin-mineral supplements. The new regulations limit vitamin A to dosages of 10,000 International Units (IU) and vitamin D to 400 IU for dietary supplements.

Both of these amounts are within the range of the Recommended Dietary Allowances established by the Food and Nutrition Board of the National Academy of Sciences—National Research Council, the recognized authority for determining vitamins and their nutritional requirements in humans. The action was prompted by reports of misuse of these essential substances for various medical problems, even though large doses may have harmful effects.

Most people receive adequate amounts of vitamin A from green and yellow vegetables, tomatoes, liver, egg yolks, and dairy products in their diet. Vitamin A is needed for normal growth and health, but excessive intake may result in nausea, dry and cracking skin, liver enlargement, bone and joint pain, and growth retardation in children.

Vitamin D is produced in the body by the action of sunlight on the skin and is also found in Vitamin D-fortified milk. It is necessary for proper absorption of calcium from foods.

However, larger amounts of Vitamin D can lead to weakness, weight loss, constipation, impaired kidney function, and premature calcification of the bones. High-dosage products will still be available through a physician's prescription for those persons who require supplements of these vitamins.

Chinese drugs. In late 1973, a visiting group of U.S. businessmen brought back *Chinese Patent Medicines,* an export catalog published by the China National Native Produce and Animal By-Products Import and Export Corporation. Among the remedies available in pill form are "essence of chicken with *Cordyceps*" (a parasitic fungus on insects), which "is efficacious to the lungs, to the sperm, and for the treatment of general weakness"; and pontocrin (made of deer antlers), listed in the catalog as "an effective remedy for neurasthenia, heart failure, impotence, loss of memory, lumbago, poor appetite, and malnutrition."

Also included are medicines from antelope and rhinoceros horn, tiger bone, ginseng root, the glandular secretions of bees, and a sugar-coated tablet "made from the placentae of healthy mothers." The latter contains female hormones and is suggested for the treatment of anemia and agalactia, the absence of milk in the breast after childbirth. These medicines are being studied by investigators to identify and characterize their active constituents pharmacologically.

In order to learn more about the use of herbs in Oriental therapeutics, the Committee on Scholarly Communication with the People's Republic of China sponsored a month-long trip to China in June, 1974, of 12 distinguished American scientists. Their visit took them to both traditional and "Western" schools of medicine, pharmaceutical manufacturing plants, and areas where the herbs used in making drugs are grown. A report and appraisal of their findings will be published and may be helpful in understanding the use

CHINESE PATENT MEDICINE

PEKING ROYAL JELLY （北京蜂王精）
(Oral Liquid)

INDICATIONS:
1. In cases of loss of body weight, loss of appetite, weakness after illness or childbirth.
2. Weakness in mental and physical energy, overtaxation, general weakness.
3. In chronic diseases such as liver diseases, rheumatoid arthritis, anemia, nodular phlebitis, gastric ulcer, degenerative conditions.
COMPOSITION: Each vial (10 c.c.) of oral Peking Royal Jelly contains 250 mg. of fresh Royal Jelly, together with Dangshen (Radix Codonopsis Pilosulae) 6 mg. Gouquzi (Fructus Lycii) 4 mg.
PACKING: 10 c.c. per vial, 10 vials per box, 48 boxes in a carton.
Manufactured by: PEKING CHEMICAL & PHARMACEUTICAL WORKS, Peking.

REN SHEN FENG WANG JIANG （人参蜂王浆）
(Liquid Tonic To Be Taken Orally) （口服液）

This product is scientifically and carefully prepared from Ginseng, specially produced in the Chang Pai Mountains, Northeast China, and the glandular secretion of bees as materials.
Rich in nourishment, delicious in relish, the product is suitable for anybody irrespective of sex and age with no harmful side effect. It is, indeed, a comparatively ideal nutrient and roborant in the present era
INDICATIONS:
1. Most efficacious for poor appetite, insomnia, neurasthenia, under-nourishment, and lowered energy.
2. Good for hepatitis, anemia, peptic ulcer, asthma and restoring the function of the stomach with a gastric ulcer.
3. Stimulating mental and restoring physical energy in case of under-growth, senility and debility after convalescence and childbirth.
4. Satisfactory for rheum arthritis and rheumatoid arthritis.
PACKING: It is packed in ampoules, each ampoule containing 200 mg. of Ginseng and 300 mg. of Royal Jelly. To open the ampoule, cut the neck with a file.
10 c.c. per vial, 10 vials per box.
TRADE MARK: Hsiang Yang Brand.
Manufactured by: THE THIRD PHARMACEUTICAL MANUFACTORY, Harbin.

GINSENG FENG WANG JIANG （人参蜂王浆

This product is mainly prepared from Ginseng — a specialty of the Chang Pai Mountains in the North east of our country, and the glandular secretion of bees — victuals for queen bees, supported with precious Chinese medicines: Radix Astragali, Cordyceps Sinensis, Radix Angelicae Sinensis, Radix Polygoni Multiflori, etc. It acts as a roborant, haematinic and sedative for the treatment of general debility, hepatic disease, gastric ulcer, rheumatism, falling off of hair, etc. Constant taking of it will extend one's life.

Drugs

Continued

A Chinese catalog lists the use and composition of patent medicines. The ones described, *above right,* contain royal jelly and other material secreted by bees, and ginseng, a root that Chinese doctors have used for many centuries.

and value of the many different herbs and plants found in ancient and modern Chinese medicines.

Drugs and athletes. Dr. Roger Bannister announced on Oct. 31, 1973, that a British research team at St. Thomas's Medical School in London, headed by Professor Raymond Brooks, had developed a method of detecting anabolic steroids. These body-building substances are used by athletes to improve their performance. Dr. Bannister is a former distance runner. In 1954, he became the first man to run the mile in less than 4 minutes. He is chairman of the sports council which sponsored the research project on the drugs.

Anabolic steroids, which increase muscle mass by promoting the body's production of certain proteins, are used in medical conditions where muscle wasting is a problem. However, it is believed that many athletes also take them, even though their use is against the rules of most sports competitions and may even be injurious to the athlete. There is evidence that large doses can injure the liver and reduce fertility.

The new test has been presented to the International Olympic Committee and other sports-governing bodies. It will make possible for the first time the detection of such drugs by spot checks of blood or urine samples from athletes participating in a contest.

New Drugs introduced in the United States in 1974 included:

• Blenozane (bleomycin), a new cancer-fighting antibiotic derived from a strain of soil bacteria. Effective in producing short-lived partial regression of certain forms of cancer in some patients, it differs from many other anticancer drugs in not depressing the bone marrow that forms blood cells. It thus may be useful if given with or between courses of treatment with other drugs.

• Aarane; Intal (cromolyn), a drug for the prevention of asthmatic attacks. The compound differs in its mode of action from other drugs used against asthma. It probably prevents the histamine release from special cells in the air passages that produces the symptoms of an asthmatic attack. It is not effective once an attack has begun. [Arthur H. Hayes, Jr.]

Curious youngsters who collect assorted aquatic creatures almost inevitably include tadpoles in their collections. As a result, they have watched the fascinating changes that the tadpole undergoes as it develops into an adult frog or toad. However, scientists know little about the population ecology of tadpoles, including their rates of growth and survival.

In the summer of 1973, ecologist George W. Calef of the University of British Columbia reported on extensive studies of a population of Red-legged Frog (*Rana aurora*) tadpoles in Marion Lake in southern British Columbia at the edge of the Coast Mountains. He used several techniques to count the tadpoles. In one case, he set up a network of traps on the lake bottom, and periodically counted the trapped tadpoles. He also put on scuba diving equipment and swam past selected points at which he counted tadpoles. In addition, Calef used a heavy metal box with a screen top and a sliding bottom which he dropped from a boat at random intervals. The box sank rapidly to the bottom, where it captured any tadpoles within the 1.82-square-foot (0.25-square-meter) area of its bottom. He shook the mud out through the screen top, leaving the tadpoles in the sampler.

Based on these techniques and a count of eggs, Calef determined that 300,000 tadpoles hatched each spring in Marion Lake. During the first three to four weeks after hatching, the number of tadpoles dropped to 75,000. The tadpole population declined less rapidly thereafter, until about 15,000 remained at metamorphosis, when the tadpoles begin changing into frogs. This occurs three to four months after hatching. During the two- to three-month metamorphosis, additional tadpoles were killed, mostly by predators, allowing only 1,200 to emerge as adult frogs.

To investigate the effects of several factors upon the growth of tadpoles and to study the impact of predators, Calef embedded enclosures in the bottom mud in shallow parts of the lake. These enclosures, about 6.6 feet on each side and about 6.4 feet high, were made of heavy plastic attached to an iron-pipe framework. Calef captured tadpoles, keeping some of them in the enclosures and taking some to his laboratory. He measured the body lengths of tadpoles living freely in the lake, those kept in the enclosures, and those kept under constant temperatures in the laboratory.

Calef measured temperatures where the mud and water meet at selected points on the lake bottom three days a week. He estimated temperatures on the other days by using these data. To study the effect of these temperatures on growth, he first estimated the degree-days experienced by tadpoles living in various parts of the lake. The degree-days were determined by taking the mean temperature for each 24-hour period over a given number of days, subtracting 4 degrees on the Centigrade scale per day as a correction factor (because tadpoles will not grow below this temperature). The only degrees used for calculations were those above 4° C. (39.2° F.). He then added the temperatures together for the four-month period from May through August. This came to about 800 degree-days for the various parts of the lake.

He then compared the degree-days with the sizes of captured tadpoles from the various areas. He found that the size of the tadpoles was strongly correlated with the total number of degree-days since they had hatched. Tadpoles raised in his laboratory at several different temperatures confirmed this finding. Those raised at 5° C. had the slowest growth rate; those at 20° C., the highest. Using these data, Calef found he could accurately plot the body length of tadpoles throughout the season.

He tested the effects of predation on the tadpole population by using plastic wading pools and two species of salamanders. The salamanders—*Taricha granulosa* and a larger species, *Ambystoma gracile,* or mole salamander—are voracious eaters of tadpoles.

Calef conducted controlled feeding experiments to determine how many tadpoles the salamanders could eat. He placed enough tadpoles in the wading pools to duplicate population densities at various parts of the lake. He then dropped in hungry adult salamanders and covered the pools with plywood to simulate the nocturnal conditions under which salamanders normally hunt. He allowed the salamanders to hunt for three hours, removed them, and examined the contents of their stomachs. Based on the analysis of the stomach contents, Calef estimated that the *Taricha* salamanders in Marion Lake consumed

Ecology
Continued

slightly more than 100,000 tadpoles and the *Ambystoma* salamanders about 48,000 tadpoles during the four weeks after the tadpoles hatched. This is about 75 per cent of the tadpoles lost during this period. The remainder of the tadpoles that died during this time were killed by fish and insects.

This study illustrated a number of important ecological principles. First of all, the rate at which the tadpoles were preyed on was related to their abundance. In the first four weeks after hatching, the salamanders ate about half of the 300,000 tadpoles. But the rate at which salamanders consumed tadpoles declined progressively between early June and late August as the tadpole population dropped from 75,000 to 15,000, about 5 per cent of the original population.

It also illustrated how evolution has shaped the strategies of natural populations. Substantially more tadpoles are produced than can survive. Although 300,000 tadpoles are born each year, only 1,200 grow to be adult frogs, the number needed to maintain the lake's frog population level. But the excess of tadpoles feeds other animals and so helps to maintain the ecological balance, or web of life.

Balance by fire. In recent years, ecologists have become increasingly interested in the role that fire has played in the evolution and maintenance of many plants and, indirectly, animals. Changes brought about by fire prevention, especially in U.S. national parks, may not, in the long run, be beneficial to the creatures that live there.

In the summer of 1973, ecologist Douglas B. Houston of the Office of Natural Science Studies of Yellowstone National Park reported on the historic role of wild fires in northern Yellowstone. He studied the past frequency of fires by counting and examining growth rings in cross sections of fire-scarred living trees. This enabled him to determine exactly when fires occurred. He selected the trees from areas known to have burned in 1870, 1886, and 1949, so he could determine exactly how old the trees were at the time of the known fires. He also counted growth rings on the charred remains of other trees and studied fragments of charcoal found at different levels in the

Cichla Dispersal in Gatun Lake

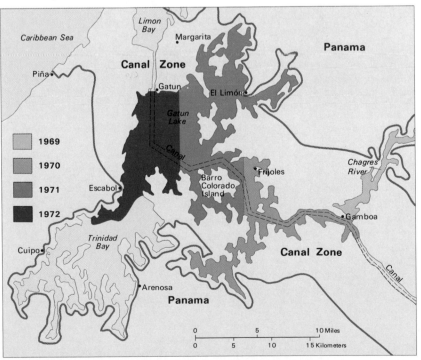

Chicla ocellaris, a voracious tropical fish, was accidentally introduced into the Chagres River in the Panama Canal Zone in 1967. A 1973 report showed it had destroyed most native fish species and had taken over much of connecting Gatun Lake by 1972.

Ecology

Continued

Sphaeroma terebrans, a 10-mm-long wood-boring crustacean, is boring into and severing the supporting prop roots of red mangroves on the southwest coast of Florida. The resulting destruction of these trees, which act as a barrier against ocean water, endangers the coastal ecosystem.

soil. Based on these data, he estimated that major fires occurred at intervals of from 20 to 25 years during the past 300 or 400 years in northern Yellowstone.

For the past 80 years or so, man has prevented frequent natural fires in this area of the park. Since plant life has not been burned out and replaced with new plants, some plant species have increased and others have decreased.

The number of aspen, an important forage tree for large animals such as elk, is declining in the park. Researchers once attributed this to the foraging of beaver or overgrazing by elk. But Houston suggests that the reduction in aspen is primarily caused by fewer fires. The present stands of aspen consist of large, old trees. Until the past 80 years, natural fires burned down such large trees, allowing great numbers of new ones to spring up.

There never has been good evidence that overgrazing by elk is responsible for the reduction in aspen. A deliberate reduction of 60 to 70 per cent in the elk population by killing animals or removing them from the park from 1955 to 1968 failed to increase significantly the number

of aspen trees. But evidence collected in areas where forest fires occur naturally suggests that many young plants grow only if they are freed from competition with old, larger plants.

At the same time, the long-standing controversy about a desirable size for the park's elk and bison herds continues. Houston believes that a more careful examination of the effects of fire on plant life and its indirect effect on these animals is needed before any decision can be made about the size of the herd. If fire is allowed to burn old trees so that many more young, edible aspen shoots can sprout, the park might be able to support more elk and bison. The U.S. government took an initial step in this direction in 1972 by establishing two large zones covering 301,340 acres in Yellowstone National Park where natural fires will be allowed to run their course.

Hurricane effects. Hurricanes are one of the great natural destructive forces that man has to contend with. We have ample information about the physical and economic damage to property, but little on the extent of ecological damage

Ecology
Continued

wrought by hurricanes. Ecologists Robert H. Chabreck and A. W. Palmisano of Louisiana State University reported in the summer of 1973 on the effects of Hurricane Camille on the marshes of the Mississippi River delta. The scientists, who had sampled this area in August, 1968, for a broad-scale study, were presented with a unique opportunity to study the effects of a hurricane when one struck the area in August, 1969.

For their study, the scientists surveyed the vegetation, soil, and water of the marshes at sampling points throughout the Mississippi River delta. They established 289 sampling points about a quarter of a mile apart along three north-south lines. Each point was identified by a marker clearly visible from the air. Using helicopters, they estimated the amount of vegetation and the extent of unvegetated areas — water or land — in a line extending 5 feet from the marker. They landed every 2 miles to collect soil and water samples and to measure vegetation and unvegetated areas.

They conducted this analysis three weeks after the hurricane struck in 1969

to determine the immediate effects on the vegetation, soil, and water. They visited the stations again one year later to measure the recovery of vegetation and changes in soil and water chemistry.

The hurricane caused a drastic reduction of vegetation, mainly through the sweeping action of wind and water. Plants were either uprooted or ripped apart and carried away by floodwaters. But the vegetation in the delta marshes grew back again rapidly. After one year, there were as many plants as before the hurricane. Plant life recovered more slowly in the ponds and lakes. However, the scientists' measurements indicated that total recovery would likely occur within two years. The amount of salt in the water increased because the hurricane swept seawater over the area; but it had declined again by the following year. This appeared to have little effect on the amount of vegetation growing in the marshes.

These findings suggest that natural ecosystems have evolved the capacity to recover from major natural catastrophes, which undoubtedly have always occurred at periodic intervals. [Stanley I. Auerbach]

Electronics

Complete, though primitive, computers in as few as four or five tiny packages were introduced in late 1973. They bear witness to steady advances in the technology of large-scale integration (LSI), the same technology that revolutionized electronic calculators. LSI is the ability to produce simultaneously thousands of interconnected microscopic electronic components on silicon chips.

The heart of such a small computer is the single-chip microprocessor, which basically consists of the central data processing unit common to all computers plus some control memory. Additional program memory plus input and output circuits for connection to peripheral equipment, such as magnetic tape readers or teleprinters, form the complete computer. Although limited and slow, these chip families cost under $50, far less than the $10,000-and-up price tag of more complex minicomputers.

The major difference between the microprocessor and its more expensive cousins is that the latter have logic circuits to control program sequences that are permanently wired into the computer.

These logic circuits, called gates, are relatively expensive and cannot be easily changed. Microprocessors use memory circuits rather than logic circuits to control program sequences. The commands are stored more or less permanently in devices known as read-only memories (ROM), which are much cheaper to produce than logic circuits. To change the control sequence, the designer simply replaces the ROM.

Low-cost computer power in this form can be used where digital computation was previously uneconomical. Microprocessors can be economically built into instruments that not only measure but also process the measured data; central control stations that control engine performance in cars to conserve fuel, diagnose malfunctions, and operate displays and safety equipment; retail store point-of-sale equipment that checks credit and totals the bill while entering data for inventory control; and traffic-light controllers that sense traffic-load changes and adjust the light timing accordingly.

Early microprocessors were capable of handling data and instructions in the

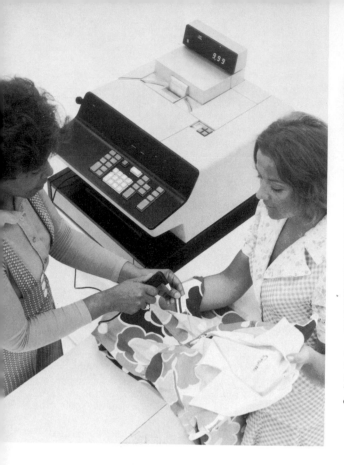

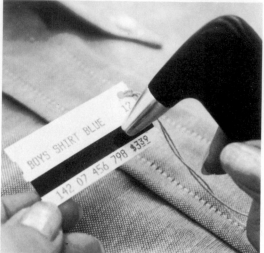

A computerized checkout system, *left,* computes the amount due, displays the price, and prints a cash receipt. A sensor "reads" sales information that has been encoded on a magnetic strip, *above.*

Electronics

Continued

form of words only 4 bits long. A bit is the basic unit of information in a binary digital computer. Subsequent 8- and 16-bit models now provide greater performance for more complex applications.

Although it is too early to assess the full impact of the LSI microprocessor, its potential is so great that many believe another revolution is brewing in the dynamic technology of electronics.

Solar energy. The 1973-1974 energy crisis triggered a serious, if not frantic, search for alternatives to fossil fuels such as coal and natural gas, and spurred interest in photovoltaic devices, or solar cells. These relatively simple devices, which convert light directly into electricity, have been ideal sources of on-board power for satellites and spacecraft. But, because they are costly to produce in terms of their power-generating ability, their use on earth has been limited to providing power for buoys, unattended lighthouses, and radio repeater networks.

Solar cells are made from layers of silicon about 10- to 12-thousandths of an inch thick or even thinner films of cadmium sulfide. Microscopic impurities in-

tentionally added to the silicon or cadmium sulfide create junctions of positively and negatively charged regions. Light shining on these junctions causes electrical current to flow. In practice, the devices are produced in panels or arrays, in which large numbers of the cells are connected together to produce the desired voltage and power.

Solar panels can be built into the roof to generate power for a building. One such system, capable of developing 1 kilowatt of peak power, is being perfected by the MITRE Corporation, Bedford, Mass. It is the largest photovoltaic energy converter ever installed. Its solar-generated electricity is used directly and also to break down water into oxygen and hydrogen in an electrolysis unit. These gases are fed into a fuel cell to generate electric power at night or on cloudy days.

Both the United States and Japanese governments have increased efforts to reduce the cost and increase the efficiency of solar cells. Most of the U.S. work is sponsored by the National Science Foundation (NSF) as part of a larger program to develop means of using solar

Supermarket checkout counter has a laser-light scanner that "reads" series of black bars printed on each package, *top*. Sales terminal then prints the name and price of each item on receipt, *above*.

Electronics

Continued

energy. One NSF official has estimated that solar arrays will be producing about 5,000 megawatts of power by 1990 and 20,000 megawatts by the year 2000. The Japanese effort is part of a multibillion dollar program called Sunshine, which is designed to provide clean energy and also eliminate the everpresent smog that plagues the islands.

Medical electronics. In a dramatic development, researchers at the University of Utah's Institute for Biomedical Engineering tested an artificial vision system that may eventually enable blind persons to move about unaided and read a conventional printed page. Although years away, this device would incorporate present-day technology such as a tiny microprocessor computer mounted in dummy eyeglass frames, a solid-state sensor located in an artificial eye, and a receiver implanted in the wearer's scalp. See NEUROLOGY, Close-Up.

Another dramatic medical electronics development allows doctors to, in effect, visually slice through a patient and examine the slice by using X-ray probes. Robert S. Ledley, professor of physiology

at Georgetown University Medical Center and president of the National Biomedical Research Foundation, developed a new X-ray scanner called the ACTA-scanner. Now in use at the university's hospital in Washington, D.C., it incorporates a computer that produces color representations of cross sections for any part of the body. This development allows doctors to see finer detail inside the body than conventional X-ray machines provide. For example, they can distinguish among such soft-tissue structures as blood vessels, muscle, and parts of internal organs.

The system operates by passing a beam of X rays the size of a pencil through the body from many different directions in a single plane. Sensors detect the emerging X rays and convert them into signals for the computer, which transforms them into color pictures. The pictures are immediately displayed on a TV monitor.

At Stanford University, James D. Plummer, James D. Meindl, and Maxwell G. Maginness developed a system called Ulisys (for ultrasonic imaging system), which permits cardiologists to observe human heart action. The core of the

283

Super
Switch

A phenomenon that only 10 years ago was purely a subject of basic research may soon make possible computers whose speed dwarfs that of fastest machines operating today.

For their discoveries about the phenomenon, Brian Josephson of Cambridge University in England, Leo Esaki of the International Business Machines (IBM) Corporation, and Ivar Giaever of the General Electric Company shared the 1973 Nobel prize in physics (see AWARDS AND PRIZES). The phenomenon, called electron tunneling, is the ability of electrons to get through seemingly impenetrable electrical barriers.

Electrons obey the physical laws of quantum mechanics rather than the laws of classical mechanics that govern the behavior of such "particles" as baseballs or planets. As a result, electrons possess wavelike features that enable them to tunnel through barriers that would stop them if they behaved like their classical counterparts.

IBM scientists announced in 1973 that electron tunneling between superconductors — metals which lose all resistance to electric current flow at temperatures near absolute zero — can be used to make electronic switches that could replace the transistors now used in computers. Cooled by liquid helium, such Josephson junctions switch at speeds of 5 to 10 picoseconds (trillionths of a second) and generate less than a millionth of a watt of heat during each operation. This is 100 times faster and 10,000 times cooler than present transistor circuits.

Giaever's experiments in the early 1960s showed that electrons could tunnel through a thin insulating layer between two superconductors in a way similar to that found earlier by Esaki in semiconductor junctions. Josephson then predicted that the insulating layer itself would act as a weak superconductor, allowing current to pass through without a drop in voltage, if it could be made thin enough — about 10 atomic layers thick. His theory also predicted that a small magnetic field would disrupt superconductivity and cause current flow to revert to the kind observed by Giaever in which there is a small drop in the voltage across the insulator.

These results prompted Juri Matisoo, a young IBM research physicist, to see if he could make a computer switch in which the presence or absence of the small magnetic field creates the two stable "1" and "0" states basic to binary computer logic and memory devices. He published measurements in 1966 indicating that such devices were indeed possible.

But two tough problems remained. First, Josephson tunneling occurs only through extremely thin insulating layers — usually an oxide of one of the metal electrodes — that are less than 50 angstroms thick (about 0.2 millionth of an inch). Since the amount of tunneling varies according to the layer's thickness, fabricating them repeatedly and reliably would be extremely difficult. The second problem was how to build up sandwiches of thin layers of metals and oxides that could withstand temperature changes ranging from near absolute zero to room temperature. The IBM announcements indicate that considerable progress has been made toward solving both problems.

Operation of Josephson superswitches at liquid-helium temperature is less of a drawback than it appears. At such low temperatures, chemical processes that cause most electronic circuit failures almost completely disappear. Moreover, the switches generate so little heat that the liquid-helium refrigeration needed is either available or in an advanced stage of development.

In today's computers, faster switching speed can only be obtained at the expense of heating the transistors. As a result, the transistors cannot be packed very closely together without overheating. But because electronic signals move between circuits at a finite speed, high-speed switching is defeated if the circuits are placed more than a few thousandths of an inch from one another.

Josephson junctions generate so little heat that they can be packed together as closely as desired. Basic computer logic and memory circuits built with Josephson devices have operated as expected, and there is a strong possibility that computers using Josephson switches may eventually be developed.

If so, meteorologists who need computers to process vast amounts of data on the earth's atmosphere, and many other scientists who also depend heavily on computer power in their work, will be able to cut their costly calculation time from hours to minutes using such speedy machines.   [Richard T. Miller]

Highly sensitive crystal can store hologram images as atomic patterns. Laser beams are used to enter and retrieve the patterns.

Electronics

Continued

system is an array of piezoelectric transducers, devices that convert mechanical vibrations into electrical signals, and vice versa. Electrical signals at a frequency of more than 20,000 hertz are fed into the array to generate ultrasound pulses. The pulses are beamed into a given region of the body. Echoes from tissue surfaces are picked up by the array, which converts them to electrical signals. They are then processed and displayed on an oscilloscope.

Solid-state TV cameras. Further development of charge-coupled devices (CCD) has led to practical all-solid-state television cameras. CCDs are relatively simple devices that resemble LSI transistors. They can also be produced as very small, very dense arrays. When one side of the array is exposed to light, packets of charge accumulate in the individual devices. The amount of charge depends on the light intensity at each point. With appropriate circuitry, the charges can be transferred from one device to the next and out of the array a line at a time, producing a scanning effect similar to that of television camera tubes.

In August, 1973, Fairchild Camera and Instrument Corporation, Syosset, N.Y., announced the first commercial solid-state camera, the MV-100. About the size of a cigarette pack, it produces black-and-white images and is designed for closed-circuit TV applications that do not require the high-quality picture dictated by broadcast standards. It produces about 80 horizontal TV lines per picture, compared with the conventional 525 lines of broadcast cameras. The active sensor consists of 10,000 CCD elements.

Fairchild's MV-100 was followed in February, 1974, by even better performing experimental CCD cameras developed by scientists at Bell Laboratories, Murray Hill, N.J., for projected Picturephone service. The Bell cameras had six times the resolution of the Fairchild unit, and both black-and-white and color units were assembled. In March, RCA Corporation announced it had developed a CCD camera that could equal a conventional broadcast camera in performance. It uses a 512- by 320-element array on a silicon chip that is 500- by 750-thousandths of an inch. [Samuel Weber]

Energy

The Arab oil embargo of late 1973 and early 1974 prompted the U.S. government to take steps ensuring that the nation would not become too dependent on foreign oil. In November, 1973, President Richard M. Nixon announced Project Independence, a national commitment to making the United States self-sufficient in energy production. The Nixon Administration set up two new agencies, the Federal Energy Administration and the Energy Research and Development Administration, to help achieve the U.S. energy goal by 1980.

Oil beneath the deeps. Oil companies believe that large oil deposits exist off the Atlantic Coast in water more than 600 feet deep. This is too deep for development with existing technology, so Exxon and Mobil Oil companies are developing new drilling techniques. In one, workers drill from inside a man-made bubble installed on the ocean floor. When the drilling is completed at one site, the bubble is moved to a new location. Oil is pumped out of these wells by electrically driven equipment fed by power cables dropped down from the surface.

Pumping wells dry. As it becomes more difficult to find and produce oil from remote fields, oil companies are considering relatively costly methods of recovering the remaining oil from existing fields in which productivity has declined. The companies have been investigating these recovery methods in their laboratories for more than 20 years and have been conducting limited field tests since the early 1960s. The potential is enormous, because only about one-fourth of the oil in existing wells has been recovered. These still hold almost 300-billion barrels, a 70-year supply at today's usage rate.

When a new reservoir is first tapped, expanding gas trapped above the oil or pressure from water beneath it drive the oil to the surface. This natural pressure decreases as oil is taken out, and the so-called primary production of oil declines. From 5 to 25 per cent of the oil in the reservoir is recovered this way.

Secondary oil production begins at this point. Water injected into the reservoir pushes more oil to the surface. Eventually, however, the water-flood process be-

"Now look who's wasting watts!"
Drawing by Alan Dunn; © 1972 The New Yorker Magazine, Inc.

Experimental aluminum power cable, chilled to −320° F. by liquid nitrogen in surrounding pipe, transmitted up to 435,000 volts of electricity. It marked a further step toward proving the practical use of low-resistance, supercold cables for high-power transmission.

Energy

Continued

comes too costly in relation to the value of the oil produced. By that time, water usually makes up more than 90 per cent of the oil and water mix, the oil is more viscous (sticky) than the original oil mixture, and water channels cut into the surrounding rock may allow injected fluids to by-pass much of the remaining oil in the reservoir.

So, tertiary, or third-level, processes are being designed to overcome these problems. To make the oil less sticky and immobile, carbon dioxide (CO_2) can be injected into the reservoir and dissolved in the oil. The CO_2 thins the oil so that a higher percentage of it is contained in the oil and water mixture pumped out of the well. Shell Oil Company has been testing this process since 1972 at the Crossett field in west Texas. Although it is too early to know how much extra oil can be recovered in this CO_2 injection test, company officials report that results are encouraging.

Other recovery processes. A "slug" of special liquid can be injected into a well, and it will form a viscous layer when it encounters the oil. Water is used to push this slug layer through the reservoir, sweeping the oil ahead of it. Esso Production Company uses a caustic solution as a slug to recover acidic crude oils at a field in southeast Texas. A thick emulsion forms a slug layer when the acidic oil meets the caustic liquid, allowing the water to force the oil out.

Micellar fluids, emulsions of petroleum sulfonate and brines, thin out thick crude oil so that it can more easily be forced to the surface. Field tests of a process developed by the Marathon Oil Company on the Bradford field in Pennsylvania indicate that from 35 to 60 per cent of the oil left in the reservoir can be recovered after injecting micellar fluid.

Heat, which thins out oil, is also used to make it easier to recover. Mobil Oil Company is using a steam-injection process at one of its oil fields in California. Treating the oil with steam has increased production three to four times. Mobil extracted an additional 3 million barrels of oil from this field by injecting 11 million barrels of steam into its wells.

In another heat-treatment process, a fire is set in the well and air is injected to

Energy

Continued

France's breeder reactor atomic power plant near Tours, first of its kind in the West, was linked up with the French electric power system in December, 1973.

keep it-burning. The hot combustion gases drive oil to the surface. Gulf Research and Development Company has been operating such a "fire-flood" at the Miga field in eastern Venezuela since 1964. As of 1974, Gulf had recovered more than twice as much oil by the process than by primary production.

Laboratory fusion. On May 13, 1974, KMS Industries, Inc., of Ann Arbor, Mich., announced success in using a laser to achieve nuclear fusion in the laboratory. The fusing of two hydrogen-isotope nuclei to form one helium atom is the same reaction used to explode hydrogen bombs. Unlike fission, or atom splitting, scientists have had difficulty producing the fusion reaction for controlled, peaceful uses because temperatures of more than 100 million degrees are needed for the reaction.

The KMS scientists used a laser beam to heat a pellet of the hydrogen isotope deuterium enough to release high-energy neutrons. Although the reaction was brief, an Atomic Energy Commission spokesman described it as a significant step toward achieving laser-fusion power.

Unique solar collector. In January, the National Science Foundation awarded physicist Roland Winston of the University of Chicago and the Argonne National Laboratory $500,000 to develop a new type of solar light collector. The Winston collector consists of rows of deep, curved trenches lined with a reflective film. Sunlight passing over the trenches is concentrated at the narrow bottom and the heat produced is converted to energy.

The Winston collector can produce about 1 kilowatt for every 3 square feet of collecting surface. Other solar collectors have proved impractical because they are less efficient. Also, other collectors must employ complex tracking equipment to follow the motion of the sun. But the troughs of the Winston collector allow the sunlight to follow the curves of the collector. The new solar collector is efficient enough at harnessing the sun's energy to be used for either heating or cooling individual buildings or for operating electric power plants. See CHEMICAL TECHNOLOGY; CAN COAL MAKE A COMEBACK?; NUCLEAR POWER: HOW GREAT IS THE RISK? [Darlene R. Stille]

Environment

Two national concerns, energy and the environment, met head-on in 1973 and 1974. Automobile companies, electric power companies, and oil companies launched massive advertising and lobbying campaigns to ease pollution regulations as deadlines set by the federal Clean Air Act approached. They cited the apparent shortage and rising prices of all fuels as reasons to use some of the "dirtier" fuels and ease up on antipollution equipment, which adversely effects fuel efficiency.

The Middle East war in October, 1973, followed by the Arab oil embargo, created a sudden crisis for the United States and other nations. But fuel supplies, particularly petroleum products, had been slowly declining before that. The source of the shortage was not a lack of oil in the ground, but a reluctance on the part of the major oil companies to do further drilling and to build more refineries in the United States.

Exploration for natural gas, its price kept low by government regulation, had fallen off even earlier. Oil and gas companies claimed they made too little money on U.S. operations, and were forced to invest heavily abroad.

Critics accused the oil companies of a giant blackmail plot. Several state governments and the Federal Trade Commission filed lawsuits that charged collusion among the big oil companies to restrict oil supplies and drive up prices.

Drive against air laws. Whatever its causes, the fuel shortage provided ammunition for a massive attack on clean-air laws. Auto companies claimed that cleaning up car emissions would be too costly and would waste fuel. Power companies advertised that they would have to burn coal, which is more polluting.

Oil companies persuaded Congress to permit construction of the Alaska pipeline to carry oil from Alaska's North Slope for shipment to ports on the West Coast. Opponents continued to charge that the pipeline was ill-conceived, and that the oil would go to Japan, at better prices, rather than to the United States.

Advertising campaigns attacked efforts to clean up the air, restrain offshore oil drilling, and regulate oil refineries. In response to great pressure, Congress con-

As no-deposit, no-return containers are laid to rest in Oregon, few mourners are present. A state law reducing the containers' use sharply cut roadside litter and saved energy used in making them.

Environment

Continued

sidered permitting automakers to defer cleaning up exhausts for at least another year, allowing more extensive use of coal, and easing federal pressure on individual states to enact effective air-pollution-control laws.

Atomic ace in the hole. Among those most eager to take advantage of the fuel shortage were the nuclear power industry and the U.S. Atomic Energy Commission (AEC). Nuclear power plants, which are fueled with uranium, were hailed as the answer to energy problems. The government called for a speed-up in nuclear plant construction, which has been bogged down by safety, labor, and cost problems and opposition from environmentalists. The Federal Energy Administration and the AEC proposed easing licensing procedures for nuclear plants. But most observers felt there was little possibility of building the plants faster.

Financial difficulties, caused in part by rising oil prices, led several utilities to delay existing orders for nuclear power plants. The AEC reduced its estimate of the nuclear power that would be available in 1980 by about one-third.

President Richard M. Nixon and the AEC had in previous years announced that a new type of nuclear power plant, the liquid metal-cooled fast-breeder reactor (LMFBR), would have the government's highest energy priority. The LMFBR was hailed as the solution to the nation's energy problems. Nearly all of the nation's power production, according to the AEC, would eventually come from the new reactors.

LMFBRs recycle a portion of their fuel, turning otherwise wasted uranium into plutonium, a man-made element that can be used as fuel. They would make even more fuel than they burned, and would lessen the need for fossil fuels and uranium, also expected to be in short supply.

Slower track for fast breeder. The Congress had already authorized funds for a commercial-size prototype LMFBR, to be built by private industry. In June, 1973, however, a federal appeals court dealt a blow to the LMFBR program in a suit brought by the Scientists' Institute for Public Information (SIPI). The suit argued that the National Environmental Policy Act of 1970 required the AEC to

Environment

Continued

issue a statement of the costs and benefits of the LMFBR program and seek the comments of other federal and state agencies and the public.

The appeals court ruled in favor of SIPI and gave the AEC one year to draw up its statement. This was the first time a federal agency had been forced to make a public evaluation of a technological program at the research and development stage. The decision was hailed by environmentalists as an important precedent in the evaluation of new federal programs.

In March, 1974, the AEC issued a draft of its "environmental impact statement" for the LMFBR program. But the draft was condemned as "inadequate" by the U.S. Environmental Protection Agency (EPA) at hearings held from April 14 to 16, 1974. SIPI and the National Resources Defense Council termed the draft "frivolous," and called for the AEC to submit a better document.

The beleaguered AEC asked the court for an extension of the original June 14 deadline for the impact statement. An indefinite extension was granted.

High stakes. The government's major energy program faces some of the most serious charges of environmental hazard ever leveled against an industry. Opponents claim that the LMFBR fuel, because it contains plutonium in large quantities, could be used illegally to make nuclear weapons. This is not true of the fuel in existing nuclear plants. Because the LMFBR can undergo uncontrolled nuclear reactions of the kind that occur in weapons, there is also the possibility that a flaw in the reactor or an accident could set off a small nuclear explosion inside the LMFBR plant, thus releasing large amounts of radiation.

Critics also pointed to the large quantities of plutonium, one of the most toxic and hazardous materials known, that would have to be processed and shipped around the country. They also argued that adequate plans for storing the intensely radioactive wastes produced in the plants have not been made and that the AEC's calculations of the benefits to be derived from the development of the LMFBR were inaccurate, biased, and unreliable. See NUCLEAR POWER: HOW GREAT IS THE RISK?

The fundamental issue raised by critics of the LMFBR is central to the dispute over energy and the environment: Is a simple reliance on nuclear energy and constantly expanding energy production the answer to the problem? Or should the United States have a more comprehensive energy policy?

Conservation measures could substantially moderate, and even reduce, energy demand without working hardship on the population. A slower rate of growth in the energy industries would allow time to develop cleaner, less hazardous energy supplies, such as solar energy. Without a comprehensive energy policy, however, the conflict between national energy needs and environmental quality is likely to continue.

Common plastic, rare cancer. In January, 1974, the federal Center for Disease Control in Atlanta, Ga., published a report that three workers in a Louisville, Ky., chemical plant that makes vinyl chloride had died of angiosarcoma, an extremely rare form of liver cancer. This was far too many to have developed the disease by chance. Vinyl chloride is the basic component of the common polyvinyl chloride, or PVC, plastics found in products ranging from flooring material to false teeth.

Subsequent reports quickly identified more than 20 other cases of the rare disease among vinyl chloride workers at other plants, and the connection between the chemical and the liver cancer is considered established.

At an emergency meeting in New York City in May, scientists told the New York Academy of Sciences and the American Cancer Society that vinyl chloride was also implicated in a variety of other diseases and symptoms, including disturbances of the blood, liver, and spleen; bone irregularities; and impotence. In April and May of 1974, the Food and Drug Administration and the EPA moved to ban aerosol spray cans and other consumer products that use vinyl chloride gas. The EPA is now investigating whether vinyl chloride gas has affected people who live near chemical plants.

Chemical and Engineering News magazine revealed on May 20, 1974, that experiments showing the cancer-causing potential of vinyl chloride were conducted by the chemical industry in 1972 and 1973, but the results of the study were not released to the public until February, 1974.   [Sheldon Novick]

Genetics

In October, 1973, Seymour Abrahamson, Michael Bender, Alan Conger, and Sheldon Wolff of the universities of Wisconsin, Johns Hopkins, Temple, and California at San Francisco, respectively, discovered a pattern: The genetic effects of radiation in different animals and plants are strictly proportional to the amount of deoxyribonucleic acid (DNA) contained in their cells. DNA is the chemical of which genes are composed.

X rays and other forms of radiation pierce through cells like tiny arrows shot from miniature bows and often cause chemical changes in molecules in their paths. In genes, such chemical changes are called mutations; they are permanent, inheritable, and almost always harmful. Because people are exposed to many different sources of radiation—some is naturally present, some lingers in the atmosphere from previous nuclear bomb tests, more comes from routine medical and dental X-ray examinations—it is important to know how many mutations are caused by a given amount of radiation.

Mutations that occur in the cells that give rise to eggs and sperm are of greatest concern, because these can be passed from parent to child for many generations. Experiments that produce mutations in humans are unthinkable, so scientists have studied such organisms as bacteria, yeasts, fruit flies, mice, tomatoes, and barley in the hope that their findings might also apply to humans. In the past this has seemed impossible, because radiation causes more mutations in some species than in others; the same radiation is 100 times more likely to produce mutations in mice than it is in yeast, for example. But, the scientists found, mouse cells contain 100 times as much DNA as yeast.

Abrahamson and his co-workers performed little or no laboratory work in making their discovery. Almost all the data already existed in various journals and reports, but no one had thought of assembling gene-mutation rates and comparing them to DNA amounts for various species. When they had drawn up their comparative tables, only one piece was missing—the mutation rate in yeast, which had never before been measured. The scientists predicted the figure for yeast from the patterns they saw in their work. A yeast researcher verified it.

Because this relationship has been observed in all animals and plants examined so far, it is also likely to be true in humans. Consequently, the genetic effects of radiation in humans can now be predicted with much more confidence.

Behavioral mutations. Early in 1973, Yoshiki Hotta and Seymour Benzer of the California Institute of Technology in Pasadena developed a method to locate the site of action of mutations affecting fruit fly behavior.

The fruit fly is one of the most useful animals for studies of how genes influence behavior. It has long been a favorite of geneticists because of its hardiness when cultured in the laboratory, its short reproduction time, and its great reproductive ability. Many behavioral mutations have now been bred into strains of these flies. Some of these mutations cause the legs to quiver when the animals are anesthetized; others cause staggering, uncoordinated movement, and premature death. Finding out how these mutations cause the abnormal behavior should reveal more about the structure and function of the nervous system. The first step is to determine where the mutated gene exerts its effect. This can be very difficult.

In the case of the mutation that causes leg quivers, for example, the defect could be in the brain or in nerves connecting the brain to the legs. It could be in the bundles of nerves located near the legs, or in the nerves or muscles of the legs.

The new localization technique is based on the way a fly develops from the fertilized egg. Early cell divisions in the fertilized egg form a flat, oval sheet of cells called the blastoderm. Certain regions of the blastoderm are destined to become specific structures in the adult fly. The right eye will develop from one site, the left eye from another, the left and right halves of the brain from still others. The locations of many of these sites are known. For example, the sites that become the legs are close to each other near the center of the blastoderm but rather far from those that become the brain.

Hotta and Benzer employ a special breeding program that produces flies with genetically different kinds of cells. Half the cells in these animals are normal; the other half carry both a behavioral mutation and a mutation that affects body color. External parts that develop from normal cells will have normal color; from mutant cells, abnormal color.

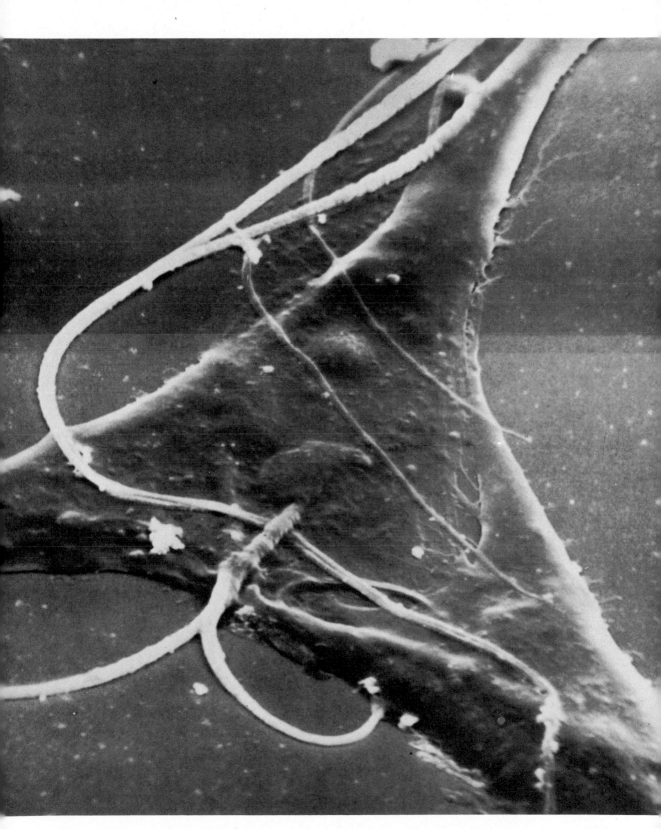

Genetics

Continued

The blastoderm of these flies is half normal and half mutant, but the dividing line between the halves can cut through the blastoderm in any one of a variety of ways, like a random slice across a pie. The farther apart two sites on the blastoderm are, the more likely it is that a slice will occur between them. Consequently, the farther apart two sites on the blastoderm are, the more likely the adult structures that arise from these sites will be genetically different. Two adjacent legs differ in color only 10 per cent of the time, for example, because their sites are close together on the blastoderm. But the rear legs and the head differ in color about half the time because their blastoderm sites are far apart.

Therefore, by finding out which structures in the adult must be the mutant color for abnormal behavior to be expressed, the site of the mutation's action can be identified. Whether internal organs are normal or mutant can be determined by examining the color of external structures that arise from nearby sites.

Hotta and Benzer have used this procedure successfully in several cases. The quivering legs result from abnormalities in the nerve masses located near each leg and not from abnormalities in the brain or legs themselves. The staggering, uncoordinated behavior of other flies results from degeneration of brain cells.

Gene regulation. Great efforts are being made to understand how genes are turned on and off. The regulation of the genes permitting digestion of lactose (milk sugar) in the common intestinal bacterium, *Escherichia coli,* has been studied particularly closely. The key is a protein, called the repressor, which can attach to a gene called the lacO gene, preventing production of the digestive enzymes. A big step has been taken toward finding out how the repressor attaches to the lacO.

In 1973, Konrad Beyreuther, Klaus Adler, Norbert Geisler, and Alex Klemm of Cologne University determined the sequence of the 347 amino acids in the repressor. At the same time, Harvard University researchers have determined the sequence of 27 nucleotides (DNA building blocks) in the lacO gene. See BIOCHEMISTRY.   [Daniel L. Hartl]

Geoscience

Geochemistry. Pictures of the planet Mercury, returned by Mariner 10 in 1974, greatly advanced geochemical knowledge of the solar system. The pictures reveal many features similar to those seen on the moon, including craters, rays, ridges, plains, and scarps (steep slopes). From a geochemical standpoint, the most significant findings were basins that were flooded by lavas. The largest basin is about 810 miles (1,300 kilometers) in diameter.

All the flooded basins appear to be exactly like the lunar maria, and they have similar crater densities. The crater density data suggests that the lavas on Mercury and the moon are about the same age, the Mercury lavas originating early in the history of that planet.

It is now also apparent from gravity data that Mercury is a chemically differentiated planet. That is, the rocks of the planet have become separated into chemical forms that are different from the original planetary mass. Therefore the planet must have existed for a long time and have undergone a series of evolutionary changes since it was formed. The same is true, of course, of the moon, and scientists have evidence that it is true of Venus and Mars. The bulk density of Mercury is about 5.5, while the silicate rocks responsible for lavas have densities of about 3.3.

Mars. Scientists continued to speculate on the source of the water that could have formed the erosional channels on the surface of Mars (see THE CLIMATES OF PLANETS). There is almost no water in the present-day Martian atmosphere, certainly not enough to create such imposing channels.

Daniel J. Milton of the U.S. Geological Survey proposed an interesting theory for the source of water by postulating ground ice consisting of carbon dioxide hydrate. If the underground pressure were suddenly relaxed, the hydrate would break down into water and carbon dioxide gas and would release a flood of water. In the present Martian atmosphere, water would tend to boil off in the daytime. However, some scientists believe that higher atmospheric pressures may have existed in past epochs.

Although the theory that water erosion

Geoscience

Continued

caused the Martian channels seems to have the widest acceptance, some scientists disagree. Stanley Schumm of Colorado State University in Fort Collins proposed that the channels are caused by fractures in the planet's crust that were subsequently modified by erosion from blown sand and dust.

Lunar science. The Fifth Lunar Science Conference, held in Houston in March, 1974, included many reports that reviewed recent accomplishments in lunar research. One aspect of these studies was the continuing search for rocks that might date the moon's formation. The moon is generally thought to have been formed 4.6 billion years ago, at the same time that most stone meteorites found on the earth were formed. As data has accumulated, however, it now appears unlikely that rocks of that age can be found on the moon. Instead, about 4.2 billion years appears to be the maximum age determined by studies of crystalline rocks, such as basalts and anorthosites. Soils from the Apollo 17 landing site, for which the most data exist, are tentatively dated at about 4.45 billion years.

The uranium-lead ages for the crystalline rocks are particularly significant. Two isotopes of uranium decay to two isotopes of lead at differing rates. By analyzing the amounts of the four isotopes, scientists can determine when a rock crystallized, and they can also determine the age of the source that produced it. So far, such studies show that the source of the crystalline rocks is only about 4.45 billion years old. This suggests that, if the moon is indeed 4.6 billion years old, its outer layer, which is the lava source, underwent extensive chemical differentiation during the first 100 to 200 million years that removed evidence of an earlier formation date.

Measurements of strontium isotopes in some rocks, however, do provide indirect evidence of a 4.6-billion-year age for the moon. The measurements are based on the decay of one isotope of rubidium of mass 87 to an isotope of strontium of mass 87. The amount of strontium-87 is compared with another isotope of strontium of mass 86 that does not decay and remains constant. Thus, the ratio of rubidium-87 and strontium-87 to stronti-

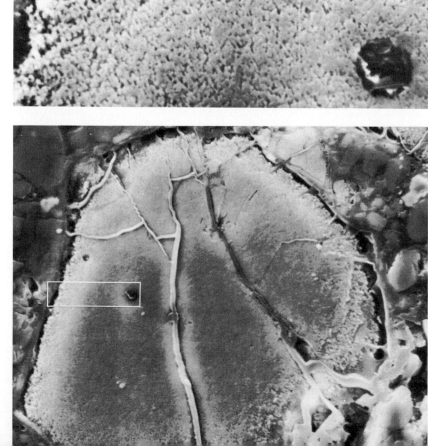

The discovery of tiny irradiation tracks in an olivine grain of a meteorite (the mottled area in the top picture) and the fact that they were mostly concentrated on one side of the grain enabled geochemists to estimate when and how the meteorite was formed. The meteorite particle, *below,* is magnified 2,000 times, and the outlined area in it is magnified 10,000 times.

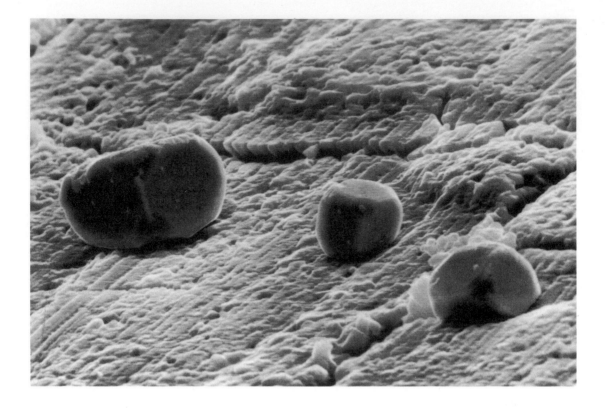

Geoscience

Continued

Continuing studies, in 1973, on rocks that were collected by the 1971 Apollo 15 astronauts led to the discovery of iron crystals in one sample. The crystals are so tiny that 1,000 of them would fit across the edge of a sheet of typing paper.

um-86 depends on its age. The results are also compared with measurements made on meteorites found on the moon. For stone meteorites, analysis of a number of samples having different rubidium-strontium ratios enables scientists to determine their age and the ratio of strontium-87 to strontium-86 when the rocks originally formed—often called "primordial strontium."

Three laboratories have now measured the ratio of strontium-87 to strontium-86 in lunar anorthosites. When small corrections are made for the strontium-87 produced by the decay of the traces of rubidium-87 in the rocks, the initial ratio is even a little lower than that for the meteorites, formed 4.6 billion years ago.

Organic matter. Significant studies of organic compounds in meteorites appeared in 1973. Investigations by Keith Kvenvolden of the National Aeronautics and Space Administration's Ames Research Center at Moffett Field in California and George Yuen of the University of Arizona demonstrated the existence of a class of organic compounds called fatty acids in two stone meteorites. Several

years ago scientists discovered another class of organic acids, amino acids, in these same meteorites.

The new finding is further evidence of a rich abundance of organic chemicals in some meteorites. Of the four so-called building blocks of life—amino acids, fatty acids, carbohydrates, and nucleic acids—two have been found in meteorites.

Still other discoveries relating to organic matter came from studies of Comet Kohoutek. Spectral studies detected water in the comet's tail, which supports the "dirty snowball" theory of cometary matter advanced 20 years ago by Fred Whipple of the Smithsonian Observatory. According to Whipple's · theory, comets consist largely of ice.

Radio astronomers also detected signals characteristic of methyl cyanide and hydrogen cyanide in the comet's tail. It is known that amino acids can be synthesized by simple irradiation experiments on mixtures of hydrogen cyanide and water. The cyanide compounds in the comet's tail could provide the amino acids needed for living matter. See A Cosmic Laboratory. [George R. Tilton]

Geoscience

Continued

Geology. Two groups of geologists successfully used different techniques in 1974 to determine the nature of the rock-forming minerals in the earth's lower mantle, the area more than 450 miles (725 kilometers) beneath the earth's surface. The groups, one in Japan and the other in Rochester, N.Y., developed methods for duplicating the tremendous heat and pressures far beneath the surface of the earth, and in the process confirmed a theory developed 35 years ago by crystallographer John D. Bernal.

The Japanese group, which published its results on February 8, consisted of Mineo Kumazawa, Hiroshi Sawamoto, Eiji Ohtani, and Kazuaki Masaki of the Department of Earth Sciences at Nagoya University. The Japanese scientists put a sample of olivine, a magnesium-silicon-oxygen mineral that makes up most of the earth's upper mantle, into a high-pressure press, which they had earlier redesigned to allow for a much greater degree of compression than was previously possible. They applied a pressure of 3 million pounds per square inch, the known pressure of the earth at a depth of 500 miles (805 kilometers), to the olivine. Then they turned on a small carbon heater that was next to the sample inside the press and heated the sample for half an hour. This reproduced the heat at that depth, about 2200° F. (1200° C.).

They reported that all the olivine had been converted to magnesium oxide, or periclase, and a dense form of silicon dioxide known as stishovite, two minerals that probably make up most of the lower mantle. The carbon heater itself had become industrial-grade diamonds.

The Rochester experiment was conducted at the University of Rochester by graduate student Li-chung Ming and William A. Bassett of the university's Department of Geological Sciences. They used a smaller high-pressure device with crystalline diamond as the hard material that squeezed the sample. Instead of using a carbon heater, Ming and Bassett focused a laser through the diamond and heated the sample to the temperature of about 2200° F. After the heat was turned off, they removed the sample from the cell and found the same minerals, periclase and stishovite.

Dome-shaped fountain of lava erupts from summit of volcanic crater on Island of Hawaii. Such unusual domes of molten rock often rise to heights of more than 100 feet.

Besides being experimental triumphs, the high-pressure results establish the crystal structure of the earth's lower mantle, which makes up almost half of the mass of the earth. Bernal predicted in 1939 that the mantle's rock-forming minerals would prove to be simple metal-oxygen compounds, or oxides, and that the sudden jumps in the speed of earthquake waves that occur between about 250 and 450 miles (400 and 725 kilometers) below the surface could be caused by reorganization of the surface minerals into more densely-packed compounds, such as periclase and stishovite.

Ophiolites. Geologist John M. Bird and co-workers at Cornell University concluded in April, 1974, that ophiolites from Josephine County in Oregon are rocks from the outer portion of the earth's core brought to the surface from a depth of 1,800 miles (2,900 kilometers) by a rising plume of flowing rock. The rocks contain 62 per cent nickel and 27 per cent iron. However, there is disagreement among geologists about the origin of these rocks. Some geologists think that the Josephine County ophiolites en-

countered a coal bed that smelted a small amount of nickel-iron in the same way that a blast furnace uses coal and iron ore to make iron metal.

X-ray diffraction. Geologists are extending the use of X-ray diffraction measurements as a result of the success of studies that geochemists have made in analyzing samples of rocks from the moon. While the technique was developing from 1900 to 1930, X-ray diffraction was used intensively by geologists to determine the crystal structure of minerals. Since a crystal is a regular array of atoms, it can be used as a diffraction grating for X rays. And the intensity of the X rays sent off in various directions from the crystal is determined by the arrangement of atoms within the crystal.

The X-ray crystallographer works backwards on the problem he is concerned with. He measures the intensity of the diffracted X rays and then hunts for an arrangement of atoms that will explain the intensities. It is not an easy search, and in recent years some of the largest computers have been used in such crystallographic problems. The machines that

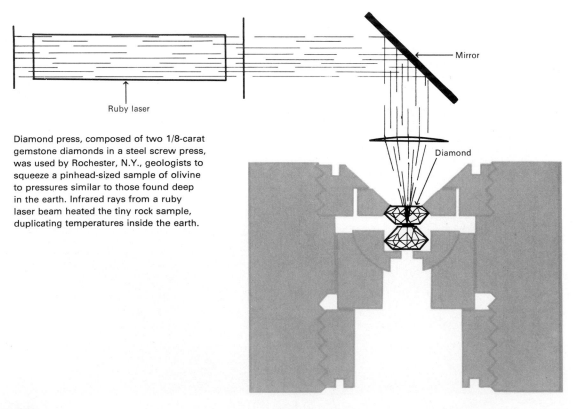

Diamond press, composed of two 1/8-carat gemstone diamonds in a steel screw press, was used by Rochester, N.Y., geologists to squeeze a pinhead-sized sample of olivine to pressures similar to those found deep in the earth. Infrared rays from a ruby laser beam heated the tiny rock sample, duplicating temperatures inside the earth.

Ruby laser

Mirror

Diamond

Geoscience

Continued

are used to measure the diffracted X-ray intensities now also contain small computers to study the measurements.

By now, almost all of the known minerals have been examined, and the characteristic atomic arrangement within the crystals of each mineral is known. So crystallographers have turned their attention to determining new structures in biology. Here, instead of examining minerals or simple chemical compounds, they are trying to determine the structures of enzymes and other biologically important molecules. Geological crystallographers would have nothing to do were it not for a whole new level of subtle variations in atomic structure that scientists recognized while studying the moon rocks, and similar variations are now being discovered in minerals on the earth.

Earlier, geologists were content to identify a mineral and to presume that all specimens of that mineral had identical crystal structures. But in any mineral there may often be substitutions of one atom for another, there are variations from fully ordered to fully disordered arrangements, and there are small stacking mistakes that occur while the crystal is growing. Small variations of these and other types are clues to the conditions under which crystals formed.

In order to determine what processes caused what variations in structure, new crystals are made in the laboratory for study and natural crystals are modified by heating so that they can be compared to crystals taken directly from the rocks.

Some interesting and useful measurements of the temperatures at which earth rocks formed have come from these studies by X-ray crystallographers. Although the scientists of the National Aeronautics and Space Administration may not have planned it that way, geologists are gaining new insights into the origin of earth rocks by applying techniques used in studying lunar samples to studies of earth rocks.

Since geologists began to use the microscope to examine rocks about a hundred years ago, they have been subjected to a certain amount of teasing, because it seemed silly to "examine a mountain with a microscope." Yet, scientists are now using the X-ray diffraction technique to measure on a scale 5,000 times smaller than the light microscope ever could, and finding that mountains have even more stories to tell.   [Kenneth S. Deffeyes]

Geophysics. Studies of rocks from deep within the earth in Africa added support to a theory of earth movement in 1973, but raised questions about previous models of the heat in the earth's interior. The rocks were taken from kimberlite pipes, formations in the earth composed of igneous rock, in Lesotho. These studies were reported by Francis R. Boyd of the Carnegie Institution of Washington, D.C., at a conference in Lesotho in August, 1973.

Because some rocks preserve evidence of the temperature at which they were formed and others preserve evidence of the pressures that surrounded them when they cooled, geophysicists can estimate the depth at which they were formed. The kimberlite pipe rocks were pushed to the surface of the earth by internal processes. The temperatures at which they were formed correlate well with the depths at which they were formed down to about 93 miles (147 kilometers). Below this depth, however, the temperature of the rocks jumped suddenly for a distance and then resumed the more gentle gradient. Either a heat source produced the sharp jump, or the thermal properties of the rocks changed. Because the rocks were all of the same type with known thermal properties, it seems likely that some heat source must have been present when the rocks were formed, probably at the 93-mile depth.

The rocks formed less than 93 miles deep were granular or crystalline, while those from greater depths were smooth, and showed signs of internal motion and shearing. Underground motions probably produced the shearing and the extra heat. It is also likely that this point, at which the temperature gradient rose and the rocks sheared, is the base of the lithosphere, the rigid outer part of the earth's shell, or mantle. If so, the sheared rocks probably came from the more plastic asthenosphere beneath it. The fact that they were sheared gives weight to the theory of earth movement.

George Kennedy of the University of California, Los Angeles, calculated in 1973 the temperature at the core-asthenosphere boundary on the basis of the melting relationships between silicate rocks and iron. The results indicated enough of a temperature rise to make the rock material in the lower mantle unstable. Further work will be required to

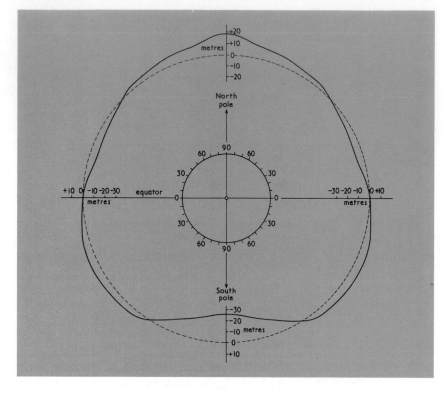

Cross-section diagram of the earth, produced on an exaggerated scale by two British geophysicists indicates that earth is more pear-shaped than previously assumed. The diagram is based on data from satellites.

eoscience

Continued

establish a physical model of the interior of the earth that is compatible with all of the new data.

Mantle motion. Geophysicists discussed the vertical movements of the giant plates that form the earth's outer shell at a conference in Columbus, Ohio, in August, 1973. The plates, about 20 in number, vary in size and shape. They move horizontally as much as an inch each year. Geophysicists do not know what causes the vertical motions both at plate boundaries and within the plates, or if these movements and the major horizontal movements of the plates are related. One of the difficulties in determining the rate of vertical movement in the plates is the problem of separating elevation changes caused by local geologic forces from those related to the regular change in sea level, and there is no clear relationship between the major movements of the plates and these vertical motions.

In the case of sedimentary basins on the continental plates, they are all slowly rising. The rate of movement is measured by the thickness of accumulated sediment in a given time, usually about 0.004 inch

(0.01 millimeter) per year. On the other hand, vertical movement caused by local postglacial uplifting ranges from 0.04 to 0.4 inches (1 to 10 millimeters) per year.

The variation in rates of elevation in the continental plates suggests that the vertical motion is oscillatory rather than in one direction, as are horizontal plate motions. The variation also contrasts with the situation in the plates that form the ocean beds. These ocean plates gradually dip down as they move away from the mid-ocean ridges, where lava from deep in the earth wells up between the plate boundaries. John Sclater of the Massachusetts Institute of Technology has proposed that heat contraction causes this dip in the ocean plates.

New instruments may soon help in measuring elevation changes. Measurements are currently being made from McDonald Observatory in Mount Locke, Tex., using the Apollo retroreflectors on the moon with an accuracy of 15 centimeters. It is possible that these measurements can be refined to accuracies of 2 to 3 centimeters. There is also a possibility of eventually building a movable ranging

Geoscience

Continued

station that can be used to measure the amounts and rates of vertical movement.

Predicting earthquakes. Such measurements could help in predicting earthquakes if they were accurate enough. The physical model for earthquakes, developed in 1973 by Christopher H. Scholz, Lynn R. Sykes, and Yash P. Aggarwal of Columbia University, suggests that the earth's crust moves vertically several centimeters before an earthquake, and the area so affected varies in size according to the magnitude of the earthquake that follows. For a modest earthquake, magnitude of 6 on the earthquake-measuring Richter scale, an area of several miles or tens of kilometers would dilate about 6 to 18 months before the earthquake. A system to monitor the California region has been proposed. It would use a laser operating in a National Aeronautics and Space Administration satellite to measure the movements related to earthquakes.

Hot spots. J. Tuzo Wilson's theory that the Pacific island chains were caused by the movement of lithospheric plates over stationary "hot spots" in the earth's mantle was tested in 1973 and 1974. The Toronto geologist's idea was refined by G. Brent Dalrymple, E. A. Silver, and E. D. Jarleson of the U.S. Geological Survey. They concluded that the hot spots were circular features some 185 miles in diameter and about 40 miles deep in the earth. One of these lies under the Pacific Ocean floor just northeast of the island of Hawaii. They suggested that lavas from this spot progressively built up the Hawaiian Islands, which range in age from Kauai (5.6 million years old), to the southwest, to Hawaii (0.7 million years old), to the southeast.

Leg 33 of the Deep Sea Drilling Project, the U.S. research program to explore the composition of the ocean floor, tested the hot spot origin of the Line Islands, south of Hawaii, and the Tuamotu chain, which includes Tahiti, with mixed results. The deepest lavas over a distance of some 800 miles (1,300 kilometers) in the Line Islands appeared to be essentially the same age, suggesting that the theory proposed for the origin of the Hawaiian chain cannot be applied there. The Tuamotu results are questionable because the deepest lavas were not reached. Because of its relation to plate tectonics, this theory of the Line Islands origin must be examined further. [Charles L. Drake]

Paleontology. For decades, paleontologists have puzzled over the unusual adaptations in some of the earliest reptiles, such as those in the genus *Dimetrodon*. This group rose to dominance in the vertebrate world during the Permian Period, between 275 and 225 million years ago. *Dimetrodon* had a long vertebral spine, which supported a thin fold of skin that stood high along its back, somewhat like a sail.

Studies by Cherry Bramwell and P. Fellgett, of Reading University in England, support the view that these "sails" gave the animals a unique method of regulating body temperature. As a result, they did not depend completely on surrounding temperatures, which determine the level of activity in most reptiles.

From estimated body weights and sail surface areas, the Reading scientists calculated that *Dimetrodon grandis,* known from fossil deposits found many years ago in Texas, could have raised its body temperature from the minimum for voluntary activity, 47°F. (26°C.), to the probable optimal activity temperature, 58°F. (32°C.), in only 80 minutes by orienting itself so that maximum sail surface faced the sun's rays. Animals of similar size, but without sails, would have required about 205 minutes to absorb a similar amount of heat.

Upon approaching a critical maximum temperature of 68° to 77°F. (38° to 43°C.), *Dimetrodon grandis* had to turn its body so as to expose a minimum sail area to the sun, thus radiating excess heat and lowering its body temperature. Such a heat-regulating mechanism apparently gave these reptiles a significant advantage, allowing them to be active during parts of the day when other reptiles and amphibians on which they preyed remained sluggish. This interesting adaptation represents the earliest known form of biological thermoregulation.

Crustaceans and fish. In June, 1973, Roger Cressey of the Smithsonian Institution in Washington, D.C., and Colin Patterson of the British Museum in London announced the discovery of fossil copepods, tiny crustaceans, in the gill chambers of two fossilized fish from the Santana Formation of Ceara, Brazil. These particular copepods were probably parasites. The fossil fish were found in rocks of late Cretaceous Period, about 100 million years old.

Geoscience

Continued

Today, some species of copepods are particularly important as food for ocean fish. Until this report, however, copepods were not known as fossils earlier than the early Miocene Epoch, from 14 to 26 million years ago. Because of their great variety in terms of species and environment, copepods were thought to have originated sometime during Paleozoic times (600 to 225 million years ago), but little else could be said about their history. The newly found fossils have an anatomical structure intermediate between two living copepod families, one parasitic and the other semiparasitic. The existence of parasitic copepods in the late Cretaceous Period suggests that their transition from a free-living to a parasitic mode of life occurred well back in the Mesozoic Era, which began 225 million years ago.

Equally important was the discovery of fresh-water ostracods, another minute crustacean, with the fossil fish. Discovery of these ostracods with the marine copepod parasites suggests that this species of fish could withstand a wide range of salt and fresh water, and perhaps migrated from one to the other as does the modern salmon. If so, this would be the first evidence of such salt- and fresh-water tolerance in an extinct fish species.

Dinosaurs and birds. Paleontologists Robert T. Bakker of Harvard University and Peter M. Galton of the University of Bridgeport in Connecticut presented compelling evidence in March, 1974, that two orders of dinosaurs, Saurischia and Ornithischia, descended from a common ancestor. Scientists had previously believed that these two groups of dinosaurs came from different members of a primitive order, Thecodontia.

The two authors cited a wide variety of anatomical features common to both types of dinosaurs. They suggested, for example, that structural similarities in the hands and feet, hip and shoulder joints, and various muscles are too numerous to have occurred independently as a result of similar evolution, as previous investigators have proposed.

Bakker and Galton also proposed that a new class of vertebrates, Dinosauria, be established. The class would include both dinosaurs and birds. To support their proposal, the scientists pointed to earlier

New species of shrewlike primate, *Chiromyoides caesor,* was given a name on the basis of a single fossil tooth, *right,* found in Wyoming. The tooth resembles that of another species found in France, the skull of which has been reconstructed, *below.*

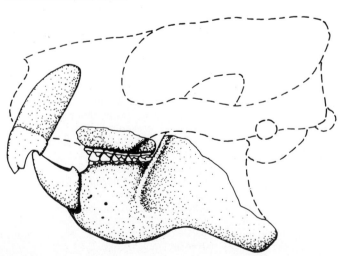

Doctors in Detroit found mummified beetle larvae in the eardrum of an Egyptian mummy, buried 2,700 years ago. The autopsy was conducted for a study of disease causes in ancient Egypt.

Geoscience

Continued

work indicating that a saurischian dinosaur was the immediate ancestor of *Archaeopteryx,* the earliest bird. They also pointed out that evidence suggests some dinosaurs were as warm-blooded as are modern birds.

This is the highest taxonomic regrouping of major vertebrates to be proposed in recent years. It is likely to trigger a great deal of controversy because taxonomists have maintained that many basic behavioral differences between reptiles and birds and the ability of birds to fly are sufficient reasons to separate members of the two groups taxonomically.

Paleoecology. Anna K. Behrensmeyer of the University of California at Berkeley has modified techniques for interpreting how prehistoric animals interacted with each other and their environment. Studying sediments from 4.5 to 1.3 million years old on the east side of Lake Rudolf in Kenya, she systematically collected all bone fragments within an area of several hundred square miles. The area included many different types of environment, including riverbeds, flood plains, and ancient deltas. The

thousands of bone fragments collected were classified and counted. The resulting data were statistically adjusted to give distribution estimates for the various fossil species that were found within the different habitats.

From her analysis, Behrensmeyer was able to compare prehistoric and modern animal distributions and distinguish those prehistoric animals that probably lived in the vicinity from those that were probably carried there after death. She showed that largely terrestrial mammals with preferences for open bush and grasslands lived in what were once grassland environments, while forest types and semiaquatic mammals lived in ancient forests and lake areas.

Her results are not surprising. But they are significant in that they show her method can be applied to fossil deposits with fragmentary bones, for which such detailed analysis was not previously possible. Such studies of animals with no living counterparts could provide much valuable evidence for an interpretation of both their mode of life and their evolution.   [Vincent J. Maglio]

Immunology

The immune system unfolded more of its mysteries and complexities in 1973 and 1974 as immunologists concentrated on trying to learn how this system is controlled naturally. They hope to use what is learned to manipulate the immune system in treating disease. This seemed reasonable in light of some encouraging applications of present knowledge. For example, transfer factor, a substance long-known but little-understood, was used successfully against a number of diseases. See Close-Up.

Thymosin. At an international conference on thymus factors in immunity held in New York City in April, 1974, a hormone called thymosin received great attention. When it was first isolated, from the thymus gland of fetal calves in 1966, there was some speculation that it might be responsible for changing primitive bone marrow cells called stem cells into lymphocytes, specialized white blood cells. Because the knowledge and tools for investigating lymphocytes were then rather primitive, this possibility lay dormant until a number of investigators confirmed it in 1973.

For example, researcher Edward A. Boyse and colleagues at the Memorial Sloan-Kettering Cancer Center in New York City added thymosin to purified bone marrow stem cells and converted them into cells with characteristics similar to lymphocytes known as T, or thymus-derived, cells. Normally, T cells are found in the body after stem cells pass through the thymus gland.

Allan L. Goldstein of the University of Texas Medical Branch at Galveston reported at the conference that thymosin can be detected and measured in the blood stream, and a number of investigators are now trying to determine if a variety of immunologically based maladies might be caused by altered levels of circulating thymosin. Goldstein and his colleagues reported that they had purified thymosin to the point where biochemical techniques should be able to determine its structure and how it works.

Perhaps the most exciting report at the conference was that some clinical trials of thymosin are now underway. The trials have generated enough optimism to suggest that thymosin could become very

B cell, *below,* and T cell, *below right,* which play different roles in the body's defense system, were photographed after a drying procedure that made them discernible from one another for the first time when they are viewed with an electron microscope. The cells are magnified over 20,000 times.

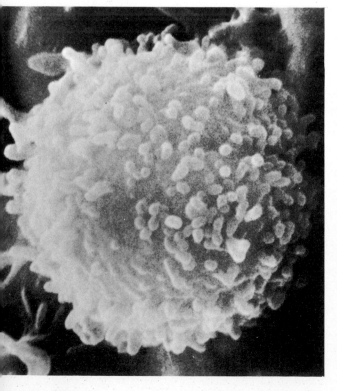

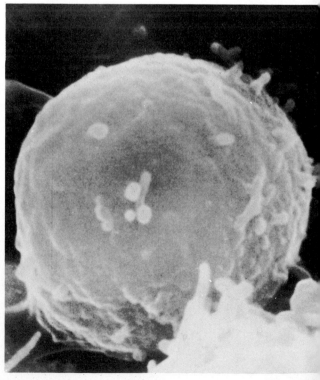

Immunity Transplant

Physicians attending young Edward (Ted) Kennedy, Jr., who had his right leg amputated because of bone cancer in November, 1973, have been considering treating him with a substance whose unpredictable effectiveness and very nature have baffled scientists around the world. The substance, called transfer factor, may help ward off metastasis, in which cancer cells that may have migrated from his leg before surgery could establish cancer elsewhere in his body.

Injecting transfer factor from one individual into another often transfers resistance against specific dangerous intruders in the body, such as bacteria, fungi, viruses, and cancer cells. Scientists extract the transfer factor from leukocytes, or white blood cells, of a donor known to have resistance to the intruder. Then doctors inject the patient and wait for possible results.

Doctors have been trying this treatment on diseases ranging from leprosy to juvenile rheumatoid arthritis as well as cancer. Results have ranged from almost miraculous to outright failure. The reasons are by no means clear.

Multiple sclerosis is among the diseases treated most recently with transfer factor. Victims of this disease of the central nervous system are ultimately incapacitated by such symptoms as blindness and paralysis. There is no known cure for multiple sclerosis, nor is its cause known. One possible clue, however, is that multiple sclerosis patients appear to have little resistance to the paramyxoviruses, of which the measles virus is one.

Doctors Virginia Utermohlen and John R. Zabriskie of Rockefeller University and a group of Scandinavian researchers have shown that transfer factor from normal individuals that have high immunity to measles virus somehow heightens the immune responses of multiple sclerosis patients to the virus.

In their small pilot study, the Rockefeller University physicians are giving transfer factor to multiple sclerosis patients to see if it alters the course of their disease. They hope to find out if measles virus plays any role in causing multiple sclerosis. The study will also determine if transfer factor is an effective treatment. Similar studies are being carried out by Doctors Casper Jersild, Bo DuPont, and others at Memorial Sloan-Kettering Cancer Center, New York City.

When and how to use transfer factor might become clearer if scientists could solve the mysteries of just what it is and how it works. Biochemist David Dressler and co-workers Steven Rosenfeld and Huntington Potter of Harvard University are front-runners in the pursuit of the solutions. In their experiments, they have found that guinea-pig transfer factor is destroyed by RNase III, an enzyme that specifically destroys double-stranded ribonucleic acid (RNA). This cell substance plays several crucial roles, including participation in the manufacture of all enzymes and other proteins needed to maintain life. "It therefore appears that transfer factor consists entirely or partly of double-stranded RNA," the investigators said in a report that was published during the summer of 1974.

Further analysis of the double-stranded RNA revealed that it was too small to take part in protein manufacture. The Harvard scientists now believe that it acts upon the recipient's lymphocytes, white blood cells that are central to the immune response. As they see it, the transfer factor may work through a process called derepression—uncovering and "turning on" certain of the lymphocytes' genes that start particular immune responses. They add that if this is so, there could be many different transfer factors—one to trigger an immune response to each of many intruders.

Other work on the characterization of transfer factor is also underway. Dr. Albert LoBuglio of Ohio State University in Columbus reported in 1974 that, working with the amount of leukocyte extract usually used as a single dose, he had isolated 250 micrograms (less than 1 one-hundred-thousandth of an ounce) of material that appears to possess most of the activity of transfer factor. LoBuglio is using this material to treat sarcoma, a type of cancer.

To Ted Kennedy, Jr., and others under the threat of cancer's return, the outcome of such treatment and research is particularly important. But, on a much broader scale, understanding how transfer factor works is of crucial importance to everyone. It should lead to a better understanding of immunological defects and their relationship to disease, to ways of differentiating between similar diseases, and ultimately to new therapies for many of man's maladies.   [Gail McBride]

important in treating certain immunodeficiency diseases.

Goldstein's measurements also show that thymosin levels in the blood stream drop off as we age. Thus, the substance may have something to do with aging. For example, the deterioration of the immune system with age could be related to thymosin levels that are too low to make sufficient numbers of T cells. This might explain why old people are so susceptible to diseases, including cancer.

Suppressor lymphocytes. A type of lymphocytes called suppressor T cells also attracted attention. In contrast to the longer-known and better-understood helper T cells, which assist B lymphocytes in producing antibodies, suppressor T cells appear to inhibit antibody formation by B cells. Immunologists are anxious to find out how they do this, because of the potential applications.

For example, Tamio Tada and his colleagues at Chiba University in Japan reported evidence that suppressor T cells may play an important role in controlling the levels of a type of antibody that causes allergies through its response to allergens such as pollen. The Japanese scientists injected suppressor T cells into rats and mice with allergies and found that the cells somehow turned off the production of allergy-causing antibody. Similar results in American and European laboratories leave little doubt about the potential use of T cells in allergy treatment.

A number of reports published within the year indicate that suppressor T cells are probably a unique population of T lymphocytes, although no identifying characteristics for this cell type have yet been discovered. Understanding T-cell suppression is potentially important to understanding immunoregulation. For example, it is possible that allergic individuals have congenital or acquired deficiencies in this suppressive activity that permit uncontrolled production of allergy-causing antibody. It may be that desensitization works in the treatment of some allergies by boosting the number of suppressor cells.

Genetic control. The ability to respond immunologically to various antigens, such intruders as viruses, appears to be determined by immune response (IR) genes. Since an immune response requires interaction between an antigen and specific receptors on the outer membranes of lymphocytes, the question is: How do the IR genes govern the expression of immunity? Perhaps they code, at least in part, for the receptors.

But, recent reports indicate that the story may be more complicated than that. IR genes may control the interaction between various types of cells involved in the immune response. For example, Ethan Shevach and Allan Rosenthal of the National Institutes of Health in Bethesda, Md., observed that certain T cells that must interact with white blood cells called macrophages had IR genes identical to those of the macrophages.

David Katz and Baruj Benacerraf at Harvard Medical School in Boston determined that the interaction between T cells and B cells that leads to antibody production also requires that both types of cell have identical IR genes.

Furthermore, Peter Doherty of the John Curtin School for Medical Research in Canberra, Australia, reported that T lymphocytes able to kill cells infected with certain pathogenic viruses could not do so unless they both recognized a viral product on the cells and shared some cell-surface element with them. The shared surface element is in some way governed, perhaps even coded for, by a gene or genes on a chromosome area that includes the IR gene region.

All of these observations point to what may be an extremely important principle in communication among cells, the recognition of mutually shared, genetically determined membrane components.

Scientists at several laboratories reported what may be a related finding. They discovered that histocompatibility antigens, those that cause the immune system to reject a graft, are associated with a small protein molecule known as beta$_2$ microglobulin. Further studies found that the membranes of all cells examined contained large quantities of beta$_2$ microglobulin. These findings have started immunologists speculating on the possible relationships between IR gene products, histocompatibility antigens, and beta$_2$ microglobulin.

Meanwhile, a function for beta$_2$ microglobulin has yet to be discovered. Scientists, who have learned from experience that nature rarely does anything on a whim, believe that such an everpresent substance must be of paramount biological importance. [Jacques M. Chiller]

Medicine

Dentistry. Fluoridation of communal water supplies continues to be the main public-health measure for preventing caries (tooth decay). However, other approaches were investigated in 1973, particularly for people living where there is no central water supply or where opposition to communal fluoridation prevails.

Fluoride options. Several studies have demonstrated that fluoridation of school water at a level of about 5 parts per million results in 40 per cent fewer cavities. This compares well with the 60 per cent reduction obtained with fluoridation of a central water source at a level of 1 part per million. Tests in which children were given fluoride tablets in school each day resulted in a 20 to 50 per cent reduction in decay.

Surface fluoride applications can also be surprisingly effective. Harold Englander and his co-workers at the National Institute of Dental Research, Bethesda, Md., have reduced incidence of decay 75 to 80 per cent by the use of concentrated gels of neutral sodium fluoride or acidulated phosphate-fluoride in a custom-made mouthpiece for six minutes a day.

The technique is now being used by dentists to treat serious decay problems.

Fluorides are most effective on decay that develops on smooth tooth surfaces and near the gum line. But they are relatively ineffective against pit and fissure decay that occurs on the biting surfaces of the back teeth. Now, adhesive materials have been developed to seal the pits and fissures from food and bacteria. Protection is greatly improved when the sealant has been combined with surface fluoride treatment, thus keeping the fluoride in contact with the enamel longer, as well as preventing bacterial contact.

Suppressing bacteria. If placed in a medium containing *Streptococcus mutans*, a common decay-causing bacteria, for 14 days, the enamel surface of extracted teeth is damaged. But teeth incubated in the same way after a brief application of stannous fluoride were protected.

Antibiotics are also being used to suppress the tiny organisms that cause decay. In one test, Vancomycin was applied to children's teeth twice daily for five days, and significantly reduced the *S. mutans* population. · [Paul Goldhaber]

An extensively decayed tooth was saved by a new technique. The tooth below center, was extracted, repaired, and the root canals filled with a sterile material. It was then replanted. Healthy tissues in the socket fostered its complete reattachment.

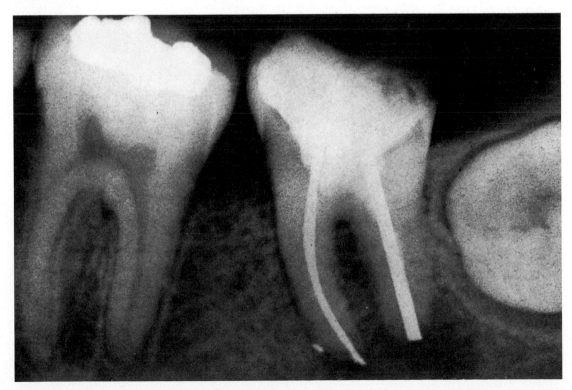

Medicine

Continued

Internal Medicine. Charles Lieber, professor of medicine at the Mt. Sinai School of Medicine in New York City, reported in late 1973 the results of a four-year study on the effects of the consumption of large quantities of alcohol carried out on 32 baboons. The study suggests that even with an adequate diet, people suffering from alcoholic cirrhosis cannot halt the progress of the disease unless they stop drinking. This is in direct opposition to the widely held belief that the ravages of alcoholism are at least partly the result of the alcoholic's poor diet.

All the test animals received a high-protein, vitamin-rich diet, but half of them had ethanol (ethyl alcohol) substituted for all other carbohydrate in their diets. As a result, from one-third to one-half of their calories were derived from the alcohol.

Successive blood tests and biopsies revealed a dramatic rise in liver triglyceride fats. This was followed by microscopic evidence of massive cell infiltration by fat particles, and finally inflamed and diseased liver cells with the characteristics of alcoholic cirrhosis. There were further signs in the tissues that the kind of structural distortion of the liver that is the end stage of alcoholic cirrhosis would eventually appear.

Adequate protein-calorie-vitamin nutrition did not protect these animals from the toxic effects of alcohol.

Virus and cancer. Recent evidence, accumulated by several groups of investigators working with New World primates, has rekindled interest in the Epstein-Barr Virus (EBV) as a possible cause of Burkitt's lymphoma, a form of cancer of the lymph system. Researchers have been aware of the association of the virus and lymphoma for some time, but they lacked evidence regarding its causal relationship to the tumor. Now they have produced malignant lymph tumors by injecting the virus into cotton-top marmosets. Then they established tissue cultures of the tumor cells and demonstrated the presence of EBV. They also produced tumors in other cotton-top marmosets by inoculating them with these cells.

As a final link in the chain, Dr. George Miller and his co-workers at Yale Univer-

These tiny viruslike particles, magnified about 110,000 times, may be the cause of infectious hepatitis, or hepatitis A. They were seen in 1973 with the electron microscope.

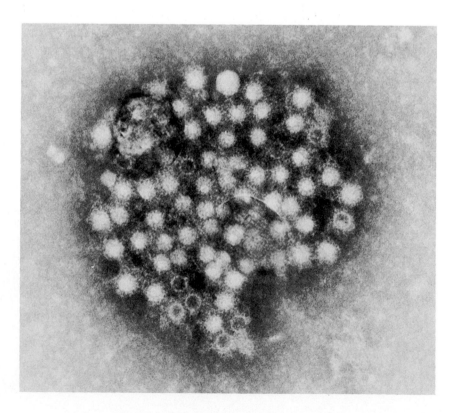

sity School of Medicine reported evidence of EBV in all the EBV-transformed cells in the test animals. This seems to confirm the hypothesis that EBV actually produces the lymphoma, rather than merely being associated with its appearance.

Diabetic danger. The most feared complication of diabetes is coma or loss of consciousness. Traditionally, this coma has been thought to be related primarily to the accumulation in the blood of acids and acid end products called ketones that results from the body's failure to break down glucose properly. But diabetic coma is also accompanied by severe dehydration, which results in an increased concentration of sodium and the sugar glucose in the body.

Several years ago, researchers noted that diabetic coma could occur in patients who did not have the excess acid, but did have hyperglycemia—profoundly elevated blood sugar. Dr. Milford Fulop and other researchers at the Albert Einstein College of Medicine in New York City reported in September, 1973, on the course of 70 episodes of coma occurring in 42 diabetic patients. They found that the coma did not correlate with the rise in blood acidity, but rather with the tendency toward dehydration and the increase in glucose and body salts such as sodium.

These results suggest that the first goal of the physician treating diabetes must now be to repair the dehydration and hyperglycemia.

The cost of medical progress. Drs. Henry E. Simmons and Paul D. Stolley suggested in *JAMA* that unless more vigilance is applied, the unfettered use of antibiotics may finally cause as much harm as benefit. Americans annually consume 8 billion doses of antibiotic drugs called for in 110 million prescriptions, 20 per cent of all prescriptions written. During the last 10 years, while the population has grown 11 per cent, drug production has increased about 300 per cent.

Undoubtedly, the widespread availability of a vast array of antibiotics has accounted for a great deal of modern medicine's triumphs. Mortality in general and the risk of succumbing to specific infections such as pneumococcal pneumonia, meningococcal meningitis, some bacterial heart inflammations, and syphilis have greatly declined.

Unfortunately, however, these desirable strides have been accompanied by less appealing changes in the medical environment. Drugs are sometimes prescribed when patients have not been examined, or when cultures have not been performed to ensure that the correct antibiotic has been selected.

Very frequently, antibiotics are prescribed when a virus, which does not respond to antibiotics, is the infecting organism. All of this inappropriate usage would be tolerable if there were not unacceptable, and perhaps dangerous, side effects of these drugs.

At the individual level, 5 per cent of all hospital patients who are given antibiotics have unfavorable reactions, and 10 per cent of these cases are classified as serious. Severe allergic reactions to penicillin and a form of anemia after the administration of chloramphenicol occur more and more frequently.

Bacteria are also changing to resist the effects of antibiotics. Increasing numbers of antibiotic-resistant strains of gonococci, the microorganism that causes gonorrhea, and staphylococci, another highly infectious organism, are appearing.

Hepatitis. The most disturbing recent development in hepatitis research has been the growing evidence that hepatitis B, or serum hepatitis, may be transmitted by other means than transfusions of infected blood, the most common cause of the disease. Heretofore, most researchers believed that only hepatitis A, infectious hepatitis, could be acquired orally. However, recent family studies have shown that hepatitis B viral material and the disease itself could be transmitted among a patient's family members whose blood did not have contact with his. Recent evidence that hepatitis B material is excreted in the saliva of hepatitis B patients may provide the explanation for this latest observation.

Drug abuse. Methadone maintenance has been an effective means of treating narcotics addicts. This orally active agent, taken in relatively large daily doses, has reduced the need for narcotic drugs, blocked the effect of intravenously administered heroin, and stabilized former heroin addicts. A large percentage of patients treated with methadone have been able to re-establish a productive life for themselves.

With an increasing number of patients committed to daily methadone treatment, the question of how long therapy must be

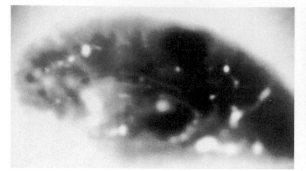

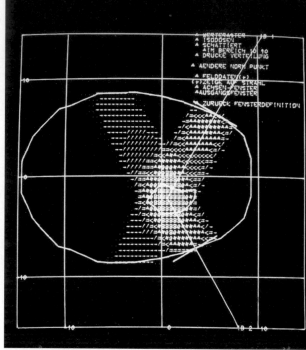

Three new procedures for viewing soft tissues are helping doctors plan more precise therapy and surgery for brain ailments. Protons beamed through the brain reveal, *above,* a tumor, the dark area at the top. Brain data produced by gamma rays appear on a German computer-display screen, *right,* where it can be manipulated to find the best angle of surgical approach to a tumor. A new X-ray technique provides more precise cross-sectional views of the brain, *opposite page,* when enhanced by computer. Cyst appears as a dark area near center of view, *left.* Cross section of a normal brain, *right,* shows no such cyst.

Medicine

Continued

continued has naturally arisen. Dr. Vincent Dole of The Rockefeller University and Paul Cushman of Columbia University have analyzed the experiences of a group of methadone-treated patients who had been withdrawn from treatment. They concluded that many such patients are capable of leading a drug-free life, but they caution against making methadone withdrawal a goal of treatment. Instead, they suggest an individualized approach for each patient, with the single aim of encouraging a satisfactory life adjustment—with or without continuing methadone treatment.

Marijuana and the heart. For some time it has been known that heart rate, peripheral blood circulation, and blood pressure all increase for a time after smoking marijuana. In July, 1973, Drs. Mahendra S. Kochar and Michael J. Hosko reported that the most active component of marijuana, delta-9-tetrahydrocannabis (THC), when given orally, can produce electrocardiographic (ECG) abnormalities lasting as long as 12 hours. These changes are similar to those produced by coronary artery disease.

The ECG abnormalities may indeed reflect true damage and the effects may be cumulative. But, on the other hand, though the abnormalities may not be serious, they might be interpreted as an indication that healthy young people had coronary artery disease.

Collagen. A February, 1974, report in *The Lancet,* published by a group of British investigators, offers substantive new hope for patients suffering from scleroderma. This progressive disease is generally characterized by rigidity and thickening of the skin as well as destruction of various internal organs.

The basic problem appears to be increased rigidity of the fibrous protein collagen, which provides the architectural framework for all body tissue. The rigidity occurs when small collagen fibers are cross-linked by amino acid bonds. These newly formed cross-links are initially unstable and easily soluble. With time, however, they become stronger and less soluble. As a result, the tissues become rigid.

The researchers have produced evidence to show that the biochemical defect results from an increased synthesis of

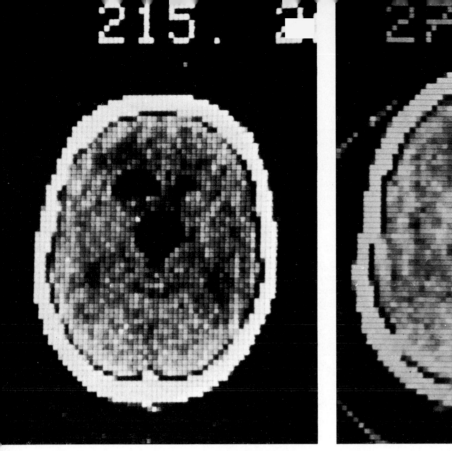
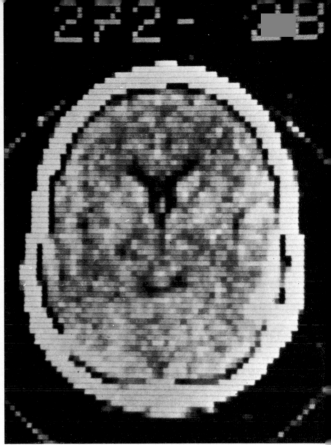

Medicine

Continued

collagen. They have found greater numbers of young collagen bonds in active disease areas of the skin. Because the drug D-penicillamine is known to cleave the cross-links of immature collagen and actually retard overall collagen synthesis, Dr. C. M. Herbert and his co-workers at Bristol Royal Infirmary, Bristol, England, treated patients with D-penicillamine in an attempt to make the collagen less rigid. Their results indicate that the drug is effective in the active phase, when excessive synthesis is occurring, but of less value in the inactive stages of the disease.

Heart disease and stroke, the number-one and number-three causes of death in the United States, appear to be declining in frequency. This was perhaps the most surprising aspect of a report issued in early 1974 by the National Center for Health Statistics. The report, made after a review of 33.6 million death certificates recorded in the U.S. from 1950 to 1969, also showed that several other leading causes of mortality declined during that period.

Heart diseases result in almost 300 deaths per 100,000 population annually. This is about twice as many deaths as the second most frequent cause, cancer, produces. But the death rate from heart disease has decreased 15 per cent, while the overall death rate from cancer has risen 3.4 per cent.

Perhaps the decline in heart disease has been obscured up to this point because earlier statistics failed to correct for age. As the American population grows older, diseases affecting the aged occur more frequently. If no adjustment is made for age distribution in the population, the statistics are distorted.

Although physicians agree on the validity of the trend, they are at a loss to explain its cause. Improvements in treatment or changes in behavior, such as less smoking, more exercise, more prudent diet — if they have occurred at all — began too late in the period covered by the study to affect the results.

The greatest changes in cause of death during the period have been homicide, up 75 per cent; cirrhosis of the liver, up 62 per cent; and death from kidney disease, down by 77 per cent, according to the report.   [Michael H. Alderman]

Medicine

Surgery. Dr. Irving S. Cooper of St. Barnabas Hospital for Chronic Diseases in New York City has developed a brain pacemaker for the control of intractable epilepsy, cerebral palsy, and the spasticity that sometimes occurs after a stroke. Electrodes are implanted in the cortex of the cerebellum, the part of the brain that regulates posture, balance, and movement. These activate the mechanism in the cerebellum, controlling the seizures and the associated muscle tension of the victim's limbs.

A battery-powered transmitter, carried by the patient, signals a small radio receiver implanted under the skin near the collarbone. The receiver is connected to the electrodes by a wire running under the skin. So far, the experimental results have been encouraging. More than 30 patients were using the pacemaker by the end of 1973.

Dr. F. A. Serbinenko of the Burdenko Research Institute of Neurosurgery in Moscow has devised a balloon-tipped tube for closing cerebral fistulae, abnormal artery and vein connections in the head. The tube is inserted through a tiny puncture in the carotid artery, the major supplier of blood to the neck and head, and is carried by the blood to the connection site. Then, a quick-hardening silicone is injected through the tube into the balloon, which swells and seals off the faulty connection. The balloon is detached and the tube is withdrawn. Of 25 cases of cerebral fistulae treated by the new method, the Soviet scientists were successful in 19.

Heart surgery. By-pass surgery, in which a vein is grafted between the aorta and the coronary artery, brings more blood to the heart, lessens the risk of heart attack, and reduces angina pectoris, the severe chest pain caused by an insufficient flow of blood to the heart. However, like any form of surgery, it carries some risk, and must be used with caution.

Two recent studies by Drs. Peter C. Gazes and Peter Hairston at the Medical University of South Carolina suggest that it is possible to determine which cases of angina should be treated with this surgery and which by medication.

Their studies distinguished between two kinds of angina. One is a stable form

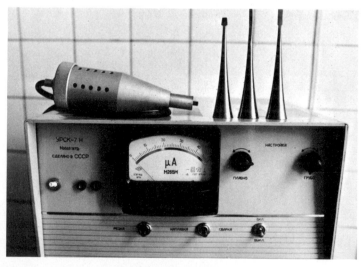

Ultrasonic surgical device invented by Russian doctors is powered by a generator and has three interchangeable tips—a chisel, a saw, and a scalpel. Bone cuts, *left,* show tool's precision.

Medicine

Continued

A metal joint was successfully implanted in an injured thumb. The operation holds promise for thousands of persons crippled by injuries or arthritis.

that can persist for years without leading to a heart attack. The other is a high risk form that almost always precedes damage to the heart muscle.

Dr. Gazes measured the 10-year survival rates of a group of 140 angina patients receiving only medical treatment, some of whom suffered from the high risk form of angina. At the end of the first year, 82 per cent of the entire group, but only 57 per cent of the high-risk patients, had survived. After 10 years, 48 per cent of the group remained alive, but only 19 per cent of the high-risk patients had survived.

Dr. Hairston studied the results of bypass surgery on 44 high-risk heart patients. They showed a survival rate of 86 per cent after one year, which compared favorably with the 57 per cent survival of those receiving only medical treatment.

Mapping conduction. A major hazard of heart surgery is heart block, which occurs when the heart's electrical conduction system is cut. When this happens there is a 50 per cent chance that the patient will die. Early in 1974, Dr. James R. Malm, of the Columbia-Presbyterian Medical Center, in New York City, described an electronic mapping procedure that tells the surgeon the location of the conduction system so that it can be avoided during surgery.

A small probe, about 5 millimeters in diameter, traces the electrical discharges given off by the conduction system as it carries impulses. These discharges are registered on an oscilloscope.

The mapping technique is particularly valuable when the surgery is complex or involves the center of the heart, because the location of the heart's conduction system can often vary.

Ultrahigh sound is becoming increasingly useful as a diagnostic tool. Because it is noninvasive — that is, no instruments or chemicals are inserted in the body — it has proved particularly valuable in studying heart defects. The technique, called echocardiography, bounces sound waves off the internal structures in much the same way that sound-detection instruments find submarines and schools of fish. The signals can be displayed on the oscilloscope.

Drs. William F. Friedman and David Sahn of the University of California, San Diego, reported in 1973 the successful use of echocardiography in studying the heart structures of some 400 babies and young children.

Ultrasound has been used in a number of other diagnostic applications. Detecting pregnancies, finding structural abnormalities in the brain, and locating tumors are among the most common.

A quite different use for ultrasonic vibrations has been devised by Russian surgeons. Early in 1974, Dr. Mstislav V. Volkov described an ultrasonic tool for cutting and welding bone, developed at the Order of Lenin Center Institute for Advanced Training of Physicians in Moscow. The device is said to be faster, safer, and more precise than the saws, cutters, and pliers in conventional use. It looks like an ordinary power tool, and has changeable tips for its different functions.

The instrument is powered by a high-frequency generator which sends electric impulses to the tool. These are translated into the ultrasonic vibrations that activate the cutting and welding tips.

In welding together fractured bone, the surgeon uses either a plastic solder or bone callus, a natural bony material found between fractured bone ends.

While the instrument is used mainly in bone surgery, the Russian doctors report that they have also used it in more than 500 operations involving soft tissues.

Preserving lost limbs. It has been more than a decade since the first successful replantations of severed limbs were reported by Dr. Ronald Malt of Massachusetts General Hospital in Boston, in 1962, and Dr. Chen Chung-Wei of Shanghai, in 1963. Since that time, advances in microsurgical technique have greatly improved the chance of successful replantation. The Chinese report that they have restored more than 300 arms, forearms, hands, and fingers. There have been only a few successful leg transplants.

Crucial to the success of a replantation is the proper care of the severed limb and the stump before surgery. In a set of guidelines prepared for *Medical World News* in early 1974, Dr. Malt suggests that both the limb and the stump be placed in plastic bags surrounded by ice.

If it is kept cool, the limb can survive the lack of blood circulation for from 24 to 36 hours. Wire tourniquets should not be used on the stump because they may injure blood vessels and nerve endings, according to Dr. Malt. The arteries should be individually clamped.

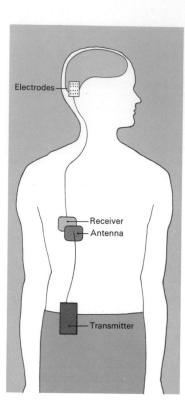

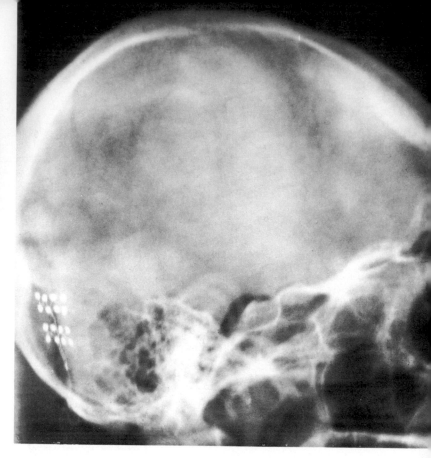

Medicine

Continued

Brain pacemaker enables patient to switch off a seizure at first sign. The transmitter sends electrical signals to the antenna, then, through a receiver in the chest, to platinum electrodes implanted in the brain's cerebellum, *above right,* blocking the seizure.

Bladder control. Paraplegics and others who have suffered injury to the spinal cord often lose the ability to empty their bladders at will. Failure to empty the vessel completely can lead to serious and sometimes fatal infections of the bladder and kidneys. Two new surgical techniques, one developed in Russia, the other in the United States, have provided paraplegics with means of control.

The Russian procedure, described by Dr. A. A. Vishnevsky of Moscow, one of the developers, employs six electrodes embedded in the front and back bladder walls. They are attached to a small electronic receiver, which is implanted near the bladder. Electric signals sent by an external transmitter cause the bladder muscles to contract, emptying the vessel.

The American technique uses a similar approach, in a different area of the body. Dr. Blaine S. Nashold, Jr., of Duke University Medical School in Durham, N.C., implants a small electrode at the precise point along the spinal cord where the bladder-emptying nerve reflex is strongest. Surgical testing along the cord is used to find this area.

As in the Russian procedure, an external transmitter activates the electrode. An electrical impulse prompts the spinal reflex which empties the bladder. One advantage of the American method is that bladder surgery is not required.

Easing pain. Tic douloureux, facial pain caused by pressure on, or degeneration of, the trigeminal nerve in the head, has been described as one of the most excruciating forms of pain. Drs. William H. Sweet and James G. Wepsic of Massachusetts General Hospital in Boston reported in 1973 on their experience in treating this painful affliction. See SHUTTING THE GATE ON PAIN.

They use a needlelike electrode, which selectively destroys the small, less-protected pain nerve fibers behind the cheek with electric current. The larger and better-protected motor and sensory nerve fibers are not injured. More than 90 per cent of the 214 patients they treated were relieved of pain. Dr. John Tew of the University of Cincinnati, who has worked with Dr. Sweet, reports that he has achieved a 95 per cent recovery rate.

[Bashir A. Zikria]

Meteorology

Evidence presented in November, 1973, indicates that there may be a link between disturbances on the sun and weather in the earth's lower atmosphere. Meteorologists have long known that bursts of electrically charged solar particles have significant effects on the ionosphere—the electrically charged upper part of the atmosphere. But most scientists have been highly skeptical of studies that tried to establish a direct link between solar disturbances and the lower atmosphere, where weather is produced.

At a symposium at Goddard Space Flight Center, John M. Wilcox of Stanford University reported a statistical relationship between the occurrence of bad weather in the lower atmosphere and changes in the rate at which magnetic field lines from the sun are carried past the earth. For example, Wilcox and his research team found that the probability of bad weather in winter was lowest just after the boundary between two parts of the solar magnetic field passed the earth. As one of these boundaries sweeps past the earth, the solar field near the earth becomes disturbed for several days. This period of disturbance appears to affect low-pressure areas in northern latitudes, and Wilcox and his colleagues could statistically relate 30 per cent of the large-scale variations in the earth's winter weather to changes that occurred in the sun's magnetic field.

Just how solar disturbances might influence the lower atmosphere is still unexplained, but most meteorologists believe that there is some kind of trigger mechanism involved. One theory was proposed in late 1973 by Colin Hines of the University of Toronto. He suggested that solar disturbances at higher levels of the atmosphere, such as strong auroras, may affect the ionosphere's influence on large-scale wind patterns in the lower atmosphere. These planetary wind currents, which control weather conditions at lower levels, move in complex horizontal and vertical wave patterns around the earth. Hines suggested that as these waves build up in height until they reach the height of the ionosphere, some of their energy is reflected back to earth, where it may either reinforce or interfere with the original wave.

Thin chemical films on the ocean's surface may help control hurricanes by suppressing waves. This limits evaporation and prevents heat from being transferred into the air to provide the energy for hurricanes.

Meteorology

Continued

Global research. Final plans were made early in 1974 for the most comprehensive meteorological experiment conducted to date—the Global Atlantic Tropical Experiment (GATE). Between June 15 and September 30, more than 4,000 people from 13 nations, including researchers from the United States, are participating in the program.

GATE is an activity of the Global Atmospheric Research Program, a worldwide observation and analysis program operating since 1969 to provide the data needed to determine the accuracy of existing models of global circulation. The program is also designed to suggest how existing models might be extended and elaborated. Until 1974, the efforts have been conducted by single nations and have been limited to small tropical areas.

The purpose of GATE, the first truly international program, is to develop methods of estimating the effects of small tropical weather systems, such as cloud clusters, on the large-scale circulation of the tropics. What happens in the tropics has a significant effect on weather in other parts of the world. GATE also is attempting to obtain the data needed to determine the heat and moisture added to the tropical atmosphere by cumulus clouds, which mark areas where heat is transported up from the surface. Other GATE projects include studying the effects of phenomena that occur where the air and the seas meet and radiation exchanges between the sun and earth.

GATE participants are conducting their investigations in an area extending from central Africa to Little America, centered about 500 miles (about 800 kilometers) southwest of Dakar, Senegal. Even more comprehensive measurements are being taken in a smaller area at the center of this area. About 65 other nations have set up additional meteorological observation sites and will coordinate their measurements with those of GATE.

The researchers are using 40 specially equipped ships, 20 oceanographic-meteorological buoys, 12 aircraft, 5 satellites, radar, and high-altitude, super-pressure balloons. Their observations are being coordinated with radio soundings of the atmosphere and soundings of the temperature, depth, and salinity (salti-

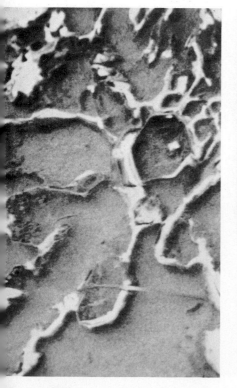

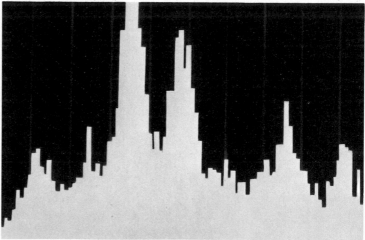

Ice nucleus smaller than a micrometer can be located in a snow crystal, *left,* with a scanning electron microscope. The microscope bombards the crystal with beams of electrons, generating X rays that show the chemical composition of the nucleus, *above.* As a result, scientists can analyze snow crystals and determine their role in cloud seeding.

Meteorology
Continued

ness) of the ocean. Data from scientific satellites permit detailed rainfall estimates. Additional information is being received from a new weather satellite, the Synchronous Meteorological Satellite, launched on May 17.

Atmospheric models. Three major global circulation models were published in 1974. They came from the National Oceanic and Atmospheric Administration's (NOAA) Geophysical Fluid Dynamics Laboratory, from the National Aeronautics and Space Administration's Goddard Institute of Space Sciences, and from the National Center for Atmospheric Research.

These numerical models use mathematical equations to calculate the effects of different variables on global wind, temperature, and moisture patterns. Among the factors incorporated in the models were the effects due to clouds, mountains, continents, snow and ice cover, the distribution of ocean temperature, and heat exchanges between the air and surface. The models have been used with varying degrees of success to make one- and two-day forecasts; to estimate average climatic conditions for several months in advance; and to simulate ice-age climatic conditions.

Other, more specialized numerical models deal with such phenomena as hurricanes and other tropical storms, squall lines, thunderstorms, the generation of weather fronts, and drylines—a kind of front with the same temperature on both sides, but with different levels of humidity on each side.

Meteorologists also can use laboratory models, or small-scale simulations, to analyze complex problems. In one such study in late 1973, a group headed by Richard Pfeffer of Florida State University in Tallahassee studied the growth and decay of the wave patterns in hemispheric circulations. The group used an array of 98 thermistors, or miniature thermometers, in a very sophisticated rotating turntable device that simulates the earth's circulation. They obtained data on temperature and wind speed that permitted them to construct weather charts for the middle atmosphere and to estimate large-scale changes in temperature and in wind speed and direction.

City weather. Meteorologists have long been aware of climate differences between cities and surrounding rural areas, but only within the last few years have they realized that the urban atmosphere, with its heavy load of industrial pollutants, might contribute significantly to increased rainfall. This was given substantial backing in 1974 by a comprehensive report from Project Metromex, a detailed field observation and analysis program covering an area around St. Louis, with a radius of 50 miles. Scientists in the program are studying changes in rainfall that are caused by aerosols—microscopic solid or liquid particles—put into the air by city industries. They are also evaluating the potential effects on water sources 50 or 100 miles away that may be affected by the changes in rainfall. Researchers use extensive networks of aerosol tracers and detectors, raindrop size spectrometers, cloud cameras, rain gauges, and impact devices to measure hail to determine if city and rural areas differ in the size of raindrops, the rate of rainfall, and the sizes of clouds.

In 1974, the researchers reported that during the first year of the program they had found significant amounts of urban pollutants in the cumulus cloud systems near St. Louis that produce rainstorms, and also in regions downwind of the city where there is heavy rainfall. The presence of such pollutants seems to change normal rainfall patterns and increase the amount of rain in the area.

Local forecasts. Although meteorologists have made considerable progress in understanding general weather circulation patterns, they are still plagued with the problem of making short-range, local forecasts. However, they have developed small-scale models of such phenomena as squall line thunderstorms, the sea breeze, and snowstorms produced by large lakes. Extensive radar and volunteer observer networks, and automation provide significant advances in warning of weather hazards. On Feb. 7, 1974, NOAA announced a plan that will allow every National Weather Service forecast office that must warn the public about weather hazards to have immediate access to a local warning radar network. A more elaborate program will eventually link more than 50 National Weather Service offices to provide automatic monitoring and computer updating of all forecasts and weather bulletins. A prototype station began operating in Washington, D.C., on July 1.   [John R. Gerhardt]

Microbiology

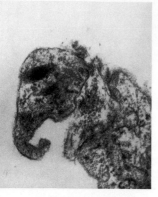

Poxviruses, which cause diseases characterized by small sores, have been isolated from many wild-animal species. This one, magnified about 25,000 times, led the researchers who found it to write that they ". . . suspect that the elephant may also harbor a poxvirus."

Most living things require oxygen. However, one group of bacteria, called anaerobic bacteria, not only grow in the complete absence of oxygen, but also are killed by mere traces of it. In June, 1973, biochemist Irvin Fridovich and his coworkers at the Duke University Medical Center reported that they had discovered why oxygen is lethal to these organisms.

For many years, microbiologists believed that oxygen killed these bacteria because they lack catalase, an enzyme found in all organisms that grow in air. Catalase converts potentially lethal hydrogen peroxide, which is produced by cells in oxygen, into water.

However, the explanation for oxygen's poisonous effect could not account for the exception to the rule, the bacteria that form lactic acid. These organisms, which are found on plants, in milk products, and in the intestines of man, require no oxygen, yet they survive where it is present despite their lack of catalase. Fridovich and his colleagues reported that an extremely toxic form of oxygen called superoxide is the substance that really kills anaerobic bacteria in oxygen.

The scientists showed that superoxide is made by all forms of life when grown in air. All of these forms of life, with the exception of the anaerobic bacteria, produce an enzyme that Fridovich named superoxide dismutase. This enzyme detoxifies superoxide. But, when the scientists found that *Lactobacillus plantarum*, a bacterium forming lactic acid, also did not produce superoxide dismutase, they seemed back at the old dead end.

On a hunch, however, they tested *L. plantarum* to see if it was using any oxygen. It was not, indicating that it escaped death by simply ignoring the oxygen and, therefore, never producing superoxide.

In February, 1974, Fridovich and his associates reported that bacteria's superoxide dismutase enzyme has several properties that are different from the enzyme in the cytoplasm, or major portion, of more complex plant and animal cells. However, superoxide dismutase is also found in the mitochondria (organelles that are involved in energy production) of these plant and animal cells. This enzyme is practically identical to the bacteria's enzyme. This adds to growing evidence that mitochondria evolved from bacteria once captured by the ancestors of modern complex cells.

New source of life energy. In October, 1973, biophysicists Dieter Oesterhelt and Walther Stoeckenius of the University of California, San Francisco, reported the discovery of a new source of adenosine triphosphate (ATP). All forms of life rely on this molecule as the immediate source of energy for movement and many other activities.

Oesterhelt and Stoeckenius have been studying a very unusual bacterium that can live only in environments extremely high in salt content, such as the Dead Sea. The scientists found that this bacterium produces, probably as part of its cell membrane, a protein very similar to the rhodopsin in animals' eyes. They also discovered that, like the animal rhodopsin, the bacterial protein reacts to light. When the protein is illuminated, a reaction begins in which the bacterium looses hydrogen ions and produces ATP.

In January, 1974, Stoeckenius and biochemist Ephraim Racker of Cornell University, Ithaca, N.Y., reported experiments in which they broke open some of the unusual bacteria. After the bacteria's contents had run out of their cell membranes, the scientists used portions of the membranes that contained the rhodopsinlike protein, with light to stimulate the synthesis of ATP.

All this raises some intriguing questions about evolution. Did these strange bacteria evolve in a different manner from other forms of life on earth? For many years, scientists have wondered if life might have come to earth from another planet. Could these bacteria, with their unique capacity for energy generation, have come from a planet where life exists in a salt brine? Or, did rhodopsin first evolve for its energy-production function, but later in evolutionary history become the photosensing pigment of the retina?

Evolution in a test tube. Darwin's theory of evolution is based on the premise that the successful organism gains properties that make it better adapted to survive and loses those that make it less able to survive than its competitors. Such changes are the result of mutation, a change in a gene that is passed along to the organism's progeny. Many laboratory experiments have demonstrated that an organism can permanently lose a characteristic because the particular gene carrying information for that characteristic is damaged or destroyed.

Slow
Virus

Some of the most exciting medical research today revolves around clues that a strange type of virus may cause chronic diseases, such as multiple sclerosis, rheumatoid arthritis, leukemia, and diabetes. Since the late 1950s, scientists have been collecting evidence that shows several neurological diseases of humans are caused by slow-acting viruses or viruslike agents. These viruses apparently survive in their hosts for years, somehow escaping detection by the immune system, before causing illness.

The term "slow infection" was first coined to describe such illnesses in 1954 by veterinary researcher Björn Sigurdsson of Iceland, who pioneered work on chronic diseases of sheep. He found that some of these fatal diseases could be transmitted from sheep to sheep, but the symptoms did not appear until years after the sheep were infected. This differed greatly from acute viral infections, such as influenza or poliomyelitis, which produce a brief illness days or weeks after they enter the body. If the patient survives, he usually has lifelong immunity.

In 1957, virus researchers D. Carleton Gajdusek of the U.S. National Institutes of Health (NIH) and Vincent Zigas of the Papua-New Guinea Health Service ventured into the Eastern Highlands of New Guinea to study a strange illness that occurs only among the Fore, a primitive people who practiced cannibalism. The Fore were being wiped out by a brain disease called kuru. Victims cannot control their body movements, and they always die within three to six months after the first symptoms appear. Scientists later pinpointed kuru as the first slow infection known to afflict humans.

The solution to the mystery of kuru began unfolding in 1959 when William Hadlow, a U.S. veterinary pathologist working in England, found remarkable similarities in symptoms and brain changes between kuru and scrapie, one of the slow infections of sheep. In 1966, Gajdusek and an NIH colleague, Clarence J. Gibbs, Jr., injected chimpanzees and other primates with a preparation made from the brain tissue of human kuru victims. They found that the disease could be transmitted; symptoms developed from $1^{1}/_{2}$ to 8 years later and progressed slowly, as it did in the New Guinea natives. In the same way, the scientists then tried to transmit a variety of other chronic human diseases to chimpanzees. They succeeded with an unusual illness called Creutzfeldt-Jakob disease, which causes premature senility and usually leads to death within a year.

Scientists believe that kuru was transmitted among the Fore people by cannibalism, because after the practice was outlawed, the incidence of kuru dropped. But they do not know how Creutzfeldt-Jakob disease is transmitted. Also, the agents that cause scrapie in sheep and kuru and Creutzfeldt-Jakob disease in man have proved to be quite a mystery. Although scientists know these agents reproduce and have transmitted them to other animals, they have never seen them. And there is no evidence that animals and humans make antibodies to fight these agents, as they do when invaded by conventional viruses. These slow-infection agents resist heat, ultraviolet radiation, and formalin. These treatments normally kill or weaken viruses, which are made up of nucleic acids and a protein coat. Because the slow infections are not affected, some scientists began to suspect that they are not viruses at all, but may represent an unknown class of infectious agents.

In studying other chronic human diseases, scientists have found more conventional slow-acting viruses. In 1969, scientists at the NIH and the University of Michigan isolated a measleslike virus from the brain tissue of patients afflicted with subacute sclerosing panencephalitis. This chronic children's brain disease eventually results in mental deterioration and paralysis. The virus appears to be a variant, or mutant, of the measles virus.

In 1971, scientists at the University of Wisconsin and at Johns Hopkins University isolated viruses from victims of a brain disease called progressive multifocal leukoencephalopathy. This disease usually occurs in adults whose immune systems are not functioning normally. It affects nerve fibers that send impulses out from brain cells—as does multiple sclerosis, a crippling disease of young adults.

Extensive research is now probing the possible role of slow viruses in chronic diseases of the joints, kidneys, lungs, and other organs, as well as the brain. Only a few years ago, slow infection was an obscure term in veterinary medicine. Today, work on slow viral infections is one of the most active and exciting areas of medical research.   [Richard Johnson]

Microbiology

Continued

In July, 1973, microbiologists John Campbell, Judith Lengyel, and John Langridge at the University of California, Los Angeles, reported the first experiments in which evolution involving the gain of a cell function has been demonstrated in the test tube. They used the common intestinal bacterium *Escherichia coli,* which grows very well when fed the sugar lactose. The bacterium needs a series of specific enzymes in order to use the lactose. The first of the enzymes is beta-galactosidase, which breaks the lactose down into simpler sugars.

The scientists isolated a mutant strain that was unable to grow on lactose. The mutant bacteria had lost the ability to produce beta-galactosidase, but it still had all of the other enzymes needed for growth on lactose.

Next, the scientists placed the mutant bacteria on a medium containing several substances including a nutrient they could grow on, lactose, and a small amount of a tetrazolium dye. Any bacteria that began feeding on the lactose would produce white colonies because of the effect that an acid formed from the

sugar has on the tetrazolium dye in the medium. The mutant bacteria, not using the lactose, grew as red colonies.

After about a month, patches of white growth appeared at the edge of some of the red colonies. The scientists isolated bacteria from the white area and confirmed that they had reacquired the ability to use lactose. These bacteria, however, grew on lactose much more slowly than did the parent organisms. The scientists gave the new bacteria the code name EBG-1, which means evolved beta-galactosidase, first isolated.

The researchers then designed experiments to try to improve upon the evolved bacterium. They grew EBG-1 bacteria on a solid lactose medium and isolated the fastest-growing colony. These bacteria, now EBG-2, contained more beta-galactosidase than EBG-1, but still did not grow as fast as the original parent organism. The scientists repeated the procedure three more times before obtaining EBG-5, bacteria which grew as rapidly as the original bacteria.

Had the EBG-5 cell reacquired the original gene responsible for formation

Knobby colonies of T mycoplasmas were discovered on the "necks" of sperm from sterile men. This helps confirm the suspected role of the bacterialike organisms in reproductive failure. Magnification is about 15,000 times.

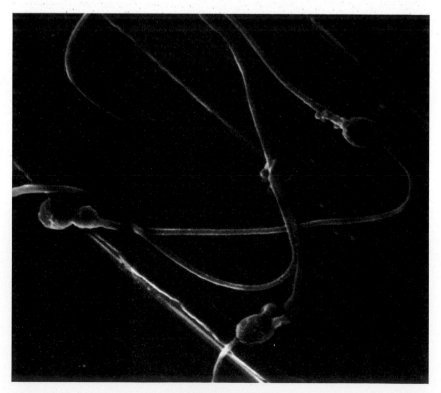

Microbiology

Continued

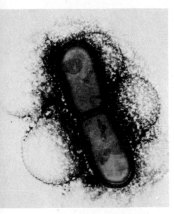

Bacterium, magnified about 10,000 times while dividing into two organisms, was found in a spring that provided a chemical environment similar to that believed to exist on Jupiter.

of beta-galactosidase, or had a completely new gene evolved to produce the enzyme? In an attempt to answer this question, the researchers isolated the beta-galactosidase enzyme from both the original strain and EBG-5. A comparison of several properties of the two enzymes showed them to be quite different. For example, the enzyme from EBG-5 weighed twice as much per molecule as the enzyme from the parent. Also, the original beta-galactosidase was controlled—that is, it was produced only when lactose was present. The EBG-5 enzyme was produced regardless of whether lactose was present. These results suggested that an entirely new gene had been evolved in the EBG-5.

In an attempt to prove conclusively that a completely new gene had evolved, the scientists carried out an experiment that took advantage of the ability of the bacteria to pass genes from one to another. It has long been known that if two strains of *E. coli* bacteria are mixed in a test tube, one will inject genes into the other. If the culture is not disturbed, the donor will inject its entire chromosome, containing all its genes, into the recipient. The genes of the donor are always injected in the same sequence—gene 1 enters first, gene 2, second, and so on. The process can be interrupted simply, by vigorously shaking the test tube.

Campbell, Lengyel, and Langridge then prepared two separate cultures. In one, they mixed the original parent strain with a recipient strain that cannot grow on lactose. In the other, they mixed the EBG-5 strain with the same recipient strain. Then they determined the time at which the beta-galactosidase gene was transferred to the recipient. They did this by interrupting the injection process at different times and testing the recipient bacteria to see if they could use lactose. The gene was received from the original bacteria after 10 minutes and from EBG-5 after 59 minutes. Thus, the two genes are located on completely different parts of the bacteria's chromosome and are different. An organism unable to use a substance for growth had acquired by mutation a new gene allowing it to do so: a clear test-tube demonstration of evolution in action.   [Jerald C. Ensign]

Neurology

What causes drug addiction? What mechanism in the body brings about physical dependence on heroin and other narcotics, and makes "withdrawal" such a terrible, agonizing ordeal, sometimes even causing death? Solomon Snyder, Candace Pert, and their associates at Johns Hopkins University School of Medicine in Baltimore may have found an answer to these questions.

Experimenting with rats, monkeys, and human brain tissue, they demonstrated in 1973 that opiates act on brain cells by combining with certain protein molecules on the surface membrane of the cells. These opiate receptors interact in a highly specific and selective manner with the molecules of the opiate. This apparently changes the normal chemical communications among affected cells in the brain.

Snyder's group is working to develop opiate "antagonists," chemicals with opiatelike structures that can occupy the receptor site and block the action of opiate "agonists," the active components of opiates. They hope to find a safe, effective antagonist that does not cause dependency. Such a chemical could be used to cure addicts by interfering with the action of the opiate agonist on the cell receptor.

Their work may also lead to the development of opiatelike substances, combining activities of both agonist and the antagonist. These would be able to block pain as effectively as opiates without causing addiction. Perhaps, too, the understanding of the biological mechanisms of pain will be advanced by this research.

Fast brain food. Chronic malnutrition, especially protein deprivation during early development (prenatal as well as postnatal), alters the chemical composition of the brain. It causes brain damage and stunted growth of brain structures. Work reported in 1973 by Richard Wurtman, John Fernstrom, and their fellow scientists in the Department of Nutrition and Food Science at Massachusetts Institute of Technology has produced the unexpected finding that the brain responds in some ways to nourishment in a very short time.

Working with rats, they found that the rate of synthesis of serotonin, one of the chemicals that transmits information be-

TV Eyes
for the
Blind

A researcher checks
television images of
the phosphenes a blind
volunteer "sees" when
electrodes implanted in
his brain are stimulated.

A dramatic development combining electronics and neurosurgery in 1973 may eventually help restore a form of sight to many blind people. Experiments by researchers at the University of Utah's Institute for Biomedical Engineering could lead to an artificial-vision device that will permit the blind to "see" well enough to read ordinary printed material.

In sighted persons, light enters the eye, strikes the retina, and the light sensation is transmitted by the optic nerve to the visual center located at the back of the brain. In this way, the visual center receives a picture of the outside world.

In 1968, British scientists Giles S. Brindley and Wallace Cambridge began experimenting with electric current to stimulate the visual centers of blind volunteers. They found that blind persons could perceive spots of light, called phosphenes, when certain points in their visual center were stimulated by electric pulses. This occurs even when the nerve path between eye and brain is partly or completely destroyed. The perceived brightness of a phosphene can also be controlled by varying the intensity of the current. The University of Utah team, led by biophysicist William H. Dobelle and computer scientist M. J. Mladejovsky, is trying to develop their artificial-vision device based on these principles.

In August, 1973, surgeons working with the Utah group installed electrodes—64 platinum wires embedded in Teflon—in the visual centers of two blind volunteers. One, a 43-year-old man, has been blind since adolescence because of eye disease. The other man, 28 years old, was blinded at 21 by a war injury.

Each man's electrodes were connected to a cable brought out through a slit in the scalp. The cable was connected to a computer, which processed signals between the brain and the electrodes; a television screen, which reproduced what the patient was "seeing"; and a stimulator, which applied weak pulses of current (about 3 milliamperes) to the electrodes.

Each patient's response to stimulation varied—the light spots appeared in different places. So the researchers tried to produce a phosphene "map" on a television screen for each volunteer by stimulating the electrodes and asking each man

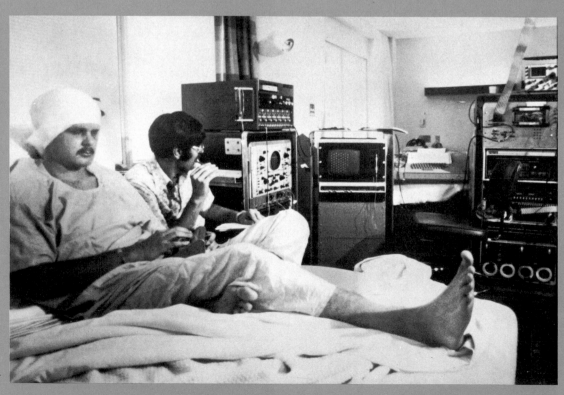

where he "saw" the spots. Because the electrodes implanted in the 43-year-old patient slipped, the researchers were unable to complete his map. But they were able to map the other volunteer.

Then the researchers sent visual signals to the patient. By aiming a light pen at points on his phosphene map, which appeared on the TV screen, they were able to stimulate corresponding electrodes in the patient's brain. They "drew" circles, triangles, and letters of the alphabet, and the volunteer could distinguish the shapes and patterns.

Although success is years away, the experiments encouraged the Utah group to work on a system for producing artificial sight. They are trying to develop a device that consists of a tiny camera inside a glass eye. The artificial eye would be mounted in the patient's eye socket and would operate somewhat like a television camera, transmitting bursts of signals to the electrodes in the brain.

Signals from the camera would be sent by a small cable to special processing circuitry—a sort of minicomputer—set in an eyeglass frame. The circuitry would transform the visual signals into electronic pulses and transmit them to a receiver implanted between the patient's skull and scalp. The receiver would be connected to electrodes surgically placed in the visual areas of the brain.

Much further experimentation will be required before the system can be incorporated in a practical visual device. For example, researchers will have to learn which materials are best for insulating the components that will be implanted in the human body. The body is extremely corrosive to metals, and the most minute pinholes in insulating material can cause problems in the circuitry. Furthermore, some of the substances used in manufacturing the circuits can have toxic effects on the body. Researchers also must learn whether continuous stimulation over long periods of time can harm the brain and nervous system.

Dobelle estimates that in mass production the new device should cost less than $5,000, plus $2,000 for the electrode-implanting operation. He warns that the device will not be able to produce normal vision. Nevertheless, any means that would help the blind lead more independent and fulfilling lives would certainly be welcomed. [Samuel Weber]

tween neurons, changes significantly, depending on the kind of food recently eaten. Some brain activity involving this neural transmitter is altered on an hour-to-hour basis. When carbohydrates are eaten, insulin is secreted from the pancreas, raising the level of tryptophan, an amino acid that is a precursor of serotonin. The insulin also lowers levels of other amino acids, which helps serotonin synthesis to accelerate. This swift response of the brain to food suggests that good nutrition has an immediate, as well as a long-term, importance to the brain.

Enzymes and goals. Recent population studies have indicated an inheritable genetic factor in schizophrenia, the most common and most disabling of mental diseases. The studies were made by David Rosenthal of the National Institute of Mental Health, Seymour Kety of Harvard, and others, using family medical histories and data on twins from a Danish government health survey. In 1973, Larry Stein and C. David Wise, of Wyeth Laboratories in Philadelphia, found further evidence of the possible physical basis of schizophrenia—the brains of schizophrenics seem to contain less of an important enzyme than do the brains of normal people.

Although the symptoms of the disease can vary widely from one patient to another, a common feature of schizophrenics is their disorganization—the lack of integrating purpose or goal in their activities. Goal-directed thinking and behavior has been associated with a particular chemical system in the brain, the noradrenergic pathways. Stein and Wise proposed that these pathways are damaged in schizophrenics. Their hypothesis seems to be partly correct.

They examined post-mortem brain specimens from 18 schizophrenics and 12 normal persons and found significantly less of the enzyme that is responsible for the final step in the production of noradrenaline, called dopamine-beta-hydroxylase (DBH), in the brains of the schizophrenics. Thus, it would seem that a deficit in DBH may well be associated with schizophrenia. If compensatory treatment could make up the deficit, the disease might be alleviated. Further research on these and other chemically coded pathways in the brain may help us to understand the basis of normal as well as abnormal moods and emotions.

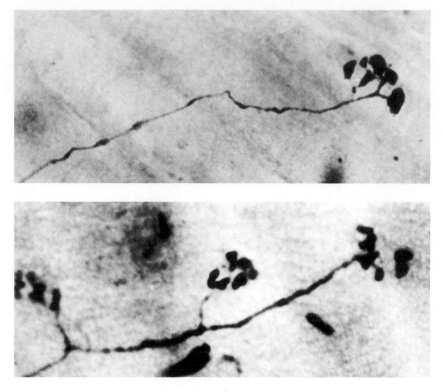

Normal muscle nerve has only one set of nerve endings, *right top.* Muscle nerve taken from a psychotic shows an abnormal number of endings, *right bottom.* Extra endings may also be present in the nerves of the brain and spinal cord of psychotics.

Neurology

Continued

New circuits for old. Brain damage does not always mean permanent loss of its functions. Sometimes motor or sensory functions drastically impaired by brain or spinal cord injury gradually return to normal. But how does this recovery come about? Nerve cells in the central nervous system of mammals generally do not regenerate as other body cells do; so, much of the recovery must be attributed to retraining or to the brain's use of uninjured nerve circuits.

But perhaps there is some form of regeneration of nerve cell connections that slightly resembles the complete regeneration seen in some invertebrates, amphibians, and fish, or in mammals, the regrowth of fibers in nerves outside the central nervous system. Gary Lynch, Carl Cotman, and their colleagues at the Department of Psychobiology, University of California, Irvine, are studying the changes that occur in cell connections in the brains of rats following experimental lesions. Working on the hippocampus, an area in the center of the brain noted for the regularity and complexity of its interconnections, they try to observe changes

that occur after small segments in other parts of the brain are removed.

In one study, they removed the entorhinal cortex, which normally has fibers extending to a segment of the hippocampus. Within 2 days in the case of 11-day-old rats and in a little more than 4 days in adults, other nerve fibers spread to the area no longer served by fibers from the removed entorhinal cortex. Electrophysiological recordings showed that these new fibers made working connections; electrical signals could be observed that appeared completely normal when compared to the signals recorded before removal of the entorhinal cortex.

Because the scientists were working with areas of the brain whose functions are little understood, only the electrical connections and certain chemical interactions within the brain could be tested. Behavioral functions could not be examined. Yet, these and other experiments now going on may help our understanding of how recovery from brain damage occurs. They may even be an early step in teaching us how to promote such a recovery.   [George Adelman]

Nutritionists studied the use of soybean protein in food products with new interest in 1973. More than 1,100 delegates from 47 countries discussed the role of the soybean in providing valuable protein in the human diet, at the World Soy Protein Congress in Munich, West Germany, in November.

While the soybean has long been a part of Oriental diets, it has been used primarily as animal feed in Western nations. It is now obvious, however, that world meat, fish, and poultry supplies will not be able to fulfill protein demands, and other sources must be found. The soybean is a rich source of protein.

The process by which soy protein is extracted is not new, but the great strides made in processing it to resemble more popular foods has increased its demand. Frank E. Horan of the Archer-Daniels-Midland Company described how textured material, which is used to make such food products as meat substitutes, is formed. The procedure is similar to the method by which nylon and other synthetic fibers are made. The protein is dissolved in a salt solution and then squirted into a bath that coagulates the protein into long threadlike fibers. These fibers are then formed into the desired shapes. Other delegates described the use of soy protein as an additive in meat, dairy foods, and bakery goods.

Nutritionists see the soybean as a much-needed source of protein, but fear that a large-scale switch to this plant protein may inadvertently decrease the intake of the various vitamins and minerals found in meat and dairy products. Some concern has also been expressed that soy protein will not supply sufficient amounts of all the amino acids that the body requires. The metabolic machinery of the body can produce some of these protein subunits, but others must be supplied directly in the diet. Soy protein is significantly lower in one of these essential amino acids, methionine, than is animal protein from beef or milk.

Protein mixes. One means of overcoming such an amino acid shortage in a protein is to mix it with a source of another protein. George G. Graham and Juan M. Baertl of the Johns Hopkins School of Hygiene and Public Health in

"No more carbohydrates until you finish your protein."

Baltimore tested several mixtures of soy protein with corn, wheat, and oat protein. They found that all of these mixtures were complete protein sources, but the body assimilated the protein from a soy and corn meal mixture best.

Ronald E. Turk and his colleagues at the University of Alabama School of Medicine in Birmingham reported similar results late in 1973. They tested a more sophisticated product that contained soy protein with egg white protein in a food which resembled chicken. Mary Korslund, Constance Kies, and Hazel M. Fox, investigators at the University of Nebraska, found that textured soy protein with methionine can be utilized by the body in the same way as beef protein.

Mineral fortification. Little is known of how to fortify food with minerals, as compared to protein or vitamins. Even less is known about the effect of mineral fortification. For example, though iron has been added to bread for several decades, there is still some question as to how much of the added iron finds its way into and is used by the body. Erik Björn-Rasmussen and his co-workers at the University of Göteborg in Sweden reported in 1973 that the added iron seems to be as available to the body as the iron naturally present in the wheat.

The Swedish scientists grew wheat, soybeans, and rice in a medium rich in ^{55}Fe, an isotope of iron, which the plants absorbed naturally as they grew. After the scientists harvested the plants, they made brown bread from the wheat, and porridges from the rice and the beans. They enriched all three foods with ^{59}Fe, another form of iron. Blood samples from volunteers who ate the foods showed that similar amounts of both forms of iron were used by the body.

Trace minerals and disease. The value or danger of trace minerals, elements appearing in the human diet in extremely small quantities, is open to more question because their roles in the human diet are unclear. Maurice L. Sievers of the Indian Medical Center in Phoenix, Ariz., suggested in July, 1973, that the trace-element intake of the Pima Indians he has been studying can be related to their abnormally high incidence of various metabolic diseases. He compared the Pima diet with the average U.S. diet and found that the Indian diet had significantly higher levels of boron,

lithium, strontium, and several other trace elements, and was significantly lower in zinc and manganese. An astonishing 45 per cent of Pima men have diabetes. It is clear that trace elements in the diet must be more closely examined.

Beef consumption has concerned nutritionists because beef contains a substantial amount of fat in addition to its desirable protein. Too much meat fat has been associated by some investigators with high cholesterol levels in the blood. The higher the blood cholesterol, the greater the chance of cardiovascular disease. To lower the risk of heart disease, people have been advised to eat less animal fat and substitute a plant fat or oil wherever possible. Few people, however, easily or readily lower meat intake.

Paul J. Nestel and his colleagues at the Australian National University in Canberra reported in 1973 a novel approach to decreasing the intake of animal fat. The type of fat consumed by an animal influences the characteristics of the fat it forms. The Australian investigators fed cattle a diet high in plant oils, and then fed the beef from these cattle to a group of volunteers. Between 45 and 50 per cent of their calories came from beef fat.

After four weeks on the diet, the volunteers showed a blood cholesterol drop of 10 per cent. This method of lowering blood cholesterol is promising because it does not require a shift in the type of foods a person eats.

Food and pesticides. The increasing changes in foods to meet modern production, packaging, and other demands have caused a renewed interest in pre-industrial styles of agriculture. Advocates of "natural foods" have indicted modern foods on a number of grounds, such as harboring pesticide residues.

Howard Appledorf, Willis B. Wheeler, and John A. Koburger of the University of Florida sampled 24 foods from a traditional supermarket and 24 from a health food store. None of the 48 samples had pesticide residues of over 0.01 part per million, the lower limit of the method employed for detection. Seven of the health foods and three of the supermarket foods contained some traces of an environmental pollutant, polychlorinated biphenyls. The 1973 report concluded that the major difference between the samples was the higher cost of the "health foods."   [Paul E. Araujo]

Oceanography

In August, 1973, the National Oceanic and Atmospheric Administration (NOAA) created the Ocean Remote Sensing Laboratory (ORSL) to study the oceans from aircraft and satellites. Research at ORSL, which is part of the Atlantic Oceanographic and Meteorological Laboratories at Miami, Fla., will concentrate on the physical and chemical aspects of oceans and estuaries. Scientists will also develop new remote-sensing devices to aid in such studies.

Scientists at the new laboratory began by using data from existing satellites, particularly NOAA spacecraft and the National Aeronautic and Space Administration's (NASA) Earth Resources Technology Satellite, ERTS-1. The remote-sensing tools used for this research include microwave radiometers, lasers and lidars (the laser equivalent of radar), acoustic sounders, and infrared sensors. Satellite observations enable scientists to receive and distribute information rapidly. For example, ERTS-1 ice maps reveal safe routes for ships through shifting Arctic ice floes. Infrared sensors define upwellings (vertical currents that bring nutrients to the

surface) and changes in ocean currents, which can tell fishermen each day where to find fish.

Satellite-assisted studies. Several major projects used satellites for oceanographic work in 1973 and 1974. NOAA began a five-year program to assess the marine ecosystem of the Atlantic coastal waters, from southern Massachusetts to New York State. The U.S. Army Corps of Engineers used data from ERTS-1 to prepare maps of the coasts of North and South Carolina and Washington state. The Environmental Protection Agency monitored water pollution by studying ERTS-1 images.

In February and March, NOAA reported that the ERTS-1 satellite had collected data on the movement and structure of sediment plumes issuing from the mouths of rivers, the location of sewage dumps and how the sewage is dispersing, and the boundaries marked by differences in temperature or salt content between major masses of ocean water.

ERTS-1 also collected data on the characteristics of internal waves, large underwater waves or oscillations. The satel-

As of August, 1973, more than 250 drill sites have yielded samples of the earth's crust cored by the research ship *Glomar Challenger.*

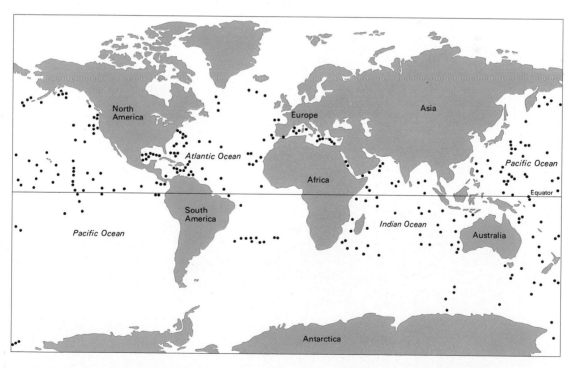

Predicting Perilous Tides

Rare alignment of sun, earth, and moon at its nearest point to earth can cause flood tides. Such conditions have occurred only about 20 times in 300 years.

Tides ran particularly high on certain days in 1974, causing flooding in some coastal areas, and they will reach similar heights several times in 1975. Exact alignments of the moon, earth, and sun combined with a very close proximity of the moon to the earth on January 8, February 6, July 19, and August 17 triggered these tides. Their flooding influence was enhanced wherever storms along the coast created onshore winds. Such a combination of tides and winds also could cause coastal flooding on or about January 28, February 25, September 6, and October 4, 1975.

Tides are produced by the gravitational attraction of the moon and sun on large bodies of water. Twice each month, at either new or full moon, the earth, moon, and sun align outside the plane that would result in an eclipse. The position is called syzygy, and the tides rise higher than usual. These are called spring tides, because the ocean waters "well" or "spring" to greater heights.

Since the moon revolves around the earth in an elliptical orbit, once each revolution (about once a month) it

reaches perigee, its closest approach to the earth. This also raises tides above normal. But on the infrequent occasions when perigee and syzygy occur within even a day or so of each other, bringing the moon exceptionally close to the earth, perigean spring tides of unusual height are produced.

In the four cases of extreme perigean spring tides in 1974, perigee and syzygy occurred within 1.6 to 23.4 hours of each other. Two weeks prior to the time that winds whipped up sea swells in the Pacific Ocean on January 8, scientists at the National Ocean Survey of the U.S. National Oceanic and Atmospheric Administration (NOAA) warned of possible flooding along the southwest coast of the United States. Thousands of sandbags, laid along lowland regions in response, greatly reduced flooding damage. However, high waters still washed away sections of the shoreline and damaged seawalls and waterfront property at Newport, Laguna, Malibu, Capistrano, San Clemente, and Mission beaches in California. On the Atlantic coast, an atmospheric high pressure system and off-

Aligned for danger

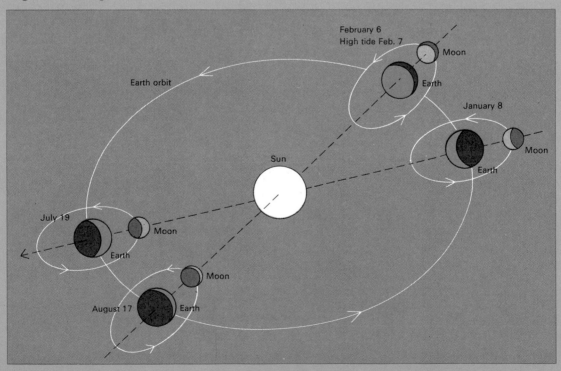

shore winds around January 8, as well as prevailing offshore winds on February 6 and 7, prevented the occurrence of any appreciable tidal flooding.

Perigean spring tides occur in Europe 2 or 3 days later than on the west coast of North America. This is because the movement of ocean water has a specific period of resonance that creates a delay time. There are also several other complex factors that affect the movement of ocean water. Thus, when a strong onshore gale occurred along the southwest coasts of England and Wales and on the islands of Guernsey and Lewis on January 11 and 12, seawalls were breached by high waters. Severe storm surges occurred at Appledore in north Devonshire; at Minehead, Somersetshire; and at Amroth, Pembrokeshire. There was widespread flooding at Lynmouth, Bideford, and Ilfracombe in Devonshire, and the inundation at Barnstaple was described as the greatest in 25 years. High waters also invaded a large portion of the airfield at Stornoway, in the Outer Hebrides off the coast of Scotland.

Based on a comparison between such special astronomical circumstances and examples of severe coastal flooding occurring in North America over a period of 281 years, NOAA has developed a statistical quantity, known as the delta omega-syzygy coefficient, indicating the likelihood of coastal flooding. It evaluates significant changes in the tide-raising forces and accelerations produced by the moon and sun, and serves as a predictor of the rate of tide growth. It expresses the potential for coastal flooding arising from astronomically induced extreme tides which are coupled with onshore surface winds. When the delta omega-syzygy coefficient was computed for numerous instances of past coastal flooding, it was discovered that the potential for tidal flooding was clearly revealed by this analytic device. To date, it has shown a direct correlation with 36 cases of major coastal flooding along both the east and west coasts of North America extending back to the year 1693, and with 31 additional cases of the highest local tides of record observed over a maximum 77-year period. Hopefully, the use of the delta omega-syzygy coefficient in the future will save lives and property loss because it will give coastal residents sufficient warning to prepare for flooding.   [Fergus J. Wood]

lite photographs showed the waves up to a depth of about 180 feet off the New York coast. The satellite was able to detect the internal waves because of the changes caused on the ocean surface as these waves passed underneath. See CATALOGING THE WHOLE EARTH.

In August, 1973, the U.S. Naval Oceanographic Office conducted a study of upwelling in the Atlantic Ocean between the Canary Islands and the northeast coast of Africa, called the Sahara Upwelling Expedition. Data from the NOAA-2 satellite were received in the Canary Islands and displayed on a television screen to aid scientists in planning daily measurements from ships in the area. These measurements were used to calibrate sensor packages aboard ERTS and Skylab. An international study of upwelling in this same region, coordinated by the Duke University Marine Laboratory, began in March, 1974.

In May, 1973, NOAA scientists completed a series of experiments on ocean currents in the Sargasso Sea. Five drifting data buoys were set out 60 miles apart in this western part of the North Atlantic Ocean. A French satellite kept track of their exact location as they drifted about with the currents.

From the experiments, scientists learned that ocean currents in the Sargasso Sea are far more erratic and unpredictable than they had thought. Some buoys moved in unexpected directions, changed direction frequently, and even floated in circles. Others moved erratically but without making any real changes in their positions for from two to three months at a time.

Deep-sea drilling. In June, 1973, the U.S. research vessel *Glomar Challenger* drilled into and removed core samples from some of the oldest portions of the Pacific Ocean floor. The drilling rig bored more than 4,000 feet into the sea floor of the Ontong-Java Plateau in the southwest Pacific, recovering sediments estimated to be 120 million years old. Analysis of the sediments, part of an investigation of the Australian and Pacific tectonic plates, indicates that when these plates converged, they created the deep trenches and volcanic formations that are major features of this area.

Other core samples taken by the *Glomar Challenger* from the Mariana Trench and from the Philippine Sea show the floor of

Oceanography

Continued

RUFAS II, a robot deep-sea diver being developed by the National Oceanic and Atmospheric Administration, dives with sonar and television cameras to inspect the ocean floor for valuable schools of fish and other ocean resources.

this basin is only about 60 million years old. It was formed either by an eastward movement of the crust or when the Pacific and Australian plates temporarily moved apart, leaving geological scar tissue. The study showed that the Sea of Japan is even younger, having opened some tens of millions of years ago.

Mid-Atlantic Ridge. While on its November, 1973, cruise, NOAA's Transatlantic Geotraverse (TAG) Expedition discovered several important geophysical phenomena associated with the Mid-Atlantic Ridge. By examining eroded rocks dredged up from the ridge, Robert Scott of Texas A&M University discovered that hot springs issue from deep fractures parallel to the median valley of the ridge. Peter A. Rona, a NOAA geophysicist, discovered large accumulations of unusually pure manganese in rocks dredged up during the TAG cruise. He believes this is the first hydrothermal mineral deposit discovered in the median valley of the Mid-Atlantic Ridge. It accumulated about a hundred times faster than the manganese nodules known to cover large areas of the sea floor.

Rona's research complemented that of Scott in understanding how hot-spring activity helps the mineral-forming process. When geothermally heated water containing minerals circulates through fissures in the rock, the minerals precipitate out onto exposed underlying layers of rock. Analyses of the manganese samples indicated that some 7 inches of manganese was deposited every million years through the action of hot springs.

The French-American Mid-Ocean Undersea Study (FAMOUS) continued research on the Mid-Atlantic Ridge in 1974. The U.S. research submersible, *Alvin,* and the French submersibles, *Archimède* and *Cyana,* were scheduled to make visual studies of the Mid-Atlantic Ridge in late 1974. This will allow scientists to examine the submarine topography and geology of the ridge firsthand. The *Archimède* made seven preliminary dives in the ridge area during summer, 1973.

Ocean resources. The *Hughes Glomar Explorer* sailed from Long Beach, Calif., on Feb. 15, 1974, to begin a series of deep-ocean mining experiments. If successful, the mining operation will harvest

Oceanography
Continued

manganese nodules from the sea floor at depths of from 12,000 to 20,000 feet. More than 1.6 trillion metric tons of nodules are estimated to lie on the Pacific Ocean floor. The nodules form continuously at an estimated rate of 6 million tons a year. If deep-sea mining becomes a reality, the present world needs for copper, nickel, cobalt, and manganese — elements that are found in the nodules — could be supplied indefinitely from the Pacific Ocean floor.

The technical difficulties in harvesting manganese nodules have reportedly been overcome by at least eight companies in the world. The Summa Corporation, controlled by Howard Hughes, is the first company to begin actual sea tests. The 36,000-ton Hughes ship houses a submersible mining vehicle connected to the ship by several miles of pipe and electrical power conduits. Details of the experimental mining operation are not available because of the highly competitive nature of the venture. However, it is likely that deep-sea nodule mining will become a commercial reality long before the legal details of such mining have been settled by the United Nations Conference on the Law of the Sea.

The Rand Corporation, conducting a study for the National Science Foundation, determined that it is possible to harvest icebergs to add to the California coast's fresh-water supply. Rand reported that icebergs could be delivered to California from Antarctica, converted to water, and sold to wholesale dealers for about $30.00 per acre-foot (enough to cover one acre with one foot of water).

Icebergs would be insulated from the warmer seawater with a special plastic film, which scientists hope will prevent most of the iceberg from melting during its year-long trip. The icebergs would be powered by large electric motors strapped to the sides, with a nuclear power plant on an escort vessel supplying the motors with electricity. Several icebergs could be controlled by one support ship. Research will continue until the scientists feel certain that the project will cause no environmental damage and until a planning conference can be held among all nations concerned with the Antarctic waters. [Richard H. Chesher]

Physics

Atomic and Molecular Physics. Researchers at Harvard University, the University of Paris, and Stanford University independently demonstrated in 1974 that they could improve by a factor of 100 their ability to distinguish between various atomic energy states having nearly the same energy. They reported almost simultaneously on a new technique called two-photon spectroscopy that uses two laser beams to eliminate unwanted effects caused by relative motions of the gas atoms that they study.

In normal atomic absorption spectroscopy, a single finely tuned laser beam, passing through a gas, boosts the atoms' orbiting electrons into higher-energy orbits. Because the frequency of the laser beam determines its energy, physicists can calculate the energy difference between the high- and low-energy atomic states if they know precisely the laser frequency. In this way, they probe the atom's detailed electronic structure.

In practice, however, when a very finely tuned laser beam is used as the probing light, only a small fraction of the atoms in the gas under study will absorb the laser light — a result of their constant random motions. For example, if the laser is tuned exactly to the absorption frequency for atoms at rest, then only those nearly at rest or moving at right angles to the direction of the laser beam absorb the laser light. Atoms moving toward the light source would be excited by light having a slightly lower frequency than the laser frequency. Those moving away would absorb light of a slightly higher frequency.

These changes in absorption frequency are similar to the change in pitch of a moving train whistle. Both are examples of the Doppler shift, the change in frequency caused by the relative motion of a source (the whistle or laser beam) and a receiver (an ear or an atom).

The research groups used two diametrically opposed laser beams, both tuned to a frequency exactly half as large as that needed to excite a stationary atom. It absorbs the light energy only if two photons (packets of light energy) arrive simultaneously. When two photons strike a moving atom from opposite directions, then the frequency of one is slightly more

Physics
Continued

than half the excitation energy required, that of the other slightly less, but their sum will be exactly right. Thus, pairs of photons can interact with any atom, regardless of its motion, provided that the laser frequency is exactly half that required to excite an atom at rest.

Two-photon spectroscopy greatly increases the number of gas atoms that are excited and makes the measurements far more precise. The Stanford research group, led by Arthur Schawlow, reported that the new technique allowed them to distinguish between energy levels in sodium atoms that were 100 times closer in energy than had previously been measured. They obtained the two laser beams by reflecting a single laser beam from a tunable dye laser back on itself, using a spherical mirror located opposite the cell containing sodium atoms.

Tunable UV laser tripler. Efforts to produce laser light in the far ultraviolet (UV) region of the spectrum were rewarded in 1974. Rodney T. Hodgson, Peter P. Sorokin, and James J. Wynne at International Business Machines (IBM) Thomas J. Watson Research Center in

Yorktown Heights, N.Y., reported in February that they had developed laser systems that produce continuously tunable UV light over four wave-length ranges: 1778 to 1817 angstroms (A), 1833 to 1875 A, 1870 to 1914 A, and 1907 to 1957 A. (An angstrom is one ten-millionth of a millimeter, which is about 1/250,000,000 of an inch.)

In their first series of experiments, the researchers extended the phase-matching technique developed in 1972 by Stephen E. Harris and his co-workers at Stanford University. They did their experiments with a frequency-tripling device in which light from a sodium fluorescein dye laser was passed through strontium vapor. The input wave length from the dye laser was varied from 5337 to 5710 A, and the interaction between this visible light and the strontium vapor produced weak UV light at about one-third the input wave length (three times the frequency) – from 1779 to 1903 A.

The IBM group observed that the output intensity increased by as much as 10,000 at input wave lengths of 5380 A, 5408 A, 5605 A, and 5681 A. The fre-

Physicists at Stanford University observe the laser system that they developed to detect closely spaced atomic energy levels. The researcher at right adjusts a spherical mirror that reflects the laser beam back through a cell of sodium atoms, in effect creating a second beam.

quencies associated with these four wave lengths are exactly half of that needed for a strontium atom to reach four intermediate excited states. Apparently, a strontium atom, having absorbed two photons to reach one of these intermediate states, is then much more able to absorb a third photon and reach an even higher energy state. These excited atoms subsequently return to the unexcited state by emitting photons having three times the energy (frequency) of the photons that had been absorbed. The photon intensity is far greater than at nearby frequencies reached without an intermediate state.

To produce their tunable UV laser, Hodgson, Sorokin, and Wynne tuned a sodium fluorescein dye laser to 5409 A, a frequency exactly half that necessary to excite strontium to an intermediate excited state. A second adjustable dye laser supplied the third photon that a strontium atom could absorb to reach the higher energy states. A rhodamine-G dye laser, it was tunable from 5608 to 6111 A, producing a corresponding UV output from the de-exciting strontium atoms that would thus vary from 1833 to 1875 A. The researchers produced the three other output wave-length ranges by tuning the fixed-frequency dye laser to the other intermediate states.

By using different metallic vapors—for example, lithium or sodium—the technique can be used to generate coherent radiation over other wave-length ranges. The tuning laser wave-length range can also be modified by using other dye laser combinations.

Although it converts only 0.01 per cent of the laser input power into output, the two-laser system produces several hundred milliwatts of power—enough for most photochemical and spectroscopic studies. Photochemists are particularly excited about the laser because its output wave lengths (1500 to 2000 A) coincide with the energies of many excited states of atoms and molecules that they study. See CHEMISTRY, CHEMICAL DYNAMICS.

Rydberg constant refined. Theodor W. Hänsch, M. H. Nayfeh, S. A. Lee, S. M. Curry, and I. S. Shahin used laser saturation spectroscopy techniques at Stanford to obtain a value for the Rydberg constant that is 10 times more precise than previous measurements. The Rydberg constant relates the frequency of light emitted by an atom to different series of whole numbers that label the excited and unexcited states of the atom. The laser saturation technique, developed in 1972 by Hänsch and others to eliminate Doppler effects, enabled the team to measure extremely small differences in frequencies, called the hyperfine structure, caused by the interaction of electrons with the atom's nucleus.

Measurements were made of transitions in the Balmer alpha series of both atomic hydrogen and its isotope deuterium. The wave lengths of these saturation-sharpened lines were measured relative to the wave length of a helium-neon laser that was stabilized by iodine absorption. In this way, the researchers were able to measure a value for the Rydberg constant of 109737.3143 inverse centimeters, with an experimental uncertainty of one thousandth.

Exciting helium electrons. In the helium atom, an energy of 24.58 volts is needed to completely remove one electron, which ionizes the atom. Because the excited state in which both electrons are excited ($2s^2$) normally has an energy of 57.82 volts above the ground state, it has 33.24 volts of energy more than is needed for ionization. Consequently, in less than about 10^{-14} seconds after excitation, the helium atom ejects an electron and returns to the ground state of the helium ion. The electron carries away the excess 33.24 volts of energy.

Frank H. Read and his colleagues at the University of Manchester in England bombarded helium with slow-moving electrons to create the excited state. However, the electrons ejected from the excited helium carried away considerably more energy than the expected 33.24 volts. For example, when the helium atoms were bombarded by 58.8-volt electrons, the ejected electrons carried away 33.69 volts of energy.

The energy difference increased as the energy of the bombarding electrons approached the minimum excitation energy of 57.82 volts. The experimenters believe the discrepancy arises because the self-ionizing transition is so rapid. Ejection takes place before the slow-moving bombarding electron has left the atom's vicinity, and it can still influence the helium atom and the ejected electron. The energy discrepancy is a measure of this effect.   [Karl G. Kessler]

Elementary Particles. An unexpected discovery late in the summer of 1973 boosted physicists' hopes that two of the four fundamental forces of nature—electromagnetism and the weak nuclear force—may be different forms of the same force. Appropriately, the findings came in the centennial year of James Clerk Maxwell's unified force theory of electricity, magnetism, and light. Like present-day particle physicists, Maxwell worked with no thought of practical consequences, but within a generation, his theory led to the development of radio and to Albert Einstein's theory of relativity. This historical parallel is very much on the minds of physicists today.

Three, not four, forces? For more than 40 years, physicists have recognized the existence of four basic forces. The two most familiar, gravity and electromagnetism, can act between two objects no matter how far apart they may be. The other two forces, which, for lack of any deeper understanding, have been named strong and weak, operate only at distances the size of atomic nuclei. Beyond a certain distance, or range, each force quickly disappears. The strong force, which holds atomic nuclei together by overcoming the electrical repulsion of their protons, has a range of a few trillionths of a centimeter. The weak force range is too short to measure. Its strength will remain a mystery until its exact range is known, because a strong force with a very short range can appear to be weak. The role of the weak force is also somewhat mysterious. Seemingly, it exists solely to allow certain elementary particles to change spontaneously into other particles. The particles do so at a very leisurely pace, about a million million times slower than changes caused by the strong force.

In the late 1950s, physicists first began speculating that the weak force might simply be a short-range version of electromagnetism. It would have the same strength as electromagnetism if its range were $1/300$ to $1/500$ as large.

There were two objections to this idea, however. One was purely mathematical: The formulas that are used to describe electromagnetism could not be readily adapted to a short-range force. The other was experimental: In all known reactions produced by the weak force, electric charge is transferred from one particle to another. If the weak force and elec-

tromagnetism were related, physicists said there should also be cases where no charge is transferred by the action of the weak force. Such a reaction is called a neutral current. Ordinary light is an example of a long-range neutral current, because it carries no electric charge.

The mathematical objections were removed in the late 1960s, largely through the work of Abdus Salam of Imperial College in London and Steven Weinberg of Massachusetts Institute of Technology. They developed formulas that indicated that neutral currents should be observed about one-fifth to two-fifths as often as the charge-changing reactions.

CERN breakthrough. This theoretical breakthrough intensified efforts to find the neutral current, and in September, 1973, a multinational team of experimenters at the European Center for Nuclear Research (CERN) in Geneva, Switzerland, announced the experimental breakthrough. The CERN team studied reactions produced by beams of neutrinos, neutral particles that are sensitive only to the weak force. Despite an energy of a billion electron-volts—a typical energy at CERN—the beams can pass through many tons of material with only 1 chance in 100 billion of reacting, because the weak force is so weak. But the CERN proton accelerator produces beams containing billions of neutrinos several times each minute. Thus, in a large detector weighing many tons, and operating for many weeks, thousands of neutrino reactions can be detected.

The CERN detector, a large French-built device called *Gargamelle,* weighs about 1,000 tons and consumes over 8-million watts of electric power. The heart of the detector is a tank 15 feet long and 8 feet in diameter that is filled with about 10 tons of liquid Freon (CF_3Br). Freon is used because it is a dense target, and has a convenient boiling point, below room temperature. The liquid is held under pressure to keep it from boiling until just before the arrival of a burst of neutrinos. If a neutrino reacts with an atomic nucleus, several electrically charged particles are usually ejected, and they heat the liquid along their path, leaving tracks of bubbles. Photographs taken about $1/100$ of a second later provide a permanent record. About a million photographs are required to obtain a few thousand containing the telltale tracks.

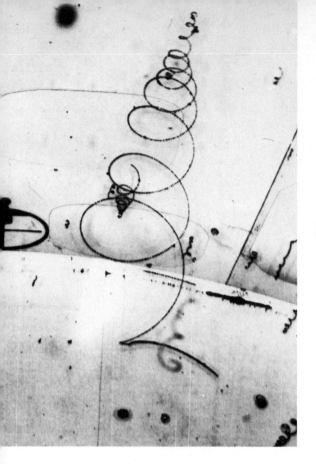

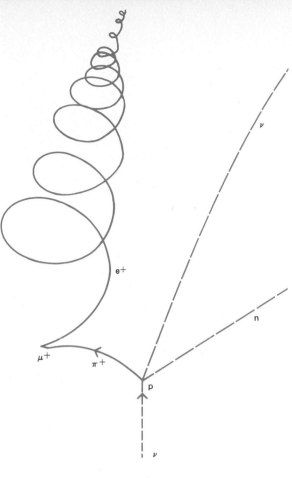

Physics

Continued

Tracks formed in liquid hydrogen by fleeting elementary particles, *above,* are the clues that two of the four fundamental forces of nature may be two different forms of the same force. Neutrino (ν) collides with a proton and veers to the right. The collision produces a neutron (n) and a pi plus meson (π^+), which changes into a positive mu meson (μ^+), and then a positron (e^+). The charge-less neutron and neutrino leave no visible tracks.

The neutrino itself leaves no track because it carries no electric charge. But after the conventional charge-changing reaction it becomes a muon, a charged particle similar to an electron. Most of the muons come to a halt in the chamber and can be easily distinguished by their track shapes and decay products from other particles blasted loose in the reaction.

In a neutral current collision, however, the neutrino remains unchanged after the collision and leaves no track. The only clue that a neutrino might be present is that the collision debris does not include a muon. But that is almost exactly what would be observed if the particle that triggered the reaction were a neutron, an ordinary constituent of the nucleus. There are always a few neutrons contaminating any neutrino beam. Nearly every one that enters the detector will induce a reaction through the strong nuclear force, and that collision debris will not include a muon.

Neutrinos or neutrons? There were many reactions without the telltale muon track in *Gargamelle,* but were they caused by neutrinos or neutrons? The CERN

group spent more than two years patiently sorting through the photographic evidence and carefully estimating the number of neutrons in the neutrino beam before they found the answer. There were more than 100 photographs showing no muon track, but neutron contamination could have produced only 10 to 20. If the rest are indeed due to neutral currents, their strength is between 20 and 40 per cent of the strength of the charged currents, just as the Weinberg theory demands.

An American team from Harvard and the universities of Pennsylvania and Wisconsin quickly duplicated the experiment. They took data using a neutrino beam at the Fermi National Accelerator Laboratory (NAL), at Batavia, Ill. They announced that they, too, detected muonless events, but spent several months rechecking their results before they felt confident that these might be true neutral currents. The NAL team had less of a problem with neutron contamination, but they used a cruder detector than *Gargamelle,* one that could miss muons if they came out slowly or at a large angle to the neutrino beam.

Physics

Continued

A flood of other confirmations followed in the spring of 1974. Examples of neutrinos colliding with electrons instead of nuclei were found at CERN. A group at Argonne National Laboratory in Lemont, Ill., found about 15 muonless events in photographs from a liquid-hydrogen bubble chamber. Though this is a small number, it is very convincing proof, because hydrogen is a simpler target than the large Freon molecules in the CERN experiment. In most cases in hydrogen, muonless reactions caused by neutrons were recognized as such and discarded.

Because it is so difficult to be sure of the origin of muonless reactions, many physicists remain skeptical that neutral currents have really been observed. The NAL neutrino beams and improved detectors should settle this question. By late 1974, they could be producing several hundred muonless events per day—data that is essential to further develop the unified force theory.

Really only two? Another major advance in experimental knowledge has come from the Stanford Linear Accelerator Center (SLAC) in California. There, experimenters have discovered that the energy released in head-on collisions between beams of electrons and their antiparticles, positrons, reappears in the form of particles that are sensitive to strong forces far more often than predicted by generally accepted theories. This confirms observations made two years earlier, at a lower energy, at the now-defunct electron accelerator in Cambridge, Mass.

In April, research teams at NAL discovered the reverse of this process—the production of electrons and muons from collisions of protons and nuclei. As was the case in the SLAC experiments, these particles appeared about 10 times more often than can be accounted for by electromagnetic forces. These results raise the hope that a link between the electromagnetic force and the strong force may be found.

Thus, a few bold theorists are looking ahead to the next, and possibly the final, step in particle theory—a grand synthesis of the strong, weak, and electromagnetic forces. Before this can be achieved, however, many questions about the nature of particles involved in the strong force must be resolved. See The Quandary Over Quarks.   [Robert H. March]

Nuclear Physics. One of the more surprising findings in nuclear science in 1974 is over 2 billion years old. Scientists generally assumed that physicist Enrico Fermi and his collaborators initiated the first nuclear fission chain reaction on earth on Dec. 2, 1942, under the west stands of Stagg Field, a football stadium at the University of Chicago. But Georges Vendryes and his colleagues at the French Atomic Energy Commission's Pierrelatte Laboratory report that nature beat Fermi to the first chain reaction.

The clue leading to this discovery was the abnormal ratio of two uranium isotopes, U-235 and U-238 in natural uranium, delivered to Pierrelatte from the Oklo Mine in Gabon, in western Africa. There was much too little U-235, the fuel isotope of nuclear power reactors.

According to the Pierrelatte scientists, the geologic processes that produced the Oklo ore first laid down the uranium about 2 billion years ago, then added water. The water acted just as it does in modern lightwater power reactors: It slowed down (moderated) neutrons emitted by U-235 nuclei and thus initiated and maintained a chain reaction. This primeval reactor operated for about a million years and delivered more than 10-billion kilowatt-hours of heat energy.

Inasmuch as such natural reactors burn U-235 out of the uranium ore, this finding raises practical questions about the availability of uranium fuels. If there are many natural reactors like the Gabon reactor, there could be much less fuel available to burn in man-made reactors than previously expected.

Spinning the nucleus. In 1973, Arne Johnson, a Stockholm physicist, discovered a striking phenomenon that may be caused by the protons and neutrons in nuclei changing from their frictionless superfluid state to their normal condition. He fired nuclei at target nuclei to set them spinning, and found that the nuclei actually spun slower despite attempts to make them spin more rapidly. This effect occurred once the nuclei had reached a critical rotational speed.

The superfluid state in nuclei is characterized by vanishing viscosity, or resistance to flow. In terms of the shell model of the nucleus, it has been understood as pairing phenomena—pairs of neutrons and pairs of protons moving back-to-back in the same shell in a stately minuet.

Physics
Continued

Superfluidity arises from the fact that nucleons obey the laws of quantum mechanics. These physical laws say that a spherical nucleus cannot rotate because all the protons and all the neutrons are identical. Spinning and stationary spherical nuclei would look alike.

However, most nuclei are shaped like footballs, and can be set spinning when hit off-center by a nuclear projectile. But if they are superfluid, the ends can slip past the spherical core, which will not spin. As the ends rotate more rapidly, centrifugal force causes them to stretch farther from the nonspinning core, and the moment of inertia, or resistance to rotation, increases slowly but steadily.

At a critical rotational speed characteristic of each superfluid nucleus, however, the neutron and proton pairs begin breaking apart, destroying the superfluid state. As this happens, the nuclear end caps can no longer slip past the central region and the whole football-shaped nucleus begins rotating. Because this configuration has a drastically higher moment of inertia, the nucleus actually spins slower despite efforts to spin it faster.

Theorists did not expect that rotational forces would destroy neutron pairs at the same critical rotational speed as proton pairs. Indeed, Gertrude Goldhaber and her collaborators at the Brookhaven National Laboratory, Long Island, reported in September, 1973, that they had found cases where two different critical rotational speeds occurred — one for neutrons and one for protons.

Weak magnetism. Theoretical studies and experiments using particle accelerators suggest that two of nature's forces, electromagnetism and the weak nuclear force, may be different forms of the same force. In May, 1974, Gerald Garvey and his collaborators at Princeton University and Brookhaven reported a new clue. They made the first direct measurement of weak magnetism, the weak force counterpart of the magnetic part of the electromagnetic force.

Physicists had long recognized that the part of the weak nuclear force that is analogous to the electric force causes certain radioactivity. But the weak force counterpart of the magnetic part of the electromagnetic force remained elusive

Drift tubes and beam hole can be seen at the center of this section of UNILAC, a heavy-ion accelerator near Darmstadt, West Germany. Beams of heavy ions accelerate as they move from tube to tube. Technicians secure metal rods that support each tube.

until Garvey's experiments. Now, any theory that attempts to unite the weak force and electromagnetism must correctly account for weak magnetism. See PHYSICS, ELEMENTARY PARTICLES.

Clocking nuclear interaction times. Georges Temmer and his colleagues at Rutgers University reported in September, 1973, that they had made the first direct time measurement in the attosecond (10^{-18} second) range—a million times faster than any previous direct measurement. Their technique opens up a whole new field of nuclear and other short-lived physical phenomena to direct time measurements.

The Rutgers physicists used the regular lattice planes of a germanium crystal as their target. The planes also served as shutters for timing bombarding protons and emitted protons in compound interactions with germanium nuclei, interactions in which the nucleus swallows up the bombarding particle and about 10^{-16} seconds later emits another particle. They measured an interaction time of 165 attoseconds—an incredibly short time interval, considering that a light beam takes about 300 million attoseconds to travel a millimeter.

Superheavy nuclei. In 1974, physicists drew closer to creating stable nuclei containing more protons and neutrons than occur naturally. In June, Jack Greenberg and his collaborators at Yale University reported that they had clearly produced quasi-atoms with 56 protons in collisions between nickel atoms (Ni-58). Quasi-atoms are short-lived atoms that are created when heavy nuclei collide. The atomic electrons behave as if they were orbiting a single nucleus containing twice the number of protons of the colliding particles, rather than orbiting the two separate nuclei.

Greenberg's group measured X rays that were emitted as the electron shells formed about the colliding nickel nuclear pair. Physicists are now more hopeful that when such heavy-ion accelerators as the UNILAC in Darmstadt, West Germany, and the SUPER-HILAC in Berkeley, Calif., begin operating in 1975, they will find superheavy quasi-atoms formed by colliding lead atoms or uranium atoms. These experiments will allow them to verify directly fundamental concepts about the nature of all matter and antimatter.   [D. Allan Bromley]

Plasma Physics. Most of the progress in plasma physics during 1974 came in the magnetic confinement and heating of plasmas needed for controlled thermonuclear fusion. Researchers have pursued two radically different approaches and have made significant advances in each.

Pellet fusion. In this approach to fusion power generation, a small, solid pellet made of the two hydrogen isotopes tritium and deuterium would absorb from 10,000 to 1 million joules of energy in a fraction of a nanosecond (billionth of a second). The energy is supplied by either a laser pulse or a high-current pulse of fast-moving electrons. Under appropriate conditions, the pellet is heated and compressed enough to undergo thermonuclear burning, thereby generating at least as much energy in the ensuing microexplosion as was required to trigger it. Attaining this "break-even" objective is the primary goal of most fusion research.

The first experimental verification of pellet compression in the laser absorption concept was reported in 1974. Using two 130-joule laser pulses of 0.37-nanosecond duration to illuminate a pellet, a group led by Keith A. Brueckner at KMS Fusion, Incorporated, in Ann Arbor, Mich., claimed, in May, to have attained a hundredfold compression of the pellet volume. Prior to this, a Russian group under Nobel laureate Nikolai G. Basov illuminated a pellet with nine laser beams of about 100 joules each. They measured a volume compression of 30.

Relativistic electron beams. In contrast to the comparatively puny lasers that have so far been built, relativistic electron beam (REB) generators that produce enough energy for pellet fusion are now available. However, researchers have not been able to focus a beam and shorten its pulse length sufficiently to meet the severe requirements for break-even.

In late 1973, Gerold Yonas and his fellow researchers at Sandia Laboratories in Albuquerque, N. Mex., reported progress in solving the REB focusing problem. They extended the 1971 pioneering work of Willard H. Bennett at North Carolina State University, who found that an electron beam generated in a vacuum diode can be focused through self-pinching—that is, the electron current's own magnetic field constricts the beam. Self-pinching occurs if a rod cathode small enough in diameter is

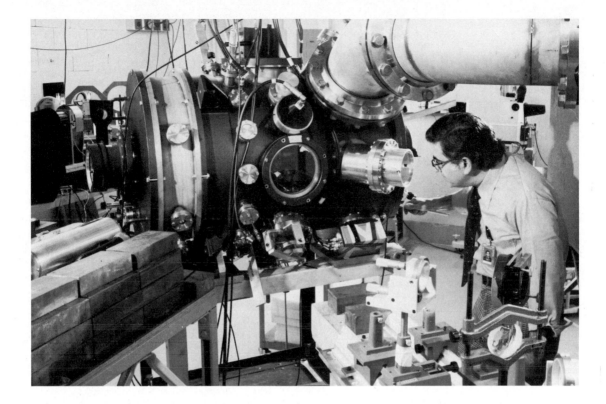

Physics

Continued

A researcher peers into a cylindrical chamber that houses a target pellet of heavy hydrogen. Laser beams compressed the pellet to 1/100th of its original volume, encouraging scientists who seek to create "solar furnaces" in laboratories on earth.

placed with its end abutting a larger-diameter anode. Unfortunately, the smaller the cathode diameter is made, the longer the pulse becomes.

Yonas's group resolved this dilemma by using a very small anode-cathode gap and injecting an auxiliary plasma near the anode prior to the arrival of the REB pulse. Experimental observations of REB-caused damage on aluminum plates agreed closely with the predictions of computer simulation.

The researchers also solved another thorny problem, the destruction of the cathode by the beam. They used a thin-shell hollow cathode instead of a solid rod to keep the destructive beam, which forms only near the cathode axis, from reaching its walls. A new REB generator incorporating all the above advances is under construction. It will generate 20-nanosecond current pulses with an energy of 200,000 joules.

Tokamaks. The traditional approach to fusion power generation is the magnetic confinement of a hot, dense deuterium-tritium plasma. But preventing the plasma from escaping the various "mag-netic bottles" designed for stable plasma containment has posed a major problem. The most promising configuration is the Tokamak, a doughnut-shaped plasma confined by an externally applied magnetic field directed along the doughnut. The applied field is supplemented by a self-generated field encircling the dough-nut, produced by current flowing in the plasma. Standard Tokamaks require an applied magnetic field strength of from 50 to 100 kilogauss to achieve break-even conditions. Establishing such a large field, even with superconducting coils, is very expensive and poses a number of severe technical problems.

Tihiro Ohkawa and his colleagues at the General Atomic Company in San Diego are developing a modified Tokamak, called the Doublet, that re-duces the required applied magnetic field strength by a factor of about three. Such a reduction would reduce the magnet costs by a factor of 10.

Ohkawa discovered that the standard Tokamak plasma cross section could be modified to reduce the applied field re-quirement. This cross section—the two circles which can be seen when a doughnut is cut along its diameter into two U-shaped halves—can be elongated and pinched, so that each circle takes on the shape of a fat dumbbell. Such a "wrinkled" doughnut decreases the ratio of the outer circumference of the doughnut to its plasma cross-section perimeter, and hence the needed applied field. Other researchers had simply tried to make the doughnut fatter to reduce the ratio, but they ran into such mechanical problems as inadequate space for the magnets.

To test their theories, the group has built two Doublet devices. In experiments conducted in 1973 with the Doublet II, a stable plasma was confined for up to 30 milliseconds using an 8-kilogauss applied magnetic field. Conventional circular Tokamaks require about 25 kilogauss to obtain similar plasma confinement. The researchers are designing Doublet III, a larger device that is expected to reach plasma densities and temperatures close to break-even conditions.

Two-component plasma. Harold P. Furth and John M. Dawson of Princeton University's Plasma Physics Laboratory reported progress in 1973 in a long-discarded fusion power concept they had revived in 1971. A beam of tritium ions can easily gain far more energy in available particle accelerators than that required for fusion. But when such a beam collides with a target of deuterium, most of the tritium ions lose all their energy in removing electrons from the target atoms, thus creating deuterium ions. A nuclear fusion reaction does not occur. The Princeton researchers plan to pre-ionize the deuterium target. They have theoretically shown that the fusion which then occurs generates more energy than that needed to accelerate the beam and form the plasma.

As an added improvement, the Tokamak's confining magnetic field can be programmed to compress the beam and plasma so as to maintain the beam energy at its optimum value for undergoing fusion. Insofar as plasma density and confinement time are concerned, the break-even conditions of such a two-component plasma device are 10 times easier to achieve than for the conventional single-component plasma. The group is designing an experimental Tokamak that they will use to test these ideas.   [Ernest P. Gray]

Solid State Physics. A new record was set in 1973, then slightly bettered, for the highest superconductivity critical temperature, the temperature at which a material begins losing all resistance to electric current flow. Below the critical temperature, current flows through the superconductor without loss of energy, in contrast with normal conductors, in which some of the energy is lost as heat.

John R. Gavaler of the Westinghouse Research Laboratories in Pittsburgh reported in September that he had made a thin film of an alloy of niobium (Nb) and germanium (Ge) that was a superconductor at −419.5° F. (−250.8° C.). This temperature is 40.2° F. (22.3° C.) above absolute zero, and bettered the previous record by 2.7° F. (1.5° C.).

Earlier in September, physicists at the Bell Telephone Laboratories in Murray Hill, N.J.—Louis R. Testardi, Jack H. Wernick, and William A. Royer—used Gavaler's method to make similar Nb_3Ge films. At the meeting at which Gavaler presented his results, they announced that one of these films had a slightly higher superconductivity critical temperature. Gavaler subsequently measured a critical temperature in one of his samples that was just under 41.5° F. (23° C.) above absolute zero, and his published data stands, however tenuously, as the new record.

Many researchers see practical significance in the new record, because the Nb_3Ge samples are superconductors at temperatures several degrees above the normal boiling point of liquid hydrogen, −426.8° F. The samples were cooled by liquid helium, a costly and scarce coolant that is normally used in laboratory cryogenic, or low-temperature, experiments. Now, many believe that abundant liquid hydrogen may replace liquid helium for commercial cooling of future energy-conserving superconducting devices, ranging from electric generators and power transmission lines to computer switches. See ELECTRONICS, Close-Up.

Gavaler made his Nb_3Ge sample—a film only a few thousand atoms thick—by modifying a proven technique called direct current (DC) sputtering. In this method, ionized argon gas molecules collide with a cathode (negative electrode) target. The target molecules "sputter" from the surface and recombine to form a thin film on a nearby heated anode.

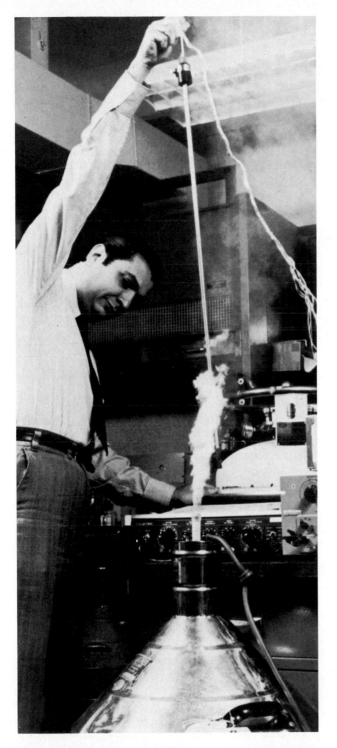

Thin niobium-germanium alloy strips became superconductive in a bath of liquid helium at about 23° C. above absolute zero, setting a record high.

Gavaler fashioned a cathode out of two strips of Nb and Ge, and placed a sapphire strip about an inch away in the argon gas atmosphere. He found that the gas pressure and sapphire temperature were critical factors in the formation of the superconductor material.

An alloy rich in Nb formed on the sapphire opposite the Nb strip of the cathode. It became superconductive at about −450° F. An alloy rich in Ge formed opposite the Ge strip, and it was not superconductive. Between the ends, however, an alloy formed that had 3 Nb atoms for every Ge atom, a mixture that is unstable and cannot be formed simply by melting and mixing the two metals. It was this 3-to-1 structure that produced the record critical temperature.

Superconductors from space also made the news last year. They were alloys of gold and germanium made aboard the orbiting space station Skylab. On earth, molten mixtures of gold and germanium settle into two layers, in much the same way that a vinegar-and-oil salad dressing separates after shaking. But molten gold and germanium, blended under weightless conditions in Skylab's special vacuum furnace, formed "a unique mixture . . . which has never before been produced on earth," according to Dr. William R. Lucas, director of the National Aeronautics and Space Administration's (NASA) Marshall Space Flight Center in Huntsville, Ala. See RESEARCH IN ORBIT.

The space samples became superconductive at a critical temperature of about 2.7° F. (1.5° C.) above absolute zero. Molten gold and germanium, mixed and quickly solidified on earth, form a metal that shows no sign of being superconductive, even though thin films of gold-germanium grown using DC sputtering are superconductors at a slightly higher temperature.

In other Skylab experiments, scientists hoped to learn more about solids by growing crystals that would be free of defects caused by gravitational settling and convection. Convection is the flow resulting from variations in density of a fluid due to its nonuniform temperature. Because hotter portions of a molten material are less dense than colder parts, gravity causes convective mixing even though only one material may be present.

The complete absence of convection in orbit was demonstrated in a Skylab experiment designed by Dr. Anthony O. Ukanwa of Howard University. Molten radioactive zinc was allowed to diffuse throughout a molten rod of natural zinc. Following resolidification and return to earth, the rod was compared to one grown in Ukanwa's lab. In the latter sample, the two types of zinc had mixed completely throughout the rod. In the sample processed in space the radioactive zinc had permeated the rod in a way predicted by diffusion theory, without any evidence of convective mixing.

The absence of convection enabled Skylab astronauts to melt and regrow portions of semiconductor crystals containing desirable impurities spread throughout them. Henry C. Gatos of the Massachusetts Institute of Technology examined indium-antimonide crystals containing tellurium that had been regrown from some of his best earth-grown crystals. The regrown portions were much more homogeneous, a desirable feature in the manufacture of semiconductor electronic components.

Another semiconductor-crystal-growth experiment was designed to grow indium-antimonide crystals—free of container walls. The molten mixture was supposed to cling to a seed crystal by molecular forces of adhesion and cohesion. In space, a small portion of each of the three samples inadvertently touched a container wall, but otherwise the melted and resolidified material formed remarkable single crystals. Their faces were flat to within about half a millionth of an inch, and microscopic studies revealed one-tenth as many internal defects as in crystals grown on earth.

NASA scientists see these Skylab experiments as the first step toward routine processing of materials in space. But whether their dreams are ever realized, scientists have now grown materials under unique conditions not available on earth, and their findings should enhance their understanding of the basic nature of solids and liquids.

Superfluid helium-3. Researchers at the University of California, San Diego, reported in February that they had produced the first direct evidence that helium-3 (He-3) becomes a superfluid at a few thousandths of a degree above absolute zero. Below about 0.0025° C. above absolute zero, a portion of the liquid He-3 called the superfluid component flows without the drag of viscosity that is present in all normal fluids. In contrast to the abundant helium-4 (He-4), He-3 is a relatively rare natural isotope that has two protons but only one neutron.

Haruo Kojima, Douglas Paulson, and John Wheatley reported measuring a phenomenon that can only occur in a superfluid liquid. Called fourth sound, it involves the passage of sound waves through the superfluid component of the liquid while the normal component is locked in place by its viscosity.

The experimenters used a device similar to one first developed by Isadore Rudnick at the University of California at Los Angeles for studying fourth sound in liquid He-4. They packed a tube with a porous material, cerium magnesium nitrate, and added liquid He-3. The normal liquid He-3, with a viscosity comparable to salad oil, was locked in the pores. But the superfluid was free to transmit sound from one end of the tube to the other.

Wheatley compares this method of measuring fourth sound to attempting to talk through a long tube packed with wet sand. If the water in the mixture were a superfluid, it would work.

The direct confirmation of superfluidity follows intensive, worldwide investigation of helium-3 that began in 1971 when Cornell University experimenters first looked for antiferromagnetic behavior in solid He-3 at ultracold temperatures. They expected that because He-3 has an odd number of nucleons, their nuclear magnetic spins would align antiparallel (up, down, up) to produce a net measurable magnetic field. They measured two magnetic changes—at 0.0026° C. and 0.002° C. above absolute zero—but subsequent experiments revealed that the changes were taking place in the liquid, not the solid. Other experiments supported the belief that these changes were caused by a pairing of liquid helium atoms to form a superfluid, in much the same way that pairing of electrons gives rise to superconductivity in metals.

These experiments point up the unexpected direction basic scientific research can take. And the strange superfluid helium-3 may hold still other surprises for investigators. It may be magnetic and, if it is, could give rise to a persistent, or undamped flow of magnetism comparable to the undamped flow of electric current in superconductors. [Robert K. Johnson]

Psychology

Psychologists in 1974 gained new insights into the sleeping-waking cycle, the most obvious daily rhythm in the lives of human beings. Most mammals, including man, spend a significant portion of every 24 hours sleeping. The actual amount of time spent sleeping depends, in part, upon the age and species of the mammal.

For some years, psychologists have been investigating the extent to which the sleeping-waking cycle in man depends upon his environment. Does sleep depend upon such external "clocks" as light and darkness, business and family routines, and watches? Would a person isolated from the usual time markers establish a pattern of daily activity based on a 24-hour cycle? Or would his internal biological clock develop another rhythm?

Altering the environment. Research conducted in 1973 and 1974 by Wilse B. Webb and his associates at the University of Florida, Gainesville, supports earlier observations that people placed in isolated environments and removed from normal time cues develop a daily rhythm that is similar to the normal 24-hour cycle, but that gradually becomes longer.

Webb's work is an outgrowth of research conducted in the 1960s by the French investigator, Michel Jouvet, who studied volunteers who spent several months in a cave.

Rather than using caves, Webb and his associates study people who spend several weeks living in 12- by 12-foot rooms in the laboratory. The rooms contain beds, chairs, ottomans, tables, sinks, toilets, well-stocked refrigerators, and even stereo music. But once inside the rooms, the subjects are removed from all of the time cues available in the outside world. An intercom system allows the researchers to communicate with the subjects at any time. The subjects' brain waves and other psychological responses are recorded continuously.

In studies that are still continuing, Webb and his colleagues have found that people who are deprived of normal time cues develop a daily cycle in which their sleeping time becomes somewhat longer each day, and the subject remains awake for a slightly longer time each day. Eventually, he develops a rhythm based on a 25- to 27-hour day, similar to the cycle

A restless, fidgety schoolchild, *below* and *center*, may be overstimulated by certain types of fluorescent lights. After the lights are changed, he moves to the front row and begins concentrating on his studies, *right*.

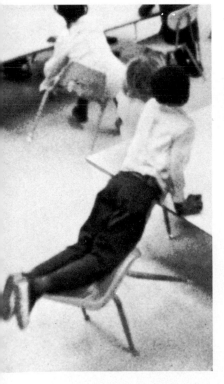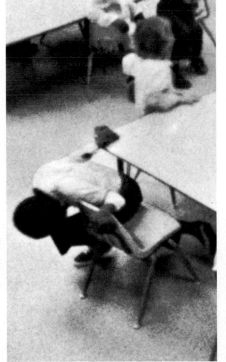

Psychology

Continued

Even a well-fed cat will attack and eat prey when a specific area of the cerebellum is stimulated electrically. The strength of the stimulus determines the specific response. Previously, scientists thought such behavior was primarily controlled by the hypothalamus.

that Jouvet had discovered earlier in the cave volunteers.

Effects of exercise. Webb speculated that sleeping-waking cycles longer than 24 hours might be due to the restriction of physical activity which occurs both in the caves and in the laboratory setting. Neither a cave nor a laboratory room allows the subject to get a normal amount of exercise.

Perhaps the low energy output of subjects in a restricted environment causes the longer sleeping-waking cycle. If this were the case, then the lengthening of the 24-hour cycle might reflect not an internal biological rhythm, but only the decreased metabolic requirements of a subject in a confined setting.

In 1974, Webb and his colleague Harman W. Agnew, Jr., investigated this possibility by studying the effect of prolonged exercise on their laboratory volunteers. Each subject rode an exercise bicycle that had been adjusted so that the riding was equivalent to a day's hard labor. Webb and Agnew found that the subjects who exercised continued to operate on a 25- to 27-hour day, just as did others who did

not exercise. They concluded that the change to longer daily cycles did not result from the lack of exercise or from low energy output.

However, they found that the bicycle riding did affect the type of sleep the subjects had. Sleep became more variable, and was more likely to be broken into short periods. However, there were more sleep periods so that the overall amount of sleep remained the same.

Webb and Agnew also found that the various stages of sleep in isolation were much the same as they are under natural conditions. Normally, as a person falls asleep, the electrical brain wave recordings show the development of a slow, rhythmic pattern. Periodically during the night, the electrical rhythms change from the slow wave pattern to an inconsistent, unsynchronized pattern similar to that of a person who is wide awake. Associated with this are many rapid eye movements (REM). This is when dreams occur.

REM sleep takes up about 25 per cent of the sleeping time of adults, and occurs regularly about every 90 minutes. The REM sleep periods last about 10 minutes

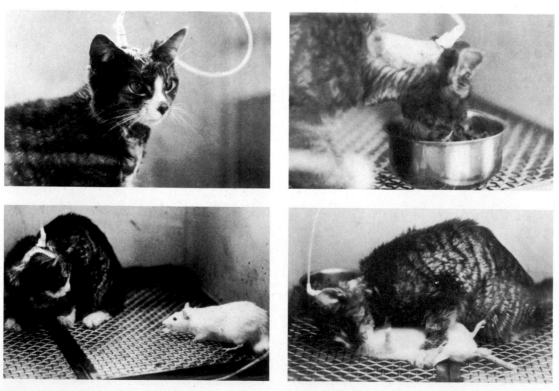

An infant rhesus monkey that was separated from its mother at 3 months of age quickly transferred its affection to a friendly dog.

Psychology

Continued

at first and gradually increase during the night to about 30 minutes near the time the person wakes up. Webb and Agnew found that neither isolation nor exercise changes the occurrence of REM sleep. They concluded that the internal clocks that regulate sleep are quite stable and are not affected by the amount of a person's activity when he is awake.

Chemical control. Sleep researchers are now trying to determine what physiological mechanisms might control sleep. Some investigators, including Jouvet, believe that a specific part of the nervous system is responsible for initiating the different substages—the deep, slow wave sleep and the erratic REM sleep. Jouvet also believes that a second, entirely separate part of the nervous system maintains REM sleep once it has begun.

Jouvet is now studying the possibility of distinguishing these two separate systems in the brain on the basis of the chemicals used by the cells in each system. He believes that the system that initiates the different stages of sleep is a set of nerve cells in the brain stem. These cells manufacture and use serotonin as a chemical

messenger to contact other nerve cells scattered in all parts of the brain. Serotonin is a hormonelike substance that is similar to adrenalin.

The second system, according to Jouvet, is also located in the brain stem. These cells manufacture and use another type of chemical messenger, the catecholamines, to contact cells in other regions of the brain.

Jouvet has associated these two chemical systems with the two major types of sleep. His evidence shows that selective reduction of available serotonin in the nerve system severely reduces both slow-wave and REM sleep.

The reduction in sleep is proportional to the reduction in the amount of serotonin. Damage to the brain stem in the area of the cells that contain serotonin also produces a permanent insomnia. On the other hand, injections of serotonin will induce sleep.

Drugs that increase the levels of catecholamines, or make them more efficient, produce long REM periods. Drugs that make catecholamines less effective abolish REM sleep. [Robert L. Isaacson]

Science
Support

There was, in some respects, a turnabout in the federal government's science support policies in 1973 and 1974. As in 1961, when President John F. Kennedy decided that scientists and engineers should work to land a man on the moon, political leaders were convinced in 1973 that the national energy shortage called for an extensive research and development effort to meet future energy needs.

As a result, the new federal budget presented by President Richard M. Nixon in January, 1974, was favorable to many fields of science and included a 25 per cent increase in funding for basic research. But problems still remained between the Nixon Administration and the scientific community. Biomedical research leaders continued their long-standing dispute with the Administration over how research should be carried out. Several prominent scientists continued to protest publicly the Administration's January, 1973, decision to transfer the functions of the White House science office to the relatively obscure National Science Foundation (NSF). However, it seemed that outrage over military research and other issues that had stirred antiwar and other dissident scientists in the past had died. Scientists spoke out on only two moral issues: Russia's harassment of the prominent physicist Andrei D. Sakharov and Soviet treatment of Jewish scientists who wanted to emigrate from Russia to Israel.

Energy and scientists. Historically, the biggest waves in science support have been shaped by outside forces over which scientists have no control. The Middle East war in October, 1973, was such a force, for after the war, the Arab nations reduced oil shipments to the West. The international crisis that resulted demonstrated how dependent the industrialized nations were on a single energy source—oil. The United States decided to strive for self-sufficiency in energy. Consequently, the Nixon Administration recognized the need for more energy research.

Earlier in the year, President Nixon had delivered a series of "energy messages" in which he anticipated summer brownouts and some winter fuel shortages. In April, the President termed the energy situation "a challenge." He gave

"Ninety per cent of all the scientists who ever lived
are alive today, and twenty per cent of *them* are out of work."
Drawing by Lorenz; © 1974 The New Yorker Magazine, Inc.

research only a passing mention, saying, "It is foolish and self-defeating to allocate funds more rapidly than they can effectively be spent." But gradually, the Administration became less complacent about the energy situation.

In June, the President promised to spend an extra $100 million in fiscal year 1974 (July 1, 1973, to June 30, 1974) on energy research. Also in June, he created the White House Energy Policy Office. And he asked Congress to establish an Energy Research and Development Administration.

In less than a year, the Energy Policy Office had three different directors. Its first chief, John R. Love, was replaced by William E. Simon in December, 1973. In April, 1974, John C. Sawhill replaced Simon, who resigned to become secretary of the treasury.

The Ray report. On June 29, 1973, the President asked the chairwoman of the Atomic Energy Commission (AEC) Dixy Lee Ray to review all ongoing energy research and development projects in the United States. She was to suggest an integrated program for meeting future energy needs, and also make recommendations for projects that should be included in the fiscal 1975 budget. Ray sought the advice of other AEC officials, other federal agencies, and private industry. The Ray report, entitled "The Nation's Energy Future," was published in December. See DIXY LEE RAY.

The fiscal 1975 budget, the so-called energy budget, was influenced by Ray's recommendations. It proposed that $1.8-billion of the $19.5 billion allotted for research be spent on energy-related projects. The budget makers not only considered the results of the Ray report, they even increased most of her recommended spending levels through fiscal 1980.

The fiscal 1975 budget included $893.3 million for nuclear fission and fusion research; $41.8 million for oil, gas, and oil shale development; $415.5 for coal production and utilization; $50 million for solar energy; and $44.7 for geothermal energy. Solar and geothermal energy had previously received only casual government interest. In some research areas, the proposed fiscal 1975 funding was up to 300 per cent over fiscal 1974.

Project Independence. In November, 1973, the President announced Project Independence, a plan to make the United

States self-sufficient in energy by 1980. The Administration proposed a $10-billion, five-year budget for achieving this goal, with spending for nuclear energy set at $5.6 billion; for coal production and utilization, $2.9 billion; oil, gas, and shale, $400 million; and solar and geothermal, $900 million.

However, Project Independence had both problems and critics. Some scientists believe that self-sufficiency is impossible by 1980. In June, a National Academy of Engineering report declared that drastic efforts by all segments of the economy might make the United States self-sufficient by 1985 — at the earliest.

There was also an absence of administrative machinery to manage the large-scale new programs. In 1970, the Administration had proposed combining the AEC's civilian nuclear power research with the nonnuclear energy research of other agencies. This would create a new Energy Research and Development Administration (ERDA). But the House of Representatives did not pass a bill to create an ERDA until December, 1973, and the Senate had still failed to move ERDA legislation out of committee as of June, 1974.

Some scientists also criticized the Administration's lack of concern for energy conservation. The new proposals emphasized research on ways to increase the supply of energy, but they placed a lower priority on finding ways to reduce the demand for energy.

The Ray report had recommended $1.4 billion for energy conservation research over the five-year period. But the Administration budget makers cut that figure in half. For fiscal 1975, they proposed $128.6 million for energy conservation. Although this represented a 78 per cent increase over fiscal 1974, critics complained this was not a large enough share of the $1.8 billion allotted for energy research in fiscal 1975.

Glenn Seaborg, former chairman of the AEC, blamed the hurried, unclear aspects of the energy plan on the Administration's earlier lack of interest in technical advice. In a February, 1974, magazine interview, Seaborg stated, ". . . For years the technical people have been warning that our energy base needed to be expanded and improved. . . . It has taken at least a decade for the decision makers to heed the fire bells that were rung."

The Rime of the Modern Mariner

Readers of *Science Year* know that a favorite nonscientific activity of scientists is to give each other prizes. These range in prestige from the Nobel prize, which corresponds roughly to being made a peer of the realm in England, to small bronze medals given by obscure scientific societies. The most sought-after awards include checks. Indeed, one of the reasons for the enormous prestige of the Nobel prize is the staggering amount of money that accompanies it.

Among the least prestigious of prizes, but still desirable to some, is the stuffed Albatross that the American Miscellaneous Society (AMSOC) awards for obscure contributions to oceanography. I was given the Bird in 1973 during the meeting of the American Association for the Advancement of Science in Mexico City.

The AMSOC Bird is not the great wandering albatross of the southern ocean that was shot down by the Ancient Mariner. Rather, it is a smaller and humbler North Pacific cousin, the Laysan albatross (*Diomedea immutabilis* Rothschild), otherwise known as the "goony" bird. Oceanographers often see these wonderful, solitary birds gliding majestically in the wake of their small ships. Indeed, the goony bird has a special place in the hearts of all sailors.

Our Albatross has certain advantages over other prizes. For one thing, it is not a medal. What can you do with a medal? If it is gold, it is too valuable to use as a paperweight. If it is bronze, it is too hard and heavy for any practical use. You can't drill a hole in it and wear it on a string—people might talk. About all you can do with a medal is to put it in a safe-deposit box (if you can afford to rent one), hide it under a mattress (if you can't), or have it made into costume jewelry.

In sharp contrast to most medals, the Albatross is photogenic. It is the only scientific award whose portrait has appeared on the front cover of *Science* magazine (Sept. 7, 1973).

Unlike the Ancient Mariner, the recipient of the Albatross is not supposed to hang it around his neck. He must display it in a conspicuous place in his home or office. It takes up a lot of space, but it makes a fine conversation piece. And just about the time the recipient's spouse decides to hide this dust collector in the darkest recesses of the basement, AMSOC awards it to somebody else.

Revelle and secretaries pose with Albatross after presentation in Mexico City.

The presentation is usually made as far as possible from the last recipient's home—preferably outside the United States. This creates transportation problems. The Albatross is not heavy, but it is big and fragile, and baggage clerks worry. Also, customs men tend to take a dim view of a large biological specimen that could be stuffed with jewels, drugs, or other contraband.

AMSOC, the group that awards this prize, has been described by *Science* as a "mildly loony, invisible college of otherwise mature academicians." The society was founded in 1952 ("to look at the lighter side of heavier problems") by three oceanographers in the Office of Naval Research—Gordon Lill, Arthur Maxwell, and John Knauss. It has no officers or dues, let alone regular meetings, but it does have an inspiring motto, *Illegitimis Non Carborundum*. It started out to conduct its business through Divisions of Etceterology, Triviology, and Generology. And, of course, it had committees. One was assigned to welcome visitors from outer space; another was to teach the lower animals their proper zoological position. So far, neither committee has had much to do. Perhaps this is one reason the society's journal, *Otherwise,* has yet to publish its first issue.

AMSOC achieved fleeting glory in the 1960s when it persuaded the National Science Foundation (NSF) to try to drill a hole through the layer that separates the earth's crust from its mantle. The NSF made grants and contracts, and the National Academy of Sciences officially designated AMSOC to guide the scientific and technical aspects of the project. But the attempt to take itself seriously ended badly for AMSOC when Project Mohole foundered in 1966 on the shoals of politics and money.

After this unhappy interlude, AMSOC went underground. It emerges only sporadically to bestow its Albatross "for the most unusual or obscure contribution to oceanography." The award was created in 1959 by Lill, Maxwell, and Knauss, who promptly made themselves the first Albatross laureates in honor of their accomplishment in thinking up the award. Other recipients include Harrison Brown, Walter Munk, John Swallow, Henry Stommel, Victor Vacquier, Sumner Pike and William von Arx. We are all very proud.   [Roger Revelle]

Peter L. Auer, director of the Laboratory of Plasma Studies at Cornell University warned in *Science* magazine in April that the Administration might be relying too heavily on science and technology to solve the energy problem. "The issues that face us now cannot be resolved in terms of clearly defined objectives, such as build an atomic bomb or place a man on the moon. . . . Scientific and technological research and development have a very proper and significant role to play in our future course of actions, but it would be foolish to consider them as the principal instruments for achieving solutions to problems at hand."

Nonenergy funding. The proposed fiscal 1975 budget contained important increases in nonenergy fields. Spending for military research and development was increased by $1 billion to $9.6 billion. The NSF's basic research budget increased 25 per cent to $363.7 million—the largest increase in recent years. Funds for agricultural research increased from $393 million in fiscal 1974 to $412 million in 1975; funds for environmental research were increased from $174 million

to $336 million. Space research funds decreased by $187 million. But money was provided for a 1978 Pioneer-spacecraft probe of Venus and a new infrared telescope at Mauna Kea, Hawaii.

Research funds proposed for the National Institutes of Health (NIH) increased by $51.8 million to $1.8 billion. The largest sums were slated for cancer and heart and lung research, both high priorities of the Nixon Administration.

Angry scientists. The scientific community continued its war with the Department of Health, Education, and Welfare (HEW) over how biomedical research should be conducted and how much independence researchers should have. During the summer of 1973, the Federation of American Scientists collected 3,000 signatures for a petition stating that the way HEW was managing biomedical research was "based on free enterprise ideology . . . that market forces will provide researchers in biomedicine" instead of steady government support.

In a January, 1974, letter to the *Washington Post,* Charles C. Edwards, assistant secretary of HEW for health, said that

Federal Spending for R & D

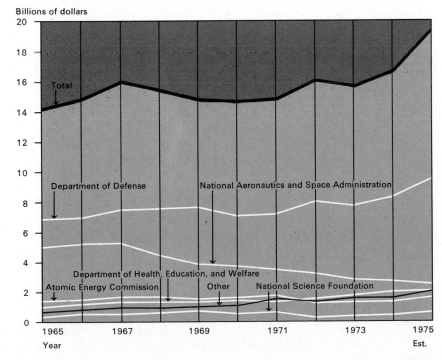

NIH should not be insulated from budgetary and managerial control. NIH leaders, Edwards said, had "a misguided sense of the place of research in the nation's efforts to solve its health problems." Some prominent NIH scientists replied that they could live with whatever funding levels their superiors dictated, but that "the nation will reap the largest benefit if scientific and medical considerations govern the programs and administration of the NIH."

The Administration made some conciliatory moves. In May, 1973, the Administration appointed New Mexico educator Robert S. Stone director of the NIH, a post that had been vacant five months. Stone had not taken sides in the funding fight. Nevertheless, high-level NIH officials resigned. One was John F. Sherman, deputy director. He resigned in January, 1974, charging that the Administration was ruining the NIH.

In July, Secretary of HEW Caspar W. Weinberger announced a replacement program for $130 million in training grants and fellowships that were cut off in 1973. The new program funds would go to individuals, not to their institutions. The fiscal 1975 budget included $27.5 million for the new training-grant program.

Scientists also continued to debate whether the post of science adviser should be restored to the White House. The Administration officially abolished the post on July 1, 1973, although it had been vacant since January. Although NSF Director H. Guyford Stever served as presidential science adviser, his main contact with President Nixon was on ceremonial occasions.

In October, 1973, all the previous science advisers met to discuss the problem at a Massachusetts Institute of Technology (MIT) symposium. Throughout the year, a number of organizational proposals were made in scientific journals. As a result of all this interest, the National Academy of Sciences set up a commission to study the science adviser problem, chaired by chairman of the corporation of MIT, James R. Killian, who had served as President Dwight D. Eisenhower's science adviser.

Soviet problems. The emotions of many scientists throughout the world were aroused by Russia's actions toward its political and religious dissidents. Many U.S. scientists rallied to the cause of Russian Jewish scientists and technicians wishing to emigrate to Israel. For years, the Russian government has regularly permitted workers and tradesmen, but rarely well-educated scientists, to emigrate.

During July and August, 1973, the official Soviet press conducted a campaign of denunciation against Russia's most prominent scientist, Andrei D. Sakharov. He is credited with having developed Russia's hydrogen bomb and with having helped Russia gain an early lead over the United States in fusion power. However, Sakharov had become identified with the Russian civil liberties movement.

During the campaign against him, Sakharov defied the authorities through such gestures as inviting Western newsmen to press conferences in his apartment. Then, in late August, 40 of his colleagues at the Soviet Academy of Sciences denounced him in a signed letter to the official newspaper, *Pravda*.

American scientists feared that Sakharov was about to be jailed, or worse. In September, the Council of the National Academy of Sciences sent a telegram to the Soviet Academy warning that if Sakharov were arrested or further harassed it would be ". . . extremely difficult to imagine successful fulfillment of American pledges of binational scientific cooperation . . ." After this rebuke and other international protests, the Russian government eased its campaign.

Cancer scandal. William T. Summerlin, a researcher at the Sloan-Kettering Institute for Cancer Research in New York City, was relieved of his post in April for allegedly falsifying research findings. He was given a one-year leave of absence to seek psychiatric help. Reportedly, Summerlin had painted black patches on white mice, claiming to his superior that the patches represented successful skin grafts. Summerlin had reported that skin grown in tissue culture can be used for grafts without the danger of rejection. If true, this would have enormous effect on cancer and transplant research. However, other scientists were unable to duplicate Summerlin's work.

Many scientists believed the incident reflected deeper problems surrounding the current cancer research program: the intense competition for government funds; pressure to make spectacular discoveries; and the ambitions of some scientists to win fame. [Deborah Shapley]

Space Exploration

The longest manned mission in space-flight history ended on Feb. 8, 1974, when the third Skylab space crew splashed down in the Pacific Ocean about 170 miles off San Diego. The astronauts, Gerald P. Carr, Edward G. Gibson, and William R. Pogue, spent 84 days in the orbiting Skylab space laboratory.

During their mission, begun on Nov. 16, 1973, the three astronauts orbited the earth 1,214 times, traveling a distance of 34.5 million miles. They also made four spacewalks outside the Skylab. Despite the record length of their stay in the weightless conditions of space, the astronauts were in better physical condition on their return to earth than the first two Skylab crews. This was probably because the third crew followed a much more strenuous exercise program.

The second Skylab crew, Alan L. Bean, Owen K. Garriott, and Jack R. Lousma, was launched on July 28, 1973. Their 59-day mission is the second longest stay of man in space. The first crew—Charles Conrad, Jr., Joseph Kerwin, and Paul J. Weitz—spent 28 days in space, landing on June 22, 1973.

The three-mission Skylab program proved that man can live and work in space for long periods of time. It also provided an opportunity for astronomical studies beyond the interference of the earth's atmosphere and allowed scientists to perfect techniques for surveying the earth and its resources. The third Skylab crew also studied Comet Kohoutek. See A COSMIC LABORATORY; CATALOGING THE WHOLE EARTH; RESEARCH IN ORBIT.

Apollo-Soyuz. With the conclusion of the Skylab program, only one manned mission remained on the U.S. space-flight schedule, the joint U.S.-Soviet mission planned for July, 1975. The space flight will bring together U.S. astronauts Thomas P. Stafford, Donald K. Slayton, and Vance D. Brand and Russian cosmonauts Alexei A. Leonov and Valery N. Kubasov in the first international manned effort ever attempted. By mid-1974, the two teams of spacemen were deep in training, including the study of each others' languages. The training sessions began with the cosmonauts visiting the Johnson Space Center near Houston in July, 1973. The U.S. team went to a

The shadow of Jupiter's moon, Io, center, and the Great Red Spot, far left, show up clearly in this photograph taken from 1.6 million miles above the planet's cloud cover by Pioneer 10.

Russian space center located near Moscow for training in November.

Pioneer probes. Pioneer 10, the first of two Pioneer outer-planet probes, passed Jupiter in December, 1973, greatly enhancing scientific knowledge about the largest planet in our solar system. As it flew past Jupiter's equatorial zone, Pioneer 10 skirted the dense and colorful clouds of the huge planet by only about 81,000 miles.

Pioneer 10's passage through Jupiter's vast and intense belt of trapped radiation (like the earth's Van Allen belt, but much stronger) was so uneventful that National Aeronautics and Space Administration (NASA) scientists announced on April 16, 1974, that they were adjusting the course of a second probe, Pioneer 11, to bring it within 26,000 miles of Jupiter in December, 1974. The modified flight path will take the spacecraft over Jupiter's south polar region, which cannot be studied in detail through earth-based telescopes. After passing Jupiter at a record-breaking speed of more than 100,000 miles per hour, the Pioneer 11 craft will "coast" through space for almost five years toward Saturn.

Both Pioneer spacecraft successfully passed through the asteroid belt between Mars and Jupiter. After Pioneer 10, scientists began to revise their conception of this region as a debris-filled obstacle course. Pioneer 11's virtually unscathed passage through this area in late 1973 permanently dispelled their concern.

Scientists were also concerned that some of the delicate electronics aboard the Pioneer 10 craft might be drowned out or weakened by the energetic particles in Jupiter's radiation belt. Fortunately, this did not occur. Although a few instruments were temporarily affected, most of the data transmitted across the half-billion-mile void of space met NASA's expectations.

Pictures of the planet transmitted by Pioneer 10 clearly showed Jupiter's Great Red Spot, and some of them revealed a second, smaller red spot. The pictures also showed white spots in the planet's southern hemisphere.

Generations of astronomers have observed the Great Red Spot, an apparently permanent, oval-shaped feature about 30,000 miles long. They have speculated about its nature, because it does not seem to stay in one place on the planet's cloud-covered surface. Some of Pioneer 10's pictures seemed to show shadows cast by the Great Red Spot, as though it towered high above the cloud cover. The Pioneer photographs also showed details of the planet's characteristic layered cloud belts.

In analyzing environmental data transmitted by Pioneer 10, scientists discovered inexplicably high temperatures in the Jovian atmosphere. Parts of the upper atmosphere reached temperatures up to 260°F. (127.3°C.), much higher than scientists had expected. Lower in the atmosphere, temperatures seemed to range as high as 800°F. (427°C.).

Some scientists interpreted this to mean that the temperature of Jupiter's surface might rival that of the sun. This seemed to reinforce their belief that Jupiter is a sort of "mini-star," an idea that came about when scientists discovered in the late 1960s that Jupiter gives off more energy than it receives from the sun.

Other data from Pioneer 10 also indicated that Jupiter may be a kind of star. For example, from a distance of 100-million miles, the spacecraft's instruments detected bursts of energy from Jupiter.

Mariner 10 carried out the first two-planet flight successfully in the spring of 1974. Launched from Cape Canaveral, Fla., on Nov. 3, 1973, the planetary probe penetrated deeper into "inner space" than any craft had ever ventured before. It skirted past Venus early in February, 1974, picking up gravitational energy from the planet for a snap-the-whip maneuver that, late in March, took the spacecraft close to Mercury, the innermost and smallest planet in our solar system. NASA controllers adjusted Mariner's trajectory to bring it back toward Mercury for a second picture-taking fly-by in September, 1974.

Unlike the Pioneer project, and earlier Mariner missions to Venus and Mars, Mariner 10 was a one-shot operation. No backup vehicle existed to carry out the mission if the first failed. This was an economy measure dictated by the tight budget constraints that have severely hampered NASA operations since Project Apollo ended at the start of 1973.

In passing Venus, Mariner 10 gathered much new data on the nature of the planet's dense atmosphere and sent back more than 4,000 photographs of its surface. At its closest approach, the spacecraft was 3,600 miles from Venus. See

Owen K. Garriott of the second Skylab crew ventures outside the orbiting laboratory to set up an experiment for collecting particles of interplanetary dust.

Space Exploration

Continued

ASTRONOMY, PLANETARY; THE CLIMATES OF PLANETS.

Mariner 10 produced the first detailed pictures of Mercury's surface. Mercury, midway in size between our moon and Mars, bore a superficial resemblance to both bodies in the Mariner pictures. Scientists said, however, that Mercury is quite different from either of these bodies. Like earth, it seems to have an iron core, which they believe the moon and Mars lack. A weak but detectable magnetic field exists around Mercury but not around the moon, Mars, or Venus.

Mercury is, however, quite different from the earth. It has no atmosphere and revolves very slowly on its axis. Because it is only about 37 million miles from the sun, it is extremely hot on the daytime side, reaching temperatures of about 625°F. (329°C.). Because of such differences in behavior and properties, scientists now believe that the planets they have studied closely—Mercury, Venus, Earth, Mars, and Jupiter—plus the moon, all evolved in different ways.

Exploring Mars. In July and August, 1973, Russia launched four spacecraft on Mars missions. Two were apparently planned as orbiters and two as landers. Mars 4 and 7 failed to achieve Mars orbit. Mars 5 went into orbit as planned and reportedly did a successful job of photomapping. Mars 5 was also intended as a radio relay to earth for Mars 6, a lander. But Mars 6 lost contact with Mars 5 and with earth during its descent to the Martian surface. Some scientists speculated that Mars 6 might have been caught up by the high winds known to sweep across the planet periodically.

The United States continued work on its Viking program for the surface exploration of Mars. Two landings are scheduled for mid-1976, including a touchdown on July 4, 1976, as part of the U.S. bicentennial celebration.

The Viking program ran into difficulties. A Titan-Centaur test rocket—the type that will launch Viking spacecraft to Mars in 1975—blew up shortly after it was launched from the Air Force's Florida missile proving ground in January, 1974. In addition, NASA budget managers worried about rising costs of the Viking project. This was traceable, they explained, to the extreme complexity of the Viking lander's payload. It includes some of the most sophisticated gadgetry ever devised, such as an automated biochemistry laboratory, which should be able to detect microscopic life if any exists on the planet. The Viking landers are being targeted for areas that scientists regard as most likely to harbor life.

Russian manned missions resumed in late 1973, the first since the fatal Soyuz 11 accident in June, 1971. The Russians conducted two flights during the last three months of 1973. Both flights were apparently rehearsals for the 1975 Apollo-Soyuz mission.

The flights had two-man crews, in contrast to the three-man crews of earlier Soyuz missions. Both crews were previously inexperienced in space flight and none of the four men was on the primary or backup crews for Apollo-Soyuz.

Soyuz 12, launched on September 29, was apparently a two-day shake-down mission for the overhauled Soyuz spacecraft. Russian space engineers had designed an improved docking and latching device to eliminate the possibility of the type of air leak that caused the suffocation of the three-man Soyuz 11 crew.

The eight-day Soyuz 13 mission, launched on December 18, marked the first time in almost 13 years of manned space flight that U.S. and Soviet spacemen were in orbit at the same time. The flight of Soyuz 13 came at about the midpoint of the third Skylab mission.

Space shuttle. On Sept. 24, 1973, NASA signed a cooperation agreement with the European Space Research Organization (ESRO). In the document, ESRO agreed to provide a spacelab unit for NASA's space shuttle.

The spacelab, costing between $300-million and $400 million, will consist of a pressurized working module and a platform for telescopes and other instruments. It will be carried in the payload bay of the reusable, delta-winged space-shuttle orbiter.

Construction began in April, 1974, on a $22-million landing runway for the space-shuttle orbiter. The concrete strip, located near Cape Canaveral, will be 300 feet wide, 15,000 feet long, and 300 feet thick. [William Hines]

Transportation

Research engineers continued their efforts in 1974 to refine innovative technological systems for mass transportation, including those using electric motors, air cushions, and computer-controlled vehicles. The public, on the other hand, became increasingly disenchanted with advanced technology, and this became a dominant factor in the selection of new transit systems.

Technological snags. Advanced systems that were widely acclaimed when they were inaugurated, such as the Bay Area Rapid Transit (BART) system in San Francisco and the Personal Rapid Transit (PRT) system in Morgantown, W. Va., are running into financial and technological difficulties.

The BART system in San Francisco has experienced continuing difficulties ever since service started in September, 1972. The system is threatened with a shutdown on Oct. 1, 1974, unless additional funds are made available. The high-speed, electric train system, widely regarded as a model for future mass transit systems, was built to take the commuter load off the Bay Bridge, which connects San Francisco with Oakland and other East Bay communities, but as of mid-1974 the connecting leg had not been opened.

The PRT system was originally planned to provide a transit system of rubber-tired, driverless passenger cars that would be operated by computer over a special 3.2-mile, concrete roadway. By mid-1974, only 2.2 miles of roadway had been completed. The system has exceeded initial cost estimates by so much that its completion is threatened, and the entire project may be demolished.

Switch in emphasis. Experiences such as these have led to rising concern that costly fixed-guideway facilities will not effectively solve the urban transportation problem in the near future. Some transportation experts now believe that the answer lies in making more efficient use of the existing systems of streets and expressways in our cities.

Cities are now concentrating on improvements to mass transit bus operations in congested urban areas. These improvements include such expedients as giving buses priority in entering freeways, reserving lanes on city streets and urban

Transportation

Continued

A new tire shape (right) promises to reduce the danger after blowouts. A conventional tire (left) collapses suddenly if punctured. But the new triangular-shaped tire is "preflattened," allowing a car to keep moving safely straight ahead after a puncture.

expressways for buses only, and allowing bus drivers to change traffic signals by remote control.

Perhaps the best-known exclusive express bus lane is on the Shirley Highway, which connects northern Virginia to downtown Washington, D.C. Another is a route from El Monte, Calif., to downtown Los Angeles along the San Bernardino Freeway, an 11-mile route that was scheduled to be completed in 1974.

Several cities are testing systems calling for the pre-emption of traffic signals by buses on arterial streets and on downtown street networks.

One such system involves a computer-controlled traffic signal system, such as that used in Washington, D.C. There, computers control the timing of traffic signals at 111 intersections. The signal changes are timed to keep traffic moving at the best possible pace. In addition, 34 of the intersections are equipped to allow buses to change the traffic signal.

Another approach, now being used in Miami, Fla., allows a bus to change local traffic signals on an intersection-by-intersection basis. As a bus approaches a red light, for example, the driver can activate the signal by remote control so that the light will change to green by the time the bus reaches the intersection.

Systems such as exclusive bus lanes and the pre-emption of traffic signals have captured the attention of traffic planners and city officials because they can be quickly implemented. Also, the cost per passenger is usually much less than that involved in major technological improvements in rail transit.

Small, high-technology systems. Relatively small, high-technology systems have had fewer problems and greater success than their larger, less fortunate transportation cousins.

In one effort, an American subsidiary of the Otis Elevator Company is working with a French company to build a 15-mile personal rapid transit system in Nancy, France. One-third of the system's guideway will be underground and the rest in the air. The 130 vehicles will ride on a cushion of air and will be propelled by linear-induction motors.

Another small-scale system is the Airtrans system for shuttling passengers be-

Spinning Wheels

Have you ever scooted about in an electric golf cart and wondered why your family car is not as quiet, smooth, and pollution free? The answer is simple: It would take about 4,000 pounds of conventional car batteries to store as much energy as a tank of gasoline holds.

But with gasoline in short supply, researchers are looking for lighter, more efficient energy storage devices to make electric vehicles practical. Many are pinning their hopes on a device that has a 4,000-year history—the spinning mechanical flywheel.

The principle that a spinning flywheel can store energy and give it up by slowing down has been put to work in many applications since the first potter's wheel. In fact, the crankshafts in today's internal combustion engines that power most vehicles are flywheels that convert the pistons' jerky back-and-forth motions into smooth circular power.

Now, Lockheed Missiles and Space Company, Sunnyvale, Calif., and Garrett Corporation, Torrance, Calif., are trying to make a flywheel-powered electric motor a realistic option. In March, 1974,

Lockheed signed a contract with the U.S. Department of Transportation to modify two test electric buses for use on San Francisco's hilly streets. Garrett has modified two standard subway cars for the New York Metropolitan Transportation Authority, and they are now being tested.

In the Lockheed bus, a combination electric motor-generator will spin a 525-pound flywheel to a top speed of 12,000 revolutions per minute (rpm) during brief charging stops, or while the bus is in contact with overhead trolley wires. Spinning this fast, the flywheel stores 12 kilowatt-hours (kwh) of energy. The energy is withdrawn by coupling the flywheel to the generator. As the flywheel slows down, the generator produces electricity for the bus's direct-current (DC) electric traction motor that drives the wheels. Thus, the flywheel system functions like a bank of electric batteries, only it is lighter and can be "charged" and "discharged" repeatedly. The bus is designed to travel six miles between "charges."

The flywheel is a single ring resembling a spinal disk—it is thickest at the center and rim. Made of high-strength steel, it

Flywheel Power

A trolley bus being built for use in San Francisco will draw current from trolley wires to run the drive motor and a separate motor/generator that revs a flywheel up to top spinning speed. With trolleys retracted, the bus can travel up to 6 miles using flywheel-generated electrical power.

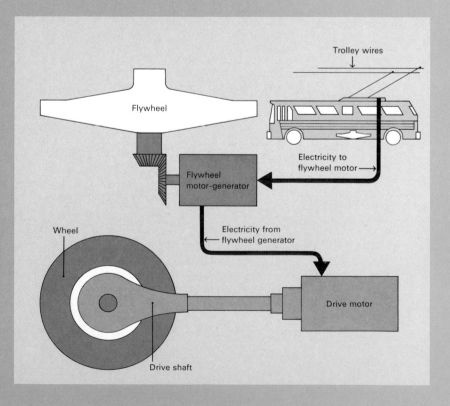

spins in a vacuum chamber held to about 1/500 of normal atmospheric pressure in order to reduce the drag of air friction at such high rotational speeds.

The Garrett subway car uses flywheels to recover energy that would otherwise be wasted as heat when the car brakes to a stop at each station. The train's traction motor, that normally drives the wheels by drawing current from an electrified third rail, can also work as a generator. Consequently, as the coasting train nears a station, it is braked to a stop by engaging the generator. The generator's electric output is "stored" in a twin flywheel system and then removed to help get the train going again. The system is similar in principle to the one in Lockheed's bus.

Built of four steel disks that are 20 inches in diameter and weigh 150 pounds apiece, each flywheel stores about 3.2 kwh of energy when spinning at 14,000 rpm. In slowing to about 10,000 rpm, they produce over half the energy needed to get the car going again. If used on all New York subway cars, the flywheel modification could drastically cut the subway system's peak electricity consumption and make electricity available for other uses.

Bus and subway flywheels are not practical for the family car. One alternative would be to use a flywheel in conjunction with a small gasoline-powered engine. But for all-flywheel power, new designs and new materials are needed.

David W. Rabenhorst of Johns Hopkins University in Baltimore is forming fiber-reinforced plastics into new flywheel shapes to take advantage of the composite material's light weight and superhigh strength. His multirim flywheel is built out from the center with thin concentric rings of composite bonded with a rubbery glue. This design reduces the problem facing any flywheel—spin it too fast and centrifugal force will tear it apart—by reinforcing the plastic in the inner rings with stretchy fibers, and using increasingly stiffer fibers for the outer rings.

Many believe such flywheels can be made compact enough for automobiles and still store enough energy for 200 miles of driving. If they can be made to work as well as designs indicate, you may someday drive into a service station and say, "Charge her up," then drive off with a spinning flywheel propelling you down the highway quietly, silently, and cleanly. [L. J. Lawson]

tween terminals at the Dallas-Fort Worth airport. It went into service in early 1974, and covers 13 miles with three routes and 24 electrically powered vehicles. Despite some early unsolved start-up problems—a piece of tin foil against the rail, or a burned-out light bulb, can short-circuit the electricity powering the cars—many transportation engineers now consider it highly successful.

Train tests. The U.S. Department of Transportation is completing a facility in Pueblo, Colo., to test high-speed train systems. Under test in 1974 were advanced systems that run on air cushions and use linear electric drive.

The facility also has conventional tracks for testing improved versions of conventional trains. Subway cars from the New York City transit system, for example, have been fitted with energy-storing flywheels and are being tested to learn how effective the flywheels are in conserving energy. See Close-Up.

One of the principal experiments at the Pueblo facility involves the new Advanced Concepts Train. This sleek, automatic, driverless transit vehicle is designed to represent the latest developments in comfort, economy, and operating efficiency. To passengers, the most obvious improvements will be a greatly reduced noise level inside the cars, and the increased comfort achieved by eliminating the bumps and jolts of a normal ride. Operators, however, are more interested in the tests to reduce maintenance costs. Different components, such as motors, control systems, and undercarriages, are being tested for long-term, trouble-free operation. The vehicles are expected to reduce maintenance costs from the present 55 cents to 30 cents per car-mile.

Transportation anniversary. The reasoning behind the need to improve public transportation has gone through several changes since the Urban Transportation Act was passed in 1964. At first, the principal concern was highway congestion. By the late 1960s, environmental concerns were foremost. And in 1973 and 1974, the fuel shortage intensified the interest in public transit. One result of the growing concern came in March, 1974, when new federal funding regulations were announced that allow states to substitute public transit projects for unconstructed sections of the Interstate Highway system. [James P. Romualdi]

Zoology

A possible way to correct a man-made imbalance between predators and wild prey was reported in May, 1974, by Carl R. Gustavson, University of Utah, and John Garcia, Walter G. Hankins, and Kenneth W. Rusiniak, University of California at Los Angeles. Man's long, concerted warfare against predators—such as coyotes, wolves, and large cats—that attack sheep and cattle has led to a population increase in their wild prey, such as deer and rabbits. This causes problems as the greater number of prey become more susceptible to starvation and disease.

In one series of experiments, the scientists trained coyotes not to attack lambs or rabbits. Lithium chloride pills, which cause temporary indigestion, were implanted into lamb or rabbit meat fed to the coyotes. After a few experiences with the chemically treated meat, the coyotes learned to avoid lambs and rabbits. They apparently first learned to dislike the flavor of the meat because it is associated with becoming sick. Given a choice, they ate some other kind of meat. Later, they refused to attack the animal.

The investigators suggest that sheep baits containing lithium chloride could be placed where coyotes are likely to hunt. Perhaps the same learning experience observed in the laboratory would occur on the range. Both the prey (sheep) and the predator (coyote) thus would be saved if the method worked.

The investigators also suggest that the altered feeding preferences of a mother coyote might be passed to her pups because her milk differs in taste, depending on what she eats. In addition, if the mother does not supply her pups with the prey that she has learned to avoid, the young coyotes may not develop a taste for those animals.

This method may work with other ecologically beneficial predators that are endangered species. For example, eagles could be trained to avoid attacking animals that are economically important.

Probing the fly palate. Vincent Dethier, insect physiologist at Princeton University, has developed a theory of taste discrimination based on many years of experiments on the neurophysiology and behavior of insects. Dethier has been studying how insects taste their food since he was a student at Harvard University in the 1930s. His early studies showed that flies have taste receptors on their feet as well as around the mouth. The receptors on the feet make the first contact with potential food; if they decide it is acceptable, sensory cells on the mouth evaluate the substance. Recordings from electrodes connected to the mouth's sensory cells show that specific cells perceive different concentrations of sugars, salts, amino acids, and water.

Currently, Dethier is studying how a fly or caterpillar identifies desirable food items. Rotting fish, for example, is delectable fare for a fly, while the caterpillar prefers the leaves of certain plants. Using their sensory systems to discriminate between food items, these insects often show highly selective preferences.

According to Dethier, an insect appears to base its food selection on the total responses of all the different types of sensory cells to a certain type of food. For example, a salt receptor responds more to salts than to sugars, but it responds to sugars to a certain extent, and the insect evidently weighs this small response in addition to the greater one. Most sensory cells behave in a similar manner, sending a pattern of responses to the brain based on the concentrations of sugars, salts, amino acids, and other substances. Each type of food draws a different pattern based on the medley of individual cell responses. The pattern provides the insect brain with the information required to make a selective judgment about the desirability of the food.

Dethier has tested his theory by determining the composition of leaves that caterpillars will or will not accept, and mixing up synthetic solutions as copies. By juggling the ingredients of the mixtures, Dethier can learn what qualities make specific leaves acceptable to the insect. With electrodes, he then can monitor the pattern of signals reaching the brain in response to each substance.

DDT strikes again. Another animal has joined the list of those endangered by DDT. Premature births of sea lions on islands off the coast of California and Mexico seem to be associated with high levels of DDT in their tissues. Robert L. DeLong of the National Marine Fisheries Service, Seattle, and William G. Gilmartin and John G. Simpson of the Naval Undersea Center, San Diego, reported in September, 1973, that premature births are occurring as early as January, compared with normal births, which occur

Zoology
Continued

Newly hatched young wolf spiders cling to knobby hairs on their mother's abdomen and avoid shaved areas. The experiment was aimed at determining the role of the hairs.

between May 15 and June 30. Tissues from females that gave birth prematurely contained concentrations of DDT from two to eight times higher than tissues from females that gave birth to full-term, normal pups.

The residues probably result from female sea lions feeding on contaminated fish. Many of the female California sea lions spend the winter off southern Baja California, but a few remain on islands near Los Angeles. The investigators found that fish around Los Angeles have higher DDT residues than those off Baja California, and they concluded that the females staying on the islands probably take in more DDT than those making the trip to Baja. The ones that winter on the islands are probably the ones that give birth prematurely.

DDT residues were previously implicated in the decline of pelicans on these islands. DDT apparently caused the birds to lay eggs with thin shells or no shells.

Plucky anemone. At the American Association for the Advancement of Science meeting in February, 1974, Richard K. Wright of the University of California

at Los Angeles described a unique form of tissue rejection.

Most animals reject foreign tissues when blood cells produce antibodies in response to the presence of foreign proteins, or antigens, in the tissue. The sea anemone seems to have a more primitive rejection system. It rejects a tissue graft from another individual by using its tentacles to reach down and pluck it off. But how does the sea anemone know where the graft is located and that the tissue is foreign? Similar grafts of its own tissue transplanted from one place to another on the same animal do not trigger the rejection mechanism. Wright plans to continue investigating how the anemone transmits information from grafts to the nervous system, which directs the action of the tentacles.

Hi-fi cricket control. Experiments on a golf course by Muniyandy Ulagaraj and Thomas J. Walker of the University of Florida in Gainesville indicate that cricket mating songs can be used to lure them to their deaths. Large numbers of two species of mole crickets were attracted to funnels placed over loudspeakers playing

Zoology
Continued

A hamster's kidney cell, magnified 16,200 times, *opposite page*, travels by a process that is called "ruffling." In a culture, the cell sprouts thin folds along its forward edge. The folds then grow upward, outward, and drop to the surface. The cell flows forward over the ruffles and repeats the process.

their mating songs. Once in the funnel, the crickets fell into traps and were later destroyed. In addition to destroying pest crickets directly, broadcasting the mating songs from loudspeakers may also reduce their numbers by interfering with the cues that lead them to their mates.

This confusion tactic may eventually be used to control other insects that depend on sounds in their courtship rituals. It is similar to using artificial odors to confuse other insects seeking mates.

Such techniques are of great value because only specific pest insects are affected; beneficial insects are not harmed. See THE BIOLOGISTS BITE BACK.

Cues for pigeons. Homing pigeons use a number of cues to navigate, including the angle of the sun and geographical landmarks. Charles Walcott and Robert P. Green of the State University of New York at Stony Brook reported in April that magnetic fields may give another important cue. They fitted pigeons with pairs of wire coils, one coil around the neck like a collar, the other around the head like a hat. The two coils were connected to a small battery and the electrical circuit produced a relatively uniform magnetic field around the pigeon's head. Each bird also carried a small radio transmitter emitting signals that showed in which direction the bird flew.

By reversing the battery in its holder, the flow of current through the coils and the direction of the magnetic field could be reversed. Reversing the magnetic field on sunny days had little effect on homing ability, but in overcast weather it hindered the pigeons in locating their home loft. Since a magnetic field encompasses the earth, it seems that pigeons, and perhaps other birds, can use information from this field to navigate. In repeated experiments, the pigeons found their way home more easily despite the reversed magnetic field. Presumably, they either adjusted their "navigation equipment" to the altered field or relied more heavily on landmarks and other cues.

Frozen snails survive. Biologists have been investigating the mechanisms used by Arctic and Antarctic animals to survive below-freezing temperatures. Allen R. Hargens and Stephen V. Shabica of the Scripps Institution of Oceanography in La Jolla, Calif., and the School of Oceanography at Oregon State University reported in September, 1973, how limpets,

a kind of small snail, escape freezing to death when they are caught in ice.

They found the limpets surviving in ice at Palmer Station, Antarctica. Laboratory experiments showed that the limpets were surrounded by small pockets from 0.04 to 0.43 inch (1 to 11 millimeters) thick, which contained a mucus secreted by the snails. Apparently, this substance has antifreeze properties not previously reported. Analysis of the mucus may lead to advances in the study of the effects of low temperatures on living creatures and to better understanding of how animals survive such a hostile environment. It may also lead to practical uses of the snail's antifreeze.

Storing frozen embryos. Experimenters at Great Britain's Agricultural Research Council reported in August, 1973, that they had frozen and revived calf embryos. Of 13 embryos that were defrosted and reimplanted in cows, 2 were born and thrived. The calf embryos are most likely to survive if they are frozen when they have developed into spheres of several hundred cells ready to implant themselves in the uterus wall.

Researchers at Jackson Laboratories in Bar Harbor, Me., are carrying out similar research with frozen mouse embryos to see whether genetic characteristics will be affected by frozen storage.

Dogs adopt monkeys. Young rhesus monkeys accepted adoption by dogs in experiments carried out at the California Primate Research Center at Davis. The experiment contradicted accepted beliefs that monkeys form irreversible bonds with their mothers. William A. Mason and Molly Donnell Kenney reported in March, 1974, that young monkeys initially raised by monkey mothers became attached not only to the first dog they were placed with, but accepted a new dog when taken from their first companion. Subsequent tests indicated that some monkeys even preferred the dog companions to their natural mothers. See PSYCHOLOGY.

Once a monkey adjusted to its new parent, it often went along when the dog was taken out for exercise. When prevented from joining the dog on such jaunts, the young monkey protested verbally and tried to escape from its cage. The investigators concluded that a gentle, accepting dog can be a highly effective mother substitute for a young rhesus monkey.   [William J. Bell]

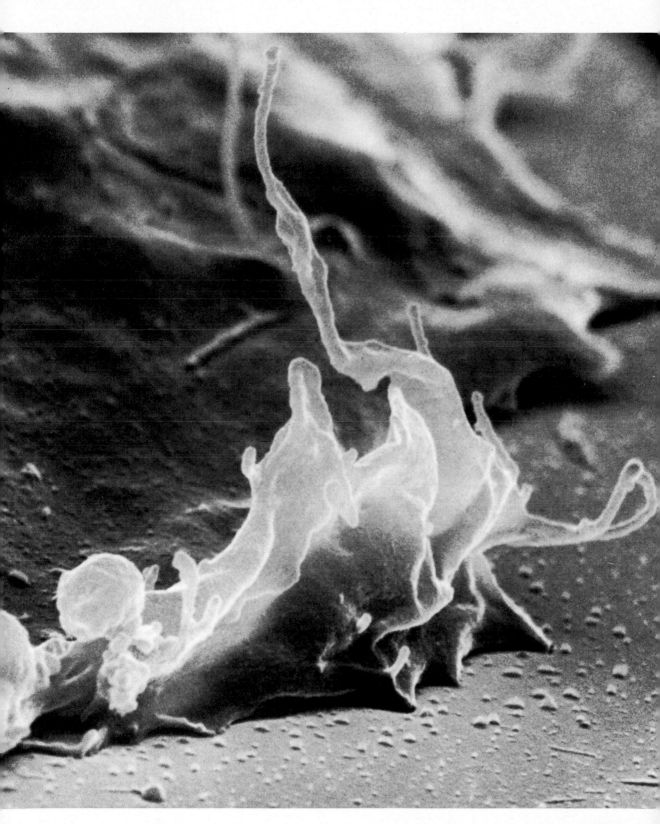

Men and
Women
Of Science

The versatility of science makes it possible for a
scientist's career to take some unexpected
turns. This section, which recognizes outstanding
scientists, features two whose accomplishments
have been, to a degree, unanticipated.

Dixy Lee Ray

By Graham Chedd

**As biologist, teacher, and head of the AEC, one of her
main concerns has been to bring science to the public**

People can be divided into two types, according to Dixy Lee Ray:
Those who think that science can do anything, and those who are
afraid that it will. "Whether science is seen as a genie or a devil is
equally bad," she says. That is why all her life she has been dedicated
to communicating the excitement of science to people, particularly to
those who know little about it. Dixy Lee Ray is passionate in her
devotion to knowing things, both as fun and as a means of understanding and coping with our world. She derives enormous pleasure from
knowledge and thinks that almost everyone else does, too—even
though a lot of them may not realize it.

This short, gray-haired marine biologist, who prefers to dress in
slacks, tennis shoes, and a rumpled sweater and is accompanied everywhere by her two dogs—Jacques, a miniature poodle, and Ghillie, a
100-pound Scottish deerhound—has been a local celebrity for years in
the Seattle area. As a teacher, research scientist, oceanographer, mu-

Dixy Lee Ray, chairman of the Atomic Energy Commission, researches
questions involving nuclear energy in her Washington, D.C., office.

seum director, television performer, and driver of a Jaguar sports car, she won the respect and admiration of both her colleagues and the public. Much of her success was founded on her great talent for communicating with people, aided by her bubbling good humor and her warm, expressive voice.

But until February, 1973, Dixy Lee Ray was little known outside her native state of Washington. Then Washington, D.C., was startled, delighted, and amused when she was appointed the chairman of the Atomic Energy Commission (AEC). She has continued to startle people ever since. She still delights quite a few, too. But everyone now takes her unexpected appointment to the AEC quite seriously.

Her influence on the AEC came during a period when the energy crisis focused the nation's attention on it as never before. "She turned on a great big light inside a dim agency," said nuclear physicist Ralph E. Lapp. "And it needed it. It was getting pretty dank in there." A few people would disagree. They are neither delighted nor amused by Dixy Lee Ray, and they have no reason to be. During her first few months as head of the AEC, she vigorously swept out some old ideas and set up new policies, greatly upsetting some other AEC officials.

But the overwhelming majority of people who have encountered Ray have become devoted admirers. They have been charmed not only by her intelligence and wit, but by her love of knowing things.

Her delight in knowledge for knowledge's sake—with an emphasis on nature, particularly the creatures that live in and at the edges of the sea—dates from a childhood spent along the shores of Puget Sound in Washington. The second of five daughters, she was born in Tacoma, Wash., on Sept. 3, 1914. Her father earned his living as a commercial printer. The family lived on the outskirts of town, half a mile from the Puget Sound waterfront. Dixy Lee Ray remembers running down a path and over a bluff to the waterfront docks. "As soon as I was old enough to be away from home for a whole afternoon, I would go down there to play," she says. "I'd use a homemade fishing line to fish for sole and flounder along the sandy bottom. I recall very clearly digging around in the sand and being intrigued by the worms and crabs and other creatures."

When she was 10 years old she joined the Girl Scouts and her life in the summer became a succession of camps on island after island and beach after beach. But the things she remembers most clearly about those days are always connected with fishing at low tide.

When she was 19 years old, Dixy Lee Ray went off to Mills College in Oakland, Calif., a liberal arts school for women. There she was introduced to literature and philosophy, which she still enjoys, while she earned her bachelor's and master's degrees in zoology. Mills College introduced her to something else, too—teaching.

Up to that point in her life, Dixy Lee Ray had not given much thought to a career beyond deciding that whatever she did, she would not teach. But while a graduate student, she became a teaching assist-

The author:
Graham Chedd, science editor for WGBH-TV in Boston, also wrote "Closing in on the Flu" for this edition.

From her attractive office in Seattle, Ray directed the Pacific Science Center from 1963 to 1972.

ant in zoology, because she needed money. This was during the Depression and the family printing business was suffering badly. "After just a little teaching I discovered what a rewarding and really fabulously interesting profession it is. Seeing comprehension dawn on the face of someone whom both you and they thought would never understand is tremendously exciting."

She graduated from Mills with a master's degree in 1938, and stayed on in Oakland to teach full time in a public high school. During the summer, she taught at a high school near Carmel-by-the-Sea on Monterey Bay. She would often take her students to the beaches to do field work at low tide, sometimes as early as 4 A.M. But, for her, high-school teaching eventually became frustrating. "By the time you'd taught the same thing to seven classes in one day," she says, "at the end of it you felt like an idiot."

So she went on to Stanford University for a Ph.D. in biology. Her Ph.D. thesis had an impressive title: "The Nervous System of *Lampayctus leucopsaurus* with Comparative Notes on Other Iniomi." Originally, Ray had wanted to work on a more ecologically oriented subject, involving marine biology. But her supervising professor convinced her that ecology would not be a good topic for her thesis. She would have to spend several seasons making observations to really understand any ecological phenomenon. And with the United States embroiled in World War II, the West Coast was under curfew. Soldiers patrolled the beaches and sent people away at dusk, so she would not be able to make any observations after dark. The professor also persuaded her that a thesis is a means to an end, in which learning the techniques of scholarship is far more important than the subject matter.

Ray followed this advice all during her graduate education. While she was doing her thesis on fish, she also worked as a laboratory assistant in microbiology, assisted in invertebrate zoology classes, and collected seaweeds for a professor who taught a course on algae. By the time she had finished her thesis, Ray saw nothing to stop her from continuing study in any of these fields. And she still believes that "one of the greatest mistakes a student can make is to regard himself forever restricted to the general area of his thesis subject."

In 1945, she joined the faculty at the University of Washington. She thought her greatest opportunities there lay in the field of invertebrate zoology. And so she began a distinguished research and teaching career in that field.

During the next 15 years at the university, Dixy Lee Ray firmed up many of the ideas that would help set the course of her later careers. Her research on a small wood-boring crustacean called limnoria showed that it is the only higher organism that produces its own enzyme for digesting wood. Other such organisms rely on the secretions of microbes. She also spent a great deal of time working with graduate students on their research. But she would not allow her name to appear on their publications. This was an almost unheard-of attitude.

The chairman of the AEC and the President of the United States confer in the Oval Office of the White House.

Scientists were under tremendous pressure to have their names appear on as many scientific research papers as possible.

She was also becoming increasingly aware of the need for a greater understanding of science throughout society. She began to believe that "the health, the tolerance, the very existence of science rests upon a general acceptance that it is a good thing."

Her life might have continued on this relatively obscure level had she not received an invitation from the National Science Foundation in 1960 to spend a few months in Washington, D.C. She was to head a committee studying what research should be done in the field of marine biology—a job that was supposed to take about six months. After finishing the study, instead of returning home, Ray stayed on in Washington for another two years. Most of that time she served as a special assistant to the National Science Foundation's associate director for administration, Paul Scherer. She was looking into the ways in which government grants for science and education are awarded. Consequently, she spent a great deal of time observing congressional hearings on almost everything that had to do with science and education. "It was a real education for me," she says, "because I had not even thought until that time, 'How does the government really function?'"

Her thoughts about public understanding of science crystallized during her stay in the capital. Most of what she saw and heard impressed her. "But, when it came to scientific questions, congressmen and scientists were talking past each other at the witness table, unable to understand each other's points. This led to frustration and irritation on both sides. After a while, the scientists tended to become condescending, and the congressmen impatient. So I determined to pay much more attention to the way we teach science. We have traditionally taught science to people who are going to become scientists. Although we live in a technological age, when the information that comes out of science affects everything we do, everything we are, we scorn the teaching of science to nonscience majors."

Dixy Lee Ray went back to the University of Washington early in 1963, having had more than enough of official and urban life in Washington, D.C. She rented a house on Mercer Island in Lake Washington, anxious to enjoy the outdoors once again and ready to immerse herself in the academic world. She also set about organizing a course at the university in science for nonscience majors. But almost immediately her desire to educate the public about science was put to a far more challenging test.

Seattle's world's fair, the Century 21 Exposition, had ended in October, 1962. A nonprofit corporation had taken over the fair's U.S. science exhibit and decided to turn it into a science resource center, called the Pacific Science Center. Dixy Lee Ray was recommended for the job of director.

At the time, in addition to her teaching, she was about to embark on her first really major oceanographic expedition, as chief scientist on the International Indian Ocean Expedition research ship *Te Vega*. But she accepted the job of director and took command of the Pacific Science Center in July, 1963. Nevertheless, she still was able to sail on the Indian Ocean research expedition by taking a leave of absence from February to June, 1964.

The first years of her directorship were mainly devoted to keeping the science center alive; indeed, people who knew her then doubt that anyone else could have succeeded. The fledgling science center existed solely because of public good will. For money, it relied on public subscriptions and government funds. And Dixy Lee Ray turned out to be a top-notch fund-raiser. Because she had good relations with the press, she presented a good public image. It seemed like everyone in the Seattle area knew her, so she became the face of the center.

Officials of the Atomic Energy Commission brief their boss on the U.S. underground nuclear test program during her visit to Amchitka Island, off Alaska, in July, 1973.

Dixy Lee Ray inspects a remote-control unit for handling radioactive materials inside an AEC facility near Las Vegas.

The staff at the center still remembers and appreciates her talent for public relations. "We were able to raise funds because of her charisma rather than because of our programs," states one of her former colleagues. "It was amazing that she kept the center flying. We didn't gain much altitude, but we didn't crash either."

People at the center still tell stories about the days when Ray was director. On one occasion she and the Seattle park district got into a dispute over spraying trees to kill insect pests. She firmly objected to the spraying for ecological reasons and would not allow the department to treat the trees around the science center.

The park district people argued that the pests had to be controlled everywhere if the infestation was to be stopped. So Dixy Lee Ray went out and bought thousands of ladybugs, which prey on other insects, and threw them into the trees. The ladybugs failed twice, but on the third try, they succeeded.

From the beginning her aim was to make the Pacific Science Center "the kind of place to which the populace would naturally turn to find

information or the answer to a question about any area in science." Although the center provided laboratories and exhibits for the schools of the region, educating the area's adult population was always Ray's main interest. "One of the most pitiful things I have ever known was the number of people visiting the science center who would say to me, 'I think it's so wonderful what you're doing for the children. They can get so much out of it, but it's too late for me.' Not only is that pitiful, but it's also untrue."

So she relied on her belief that people derive pleasure from bits of information, such as knowing how to tell a butterfly from a moth. "Such little informative things can be used as handles for getting some sort of appreciation of science," she says. "It's this sort of appreciation we need in the general public. We need to eliminate the fear that goes with ignorance."

She also has an answer for those who argue that we now know enough science, that it is time now to learn how to control and apply it properly. "There is no such thing as ever having enough knowledge about anything," she says. "You may just as well say to people, 'Stop thinking, we've had enough thinking. Quit it.' You'll succeed no more than saying to children, 'Stop growing.' It's impossible."

High up on the list of Dixy Lee Ray's qualities is her ability to communicate. She was born with this talent, honed it during her teaching days, and polished it bright at the Pacific Science Center. For a number of years she used this talent on a mass scale, hosting a regular local television show in Seattle called "Doorways to Science." The program was typical of Dixy Lee Ray—relaxed, informal (her dogs wandered about the set), and spontaneous. Often she made up her mind about the subject of a program while on her way to the studio. If the subject was snow, a pan of snow in the studio would lead into discussions ranging from avalanches to why ice crystals are six-sided. It was always easy for the audience to relate to her "fireside chats about science," as she called them.

For one program, she cooked up a Puget Sound bouillabaisse, a fish chowder, and talked about the natural history of the fish included in the dish. During the preparations, she was foiled by a can opener that refused to work. Determined that the show and the chowder would go on, she opened the can with a hatchet.

By the early 1970s, Ray had handed over much of the responsibility for the day-to-day operation of the science center to her staff and had begun to involve herself in other things. She joined the American Association for the Advancement of Science's (AAAS) Committee on Public Understanding of Science, and began preparing a special report on the role of museums in science.

One day in May, 1972, after attending a AAAS committee meeting in Washington, D.C., she was waiting at the airport for a flight back

Ghillie and Jacques make themselves at home while Ray confers with technical assistant David Jenkins at AEC headquarters in Germantown, Md.

With Jacques a very
hungry onlooker,
Ray passes out candy
to members of her staff.

home. Suddenly, she heard herself being paged over the airport's loudspeaker system. It was the White House calling. Barbara Franklin of the White House Women's Office asked if Ray would mind being nominated for the 5-member Atomic Energy Commission. The Administration was anxious to appoint a woman. Dixy Lee Ray replied that atomic energy was not her field. But the White House aide replied frankly that that did not matter. "We don't have too many women trained in science, you know."

Ray asked two questions: "Is it a full-time job? Do I have to live in the Washington, D.C., area?" The answer to both questions was yes. "I said no," she recalls. "In the first place, I like what I'm doing, and in the second place, I like where I live. So, no thank you. Find someone else." Franklin begged her not to say no and said the White House would call again the next week.

Obviously, Ray changed her mind and accepted the job. Why? "Because when you look at it like a biologist, you realize that energy is at the heart of Western civilization, and that seemed like an interesting place to be." Colleagues say that she was also flattered by the invitation and that she viewed it as a next-to-impossible challenge—her favorite kind.

So again she left her beloved Pacific Northwest, bought a motor home, and drove it across the country with Jacques and Ghillie. Along the way she visited AEC installations, and finally arrived in Washington, D.C., in August, ready to learn about atomic energy.

Within six months of joining the commission, she was elevated to the chairmanship on direct White House orders. Just why the appointment was made remains a mystery. Although it seems no one expected fireworks from this charming, humorous, open woman, it was not long before old habits and attitudes at the AEC were vigorously shaken—within the agency itself, among the commission members, and on the Joint Congressional Committee on Atomic Energy. "She is strong enough intellectually to act as a very firm leader," said one of Ray's friends. "She saw that it was necessary to break up the old

Ray delights in watching Ghillie romp at noontime on the AEC headquarters' grounds. A great believer in educating the public about science, she pauses to talk about nuclear power with a large group of students touring the agency.

AEC hierarchy. And even though she knew that many of her actions would cause trouble, she went ahead anyway."

Dixy Lee Ray contends that after about 25 years, "science agencies tend to become moribund." And the AEC was 25 years old in 1970. "Put it this way: About once in every quarter century there ought to be a good shakeup—a total relook at what you're doing and why."

She made many changes in her first few months as chairman, opening up the AEC internally and externally. She announced that AEC information on the peaceful uses of the atom would be made available to the public. Before Ray took over, most of the AEC's records were kept secret. She also agreed to file an Environmental Impact Statement on the nuclear breeder reactors under development. But the most dramatic change was her decision to completely reverse the stand of her predecessors on the issue of safety research. The fact that responsibility for research on the safety of nuclear reactors lay in the Division of Reactor Development Technology (RDT) had long been a major bone of contention between the AEC and its critics. In fact, shortly before Ray became chairman, her predecessor James R. Schlesinger had defended the arrangement to Congress. But AEC critics claimed there was a clear conflict of interest when the people responsible for developing new reactor technology were also responsible for checking on the safety of nuclear reactors.

The battle was heightened considerably by the man in charge of RDT, Milton Shaw. Shaw, a tough uncompromising man, had powerful friends where it mattered: James Ramey, AEC commissioner and liaison with Congress, and Congressman Chet Holifield (D., Calif.), a powerful member of the joint committee on atomic energy. Ray took them all on and won. Shaw resigned from the AEC shortly afterward and Ray refused to support Ramey's renomination to the commission in June, 1973.

Why did Dixy Lee Ray decide to separate safety research from reactor development? "I think that there is a real difference in the sort of research you do when you're developing and making something for the first time, and the sort of thing you have to do to make sure it continues to work. It's like the difference between building cars and repairing them. Moreover, as in basic science, you need experiments to confirm your findings. You can't just have one group saying, 'Yes, they're safe, take our word for it. We built them, and we know they're safe.' Someone else, completely independent, needs to take a look."

Ray believes this internal cross-checking arrangement should satisfy most critics. "Though if they say, 'We don't believe anything the AEC does,' we might as well shut up shop. There are people who would like to do away with nuclear power completely." She has no patience with them and they have none with her. She is also temperamentally poles apart from critics, such as Ralph Nader, who rely essentially on the adversary approach to argue scientific questions—presenting opposing viewpoints as lawyers do in a courtroom. She contends that these

Ray talks briefly with Senator Howard H. Baker, Jr. (R., Tenn.) center, and Representative Orval Hansen (R., Ida.) before testifying on nuclear reactor safety at public hearings held by the Joint Congressional Committee on Atomic Energy.

critics only choose evidence that will further their case. For scientific debate, all the evidence must be considered equally so that a reasonable conclusion can be drawn.

In scientific matters, Dixy Lee Ray regards the adversary approach as irresponsible pressure that is "both dangerous and mischievous. It is almost a call to panic and hysteria by innuendo and unsupported charge, which is just the opposite of everything I believe in. I believe that if information exists and can be made understandable, you can rely on the good sense, the general sensibilities, of most people."

But she does welcome the kind of pressure that comes from what she regards as responsible environmentalist groups such as the Sierra Club. Although these groups make public demands and may differ with her on the interpretation of the evidence, Ray believes that they do attempt to look at all the facts.

Dixy Lee Ray has brought an unlikely informality to the prestigious and powerful AEC. "She is not the kind of person to want to maintain hierarchies and keep her distance from people," according to a former colleague at the Pacific Science Center. "Anyone who works for her is

After a hard day at the office, Jacques, Ghillie, and Dixy Lee Ray relax in their motor home, parked in the country.

important enough for her to talk to." And she has carried this approachability over to the AEC. For example, Ray brings Jacques and Ghillie to her office every day. At noon she takes the dogs for a walk on the grounds at AEC headquarters and will talk to anyone she meets. Also, she will ask whoever happens to be closest at the time to do things, whether they are the "right" person or not.

Her day begins early in the morning when a chauffeured limousine picks up her and the dogs at her motor home, parked in the countryside about two miles from her office. In the office, she devotes most of her time to meeting with staff and consultants and directing operations of the huge agency. But she sets aside time for interviews with the press and meetings with representatives of environmental groups. When time permits, she enjoys stopping to talk with students or other groups touring AEC headquarters. She also feels it is important to travel to other cities—usually about once a month—to meet with civic groups and educate the public about nuclear power.

378

Dixy Lee Ray greets most visitors to her huge and imposing office at the AEC headquarters in Germantown, Md., with a captivating smile and a warm handshake and then offers them coffee, tea, or other refreshments in an informal little ceremony. She loves to feed people.

This is reflected, too, in what little time she has for a social life. Cooking and entertaining are her favorite ways to relax. In her days at the Pacific Science Center, she and four or five colleagues would eat together almost every night, so they formed a dining club. Each took turns cooking for the group, and eventually the meals turned into gourmet productions.

One of the best examples of Ray's entertaining style came soon after she returned to Washington, D.C., to take up her job as an AEC commissioner in 1972. She ordered fresh salmon specially flown in from the Pacific Northwest and entertained an impressive group of dignitaries, including Schlesinger, at her 8- by 28-foot motor home, parked on the grounds of a friend's Maryland estate.

Occasionally, Ray gets away from her duties at the AEC and returns to the Puget Sound area for a visit with one of her sisters, who lives on Fox Island. The rest of her family is scattered around the world. One sister is a missionary in Ethiopia. During these visits, Ray stops in at the Pacific Science Center and cooks bouillabaisse or chili for the staff—just as she did when she was the director.

As chairman of the AEC at a time when energy suddenly became a national preoccupation, Dixy Lee Ray found herself with a leading role in the debate about how to alleviate the U.S. energy shortage. She became an enthusiastic supporter of President Richard M. Nixon's proposal that the AEC should become the nucleus of a new Energy Research and Development Administration. Arguing eloquently before congressional hearings, she pointed out that the AEC's well-equipped laboratories and scientific personnel make it a natural focus for expanded energy research.

The President also gave her the enormous task of preparing—in five months—the nation's blueprint for energy research and development to aid in making the United States self-sufficient in energy production by 1980. For this report, entitled "The Nation's Energy Future," she consulted with more than 400 scientists, industrialists, environmentalists, and politicians. When the report was published in December, 1973, it was widely acclaimed as a monumental achievement in pulling together information about the various public and private energy research projects and the technology that might be useful in solving the nation's energy problems.

In the energy crisis, as in any other situation that requires public understanding, Dixy Lee Ray still firmly believes in the inherent good sense of a properly informed public, a public with knowledge of the scientific facts surrounding the problem. "People need to understand that science is just one more intellectual tool, one more way of knowing enough of the things that will allow society a means of survival."

Carl Djerassi

By Gene Bylinsky

The genius, insight, and vigor of this pioneering organic chemist have left their marks in the classroom, laboratory, and corporate board room

From the sundeck of his house in Portola Valley, Calif., near San Francisco, Carl Djerassi can look down at a big rectangular swimming pool. The steps leading into the pool are inlaid with lettered tile: "BUILT BY OPTICAL ROTATORY DISPERSION."

The words hint at one of Djerassi's major contributions to chemistry and typify his sense of humor. He paid for the pool with royalties from his book on optical rotatory dispersion, a physical phenomenon that he applied to biochemical analysis and thereby helped to create a revolution in chemical research.

Many of Djerassi's personal and professional interests lie almost within shouting distance of that pleasant house ringed by Monterey pines. A few miles south is Syntex Research, the investigative arm of Syntex Corporation, the company Djerassi served as a principal research executive until 1973. In the same industrial park, huge tobacco hornworm moths grow on a strange assembly line at Zoecon Corporation, a small company pioneering the development of hormonal insecticides. Djerassi is Zoecon's board chairman and president. Within a 15-minute drive of the house is his laboratory at Stanford University,

Selections from his extensive collection of contemporary paintings and pre-Columbian art from Mexico lend color and elegance to Djerassi's Zoecon office.

where he is professor of chemistry. And in the Santa Cruz Mountains, a few miles west of his house, sprawls Djerassi's 1,200-acre ranch, stocked with prize Polled Shorthorn cattle.

Whether he is at the ranch, striding through redwood groves, at an international conference on science and world affairs, serving as a U.S. delegate, or writing at his desk in Portola Valley (he has written six books and over 800 scientific papers), friends have trouble keeping up with Djerassi. This stocky man of intense gaze, eloquent tongue, remarkable mind, and, above all, boundless energy is, in the words of a friend, "an elemental force."

Carl Djerassi has jammed enough into the first 50 years of his life for three or four outstanding careers. He has successfully bridged the gap between academic and industrial science and is highly respected in both. He calls his life "a luxury—like having two cakes and eating them, too." The quality of all his scientific work has prompted a Nobel Prize-winning Stanford colleague to remark that Carl Djerassi "has won the Nobel Prize two or three times over—he has made contributions of that magnitude."

That assessment suggests the quantity of Djerassi's work as well. Djerassi's numerous contributions to science, education, and society continue today. He is deeply involved in helping countries in Africa and Latin America develop high-quality scientific programs, particularly in medical and drug research. In his Stanford laboratory, he is perfecting new analytical techniques and probing marine plants in

The author:
Gene Bylinsky, a science writer, is an associate editor of *Fortune* magazine. He wrote "The FDA: Guarding a Nation's Health" for *Science Year,* 1971.

search of new chemicals and drugs. To the consternation of some of his
students, he holds classes at 8 A.M., and because he is on the go until
late at night, his telephone rings in three places at once—his Stanford
and Zoecon offices, and in the study of his home. Colleagues quickly
discover that Djerassi has no time for social chit-chat. He is intent on
using every minute productively. Says Professor Gilbert Stork of Columbia University, who has known Djerassi since they attended graduate school together at the University of Wisconsin, "He has an absolute rule of doing at least two things simultaneously."

Djerassi believes he inherited his remarkable physical energy from
his father, who practiced medicine until he was 73 and is still spry at
81. Djerassi was born in 1923 in Vienna, Austria, where his Bulgarian
father and Viennese mother met while attending medical school. Carl
literally grew up in two doctors' offices. His parents divorced when he
was 7 and for eight years he spent the school year in Vienna with his
mother, and summers in Sofia, Bulgaria, with his father.

It was assumed by both parents and child that he, too, would eventually go into medicine. Yet young Djerassi had no early interest in
medicine or, for that matter, in any form of science. "I didn't have a
basement lab," he recalls. "I was not interested in mixing chemicals
and blowing up things, or in seeing colors change."

In 1938, with Austria under Nazi rule, Djerassi went to Bulgaria to
attend the American College in Sofia. In 1939, two months after the
outbreak of World War II, he and his mother emigrated to the United

States. He took premed courses at two small colleges before entering Kenyon College in Ohio in September, 1941. A skiing accident in Bulgaria left Djerassi with an injured knee and a 4-F draft classification. With so many other young men in the armed forces, he soon found himself to be one of only two students taking advanced chemistry. Two chemistry professors tutored the two the way students could expect to be tutored perhaps only at the universities of Cambridge and Oxford in England. The study was intensive, the lab work hard, and the results, for Djerassi at least, were inspiring. "That was really the change," says Djerassi. "It was only here that you might say I became a scientist." He decided to go into basic science rather than medicine. Drug development interested him even then, particularly because he suspected that many physicians were relatively ignorant about the substances they were administering.

After finishing two years of academic work in one at Kenyon, he received an A.B. degree, *summa cum laude,* in 1942 and then joined Ciba Pharmaceutical Company in New Jersey as a research chemist. Treated as an equal by older scientists, the 19-year-old chemist worked on a team that within a year developed Pyribenzamine, one of the first antihistamines.

Brief stints in night school at Brooklyn College and, later, New York University convinced Djerassi that full-time graduate school was the next logical step in his career. Being a young man in a phenomenal hurry, he calculated that he could his Ph.D. in only two years in the accelerated atmosphere of a university in wartime. He enrolled at the University of Wisconsin in Madison on a research fellowship. He wanted to work on steroids, a group of natural chemical compounds that includes the adrenal and sex hormones. Although the steroids had been studied for years, research on these important compounds was just moving into high gear as Djerassi began his graduate work. Steroid molecules became a lifelong interest and the foundation of his scientific career. Because he had some industrial experience, Djerassi knew more chemistry than most graduate students. Well-organized, confident, and determined, he knew what he wanted to do and how he wanted to do it. "Now that I look back," he says, "if a young Djerassi were to walk into my office now, I would certainly consider him brash, maybe even obnoxious."

But his professors were intrigued by this unusual young man. Professor William S. Johnson, now at Stanford, recalls that, even then, Djerassi's exceptional knowledgeability, diligence, dedication, and dynamism impressed them. They were impressed even more when, as part of his Ph.D. thesis work, he succeeded in converting the male sex hormone testosterone into the female sex hormone estradiol. Djerassi's solution of this extremely tough technical problem hinted at his blossoming research capabilities.

Armed with his Ph.D., Djerassi went back to Ciba in 1945, the year he became a U.S. citizen. While working for Ciba, Djerassi met

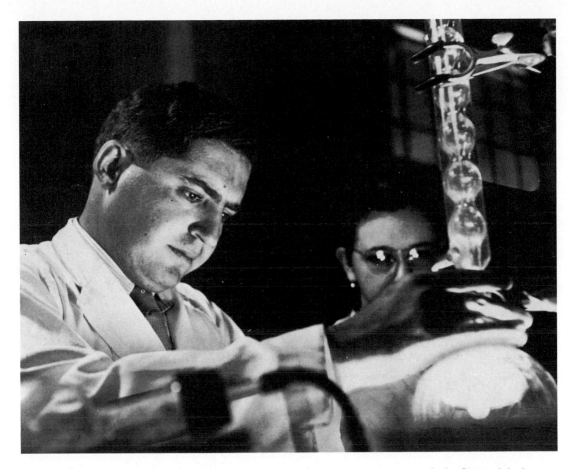

At the Syntex labs in
Mexico City, in 1951,
the young Djerassi led
a research team that
synthesized many
important steroids.

Norma Lundholm, then Manhattan program director of the National
Conference of Christians and Jews, over a plate of olives at a New
Jersey party. Their mutual taste for olives quickly ripened into a mu-
tual regard for each other and they married in 1950.

By 1949, Djerassi had become impatient with his career. The discovery that year of the therapeutic effects of cortisone in relieving
arthritis opened an exciting chapter in steroid development. But Ciba
showed little interest in cortisone. Then an offer came from a Mexican
company, Syntex, that wanted to develop new methods of synthesizing cortisone and other steroids. Djerassi was intrigued. Most American scientists then clung to the mistaken notion that good science was
not done south of the Rio Grande. Friends warned him that he would
be lost to science if he went to Mexico. But he went for an interview
anyway. He was a bit startled to see a hydrogenator in the bright
sunlight in the Syntex courtyard. Hydrogenators are normally kept
away from unnecessary heat, handled gingerly, and operated behind
heavy protective screens because the hydrogen gas they contain is
highly explosive. But neither this nor Syntex's relatively primitive
laboratories deterred Djerassi. He was convinced that good work at

Syntex would attract a lot of attention and could lead to an academic appointment at a university in the United States, which remained his primary professional goal.

Making what turned out to be the most important decision of his life, he went to Syntex in 1949. In two highly productive years there, Djerassi and Hungarian-born chemist George Rosenkranz led a team of young Mexican chemists in producing a synthetic cortisone from steroid substances obtained from Mexican yams. This would have been a spectacular achievement anywhere. Coming from an unknown Mexican company, it made an even bigger scientific splash. The synthesis also sharply reduced the price of cortisone, which had been selling for $250 a gram.

The achievement laid the groundwork for another synthesis of major importance. In 1951, using the yam material, the Syntex chemists manufactured a synthetic analogue of progesterone, a female sex hormone. This filled a great demand for an active hormonal compound that could be taken orally to treat menstrual disorders. The other compounds then on the market were not as powerful biologically and had to be administered by injection.

As the starting point for the synthesis, Djerassi chose the 19-nor steroids (so-called because the molecules lack the usual carbon 19 atom). He was convinced that they could be made into much more powerful substances than those already available. From substances originating in the yam, Djerassi first prepared 19-nortestosterone. From that, he and his colleagues synthesized norethisterone, a pure, crystalline steroid. It turned out to be a potent compound, with effects just like the progesterone manufactured in a woman's body.

Speaking of this synthesis, Alejandro Zaffaroni, a biochemist who worked with Djerassi at Syntex, says, "To conceive of that structure as something that could be made in a practical way in those days was like going to the moon." Carl Djerassi had made a successful soft landing on his scientific moon.

It did not take long for researchers to figure out that such a compound could be used as an oral contraceptive. There had been hints as early as 1937 that progesterone inhibited ovulation in the rabbit, for instance, but that fundamental observation was never extended to human beings. Then, in the middle 1950s, biologist Gregory Pincus, of the Worcester Foundation for Experimental Biology, Shrewsbury, Mass., and his co-workers used norethisterone and a closely related substance (norethynodrel) to inhibit ovulation in women. After years of investigation and clinical testing, the first commercial oral contraceptive was marketed in 1960.

Djerassi's norethisterone thus became an ingredient of birth-control pills and is still found in more than half of all oral contraceptives in use today. When he visited China at the invitation of the Chinese Academy of Sciences in 1973, Djerassi was pleasantly surprised to see the Chinese use the Syntex trade name *Norlutin* for their pill.

Free wheeling scientific discussion with students and associates forms an important part of Djerassi's day at Stanford. *Top and left,* he talks with students in the lab and on a campus stroll; later, he joins Edward Feigenbaum (left) and Nobelist Joshua Lederberg in planning their joint computer project in chemistry.

In 1952, Djerassi accepted an associate professorship at Wayne State University in Detroit. His research interest continued to be the chemistry of natural products—compounds produced by plants or animals—but he was stymied by the lack of effective analytic techniques. Only when the structure of a compound has been analyzed, can it be synthesized in the laboratory. But even after the compound has been isolated from, say, a yam or an insect, the chemist has no idea of its structure. And to complicate the problem, he often has only a minute quantity of the material to study. Thus, the chemist needs a precise, yet nondestructive, method of analysis.

Djerassi, an experimentalist rather than a theoretician, and an impatient man as well, had no intention of spending his life trying to work out the nature of a single substance as some chemists have in the past. So, with his extraordinary ability to spot a good problem—often from bits of data that have escaped the notice of others—and organizing a massive effort to solve the problem, Djerassi turned to the world of physics. He thought that optical rotatory dispersion (ORD), a phenomenon that had been known to physicists since the early 1800's, might be useful to the organic chemist.

ORD is based on a peculiar characteristic of polarized light. Ordinary light is disorderly. It is composed of waves that vibrate in all the

Norma and Carl Djerassi talk with daughter Pamela and son Dale, left, and son-in-law Steve Bush, right, in the book-lined living room of the Portola Valley home. A tree stump at the ranch provides a sunny, out-door study as Djerassi catches up on his scientific reading.

A skiing enthusiast, Djerassi starts down a slope in the High Sierra, near Lake Tahoe, only a few hours drive from his home.

directions perpendicular to the light beam. A special filter polarizes the light, allowing only the waves that vibrate in a single plane to pass through. Certain substances can rotate the plane of a polarized light beam as it passes through them. For this reason, such substances are called "optically active."

The cause of this rotation was discovered in 1874. The molecules of optically active substances come in two forms, identical in every way except that one form is reversed relative to the other, much like left- and right-handed gloves. One form rotates polarized light to the right, the other to the left. Thus, the change in the plane of polarized light passed through a sample of such a substance indicates either that only one form is present in the sample or that the two molecular forms are present in unequal amounts.

Djerassi suspected that he might be able to determine the molecular structure of an optically active substance by passing different wave lengths of polarized light through it and measuring the degree and direction that each was rotated. Verifying that intuition was not easy.

With other cattlemen, Djerassi inspects his prize Polled Shorthorns
just before the first cattle auction ever held at his SMIP Ranch.

Dealers, ranchers, and their families fill Djerassi's unusual 12-sided barn as he welcomes them to the auction. Later, he, his wife Norma, and their ranch manager, Darroll Weddell, listen to the bidding.

No adequate instrumentation existed in the early 1950s, so Djerassi and his co-workers had a device specially built.

They also needed a group of compounds whose members had similar, known structures. Naturally, Djerassi turned to his favorites, the steroids. They were ideally suited to test the new technique. They are all optically active and share the same basic four-ring carbon skeleton, but with many small structural differences. It was these differences that Djerassi hoped he could correlate with the changes in the rotation of the polarized light.

The scientists made thousands of measurements, passing many different wave lengths of light through a host of steroid compounds. Each bit of data was painstakingly graphed. Djerassi infected everyone with his energy and enthusiasm, even enlisting the wives of his graduate students to help in collecting and recording data.

From the first, the results were encouraging, but it required a great deal of work before the Djerassi team was sure that the patterns they saw in the ORD graphs actually revealed the molecular structure of the steroids. After 30 months of long hours and hard work, this new and powerful tool was added to the kit of the chemist.

ORD is now commonly used in laboratories throughout the world. With it a chemist can determine first whether a substance is left- or right-handed. This is of great importance, because many natural substances have mirror-image (both left- and right-handed) molecules, and usually only one form is biologically active. And the chemist can also use ORD to establish the geometric shape of the molecule, that is, the three-dimensional arrangement of its atoms. Such information is valuable in biology and biochemistry. Coupled with such other sophisticated advances in analysis as liquid and gas chromatography, and mass spectrometry, ORD makes it possible to solve in weeks problems that used to take years. It also extends chemical analysis to substances occurring in such minute amounts that they cannot even be detected without these techniques. Small wonder that Djerassi considers the development of optical rotatory dispersion the most satisfying scientific achievement of his career.

Syntex asked Djerassi in 1957 to return as vice-president for research to lead an expanded program. Djerassi took a leave of absence from Wayne State for two years and went back to Mexico. But teaching has always been extremely important to him and he did not want to sever his ties with graduate students whose work he supervised. So Syntex agreed to pay for Djerassi's telephone conversations with his students in Detroit. His telephone supervision proved quite effective because students wasted no time on trivia in international calls. Nevertheless, he quickly began running up $200 to $300 weekly phone bills. Djerassi also made frequent trips to Detroit. Typically, he would have graduate students meet him at the airport so that they could discuss their research during the 45-minute ride to the Wayne State campus in downtown Detroit.

During this stay at Syntex, Djerassi led the effort to synthesize a number of powerful anti-inflammatory agents, including Synalar. This drug quickly became the most effective of a class called topical corticosteroids, used to treat skin inflammations. In 1959, Djerassi resigned his Wayne State appointment and accepted a professorship at Stanford University. At first, he commuted from Mexico City to Palo Alto, then he moved there in 1960. When Syntex pondered where to establish its U.S. subsidiary, Djerassi made a strong case for the Stanford Industrial Park in Palo Alto. His colleagues agreed, and Syntex Research Center, as well as the parent corporation's American headquarters, settled in that city.

Djerassi continued as vice-president, and later as president of Syntex Research. He also became chairman of two Syntex offshoots he helped create: Syva, which specializes in medical diagnostics, and Zoecon, which produces hormonal insecticides. He combined all of this with teaching at Stanford and supervising the research of nearly 20 graduate students and postdoctoral fellows.

How has Carl Djerassi managed to do so much? He works hard—"Relaxation makes him tired," says his wife Norma. "He has an ability to make decisions very fast," says Stork. "He has enormous enthusiasm and is able to turn it on immediately . . . an ability to switch gears

With Glenn Seaborg, former chairman of the Atomic Energy Commission, Djerassi stands atop the Great Wall of China during his 1973 visit. At Peking's Institute of Zoology, he discusses the development of oral contraceptives with leading Chinese scientists.

with no time lag," says an old friend. "Well organized and well informed," says a former student. Djerassi does not sit down to write a paper or book until he is fully prepared. Then, he writes quickly. He wrote his first book, on optical rotatory dispersion, in three months.

Resourcefulness helps, too. Few opportunities escape him. Once, in a hospital room recovering from a gall bladder operation, Djerassi asked a visiting student to take a sample of the large gallstone that had been removed to the laboratory and make a detailed analysis of it. The results, which indicated for the first time the presence of cholesterol in gallstones, appeared in a scientific paper by Djerassi, and a very surprised surgeon found himself thanked in a footnote to the paper for "experimental assistance."

Refreshed by the green
beauty of his ranch,
Djerassi sits, reads,
and makes new plans.

Djerassi believes that his industrial experience has contributed significantly to how he approaches a scientific problem. For instance, he applies such business techniques as systems analysis in designing research projects. He also believes that he can operate more efficiently working in two different fields at the same time. "You frequently get discouraged in basic research. So other activities enable you to come back to research with a new view."

In January, 1973, Djerassi resigned from Syntex to devote more time to Zoecon. Zoecon is now an independent corporation and pioneers in developing insecticides that are analogues of the insect's juvenile hormones, which interfere with normal biochemical reactions and can retard adult insect growth. These substances are harmless to other types of life and are expected to emerge as important means of insect control. Fittingly, it was some of Djerassi's own analytical techniques that helped make work with these substances possible, because they occur in such minute amounts.

He brings to Zoecon remarkable financial and administrative abilities as well as extensive experience in managing and weighing research risks and benefits. Zaffaroni, himself a scientist-businessman, says, "I can't conceive of a better chief executive for that organization than Carl. He has good common sense—he is not a blue-sky scientist."

In his Stanford laboratory, Djerassi continues research as usual in a number of fields at once. He and his postdoctoral associates are perfecting still another analytical method, magnetic circular dichroism. This technique allows sensitive and precise measurements of molecules that do not exist in mirror-image form by making them optically active in a magnetic field. He is also looking at marine plants and animals as possible sources of drugs. He is collaborating with geneticist Joshua Lederberg and Edward Feigenbaum, of Stanford's Computer Sciences Department, on computerizing the creative process in chemistry. "We are trying to put Carl Djerassi's mind into a computer," Lederberg explains.

He has always been keenly interested in upgrading science in less developed countries. His prodding and ideas have helped set up advanced research institutes in Mexico, Brazil, and Africa. He is also chairman of the Board on Science and Technology in International Development of the National Academy of Sciences.

Djerassi's private life is as rich and varied as his professional life. On Friday nights, he and his wife often attend the San Francisco opera or the theater. After that, they drive to their ranch. "Sixty minutes later," says Djerassi, "we're in deep woods where there are deer, coyotes, and bobcats." The ranch is called SMIP-1 (Syntex Made It Possible). There is also SMIP-2, a ranch in Alberta, Canada, near the Canadian Rockies, where the Djerassis ski. After an operation to fuse his injured knee, Djerassi designed a special boot which enabled him to ski again.

His two children—a married daughter, Pamela, an artist, and his son, Dale, a political science student at Stanford—are building houses on the family ranch in California and that pleases him. He enjoys the ranch more and more, taking pleasure in seeing a calf born or auctioning off a prize bull. His hobbies are simple and, as one would expect, active—hiking, swimming, skiing. He once tried ballooning but promptly gave it up when his prospective instructor fell out of the balloon during a preliminary demonstration.

He is probably too busy for new interests, anyway. He wants to leave behind "something original." He works with the conviction that "whether you live to be 50 or 100, there isn't enough time for all the creative work one could do." In the first 50 years of his life, Djerassi has done quite a few original things. He admits there are many frustrations in science, but likens the occasional success to reaching a mountaintop. The view from that peak may be dull or delightful; one may see nothing but more mountains in every direction. Yet, getting to that mountaintop can be tremendously satisfying. Carl Djerassi does not intend to stop climbing.

Eight Nobel Prize winners, front row at left, await their awards in Stockholm. From left: Leo Esaki, Ivar Giaever, and Brian D. Josephson, physics; Ernst Fischer and Geoffrey Wilkinson, chemistry; Konrad Lorenz and Nikolaas Tinbergen, physiology and medicine; and Wassily Leontief, economic science.

Awards And Prizes

A listing and description of major science awards and prizes, the men and women who won them, and their accomplishments

Earth and Physical Sciences

Chemistry. Major awards in the field of chemistry included:

Nobel Prize. A German and an English scientist shared the 1973 Nobel prize in chemistry for their studies on how organic and metallic atoms can merge. Ernst O. Fischer, 54, of The Technical University of Munich, West Germany, and Geoffrey Wilkinson, 52, of the University of London also shared $122,000, the cash portion of the award. Professor Gunnar Brusewitz of the Swedish Royal Academy said their studies "may mean that the present lead in gasoline can be replaced with less dangerous metallic ingredients, creating less risks of exhaust pollution in large cities."

Fischer, a native of Munich, had his scientific studies interrupted by nearly 10 years of peacetime army service, then served throughout World War II and was a prisoner of war. He was the first to set up stable "sandwich" compounds of chromium and benzol molecules.

Wilkinson did most of the work for which he received the prize while teaching at Harvard University from 1951 to 1955. Ironically, Wilkinson was dismissed in 1955, "because I was only an assistant professor and they thought they could do without me." He also worked for the Atomic Energy Division of Canada's National Research Council from 1943 to 1946, and later worked at the Radiation Laboratory at the University of California at Berkeley, and at Massachusetts Institute of Technology (M.I.T.) before returning to England in 1956.

Cope Award. Donald J. Cram received the American Chemical Society (ACS) Arthur C. Cope Award in 1974 for significant innovations, including creation of "host-guest" synthetic chemistry. Cram has synthesized "host" molecules that can mimic the body's peculiar ability to distinguish between "twin" molecules. His work could become significant in food supplementation for balanced nutrition.

Cram was born in Chester, Vt., and studied at Rollins College, the University of Nebraska, and Harvard. He has been on the faculty at the University of California, Los Angeles, since 1947.

In addition to a gold medal, the Cope Award includes a $10,000 honorarium and at least $20,000 in research grants.

Edwin H. Land

Leo Esaki

David T. Griggs

Perkin Medal. Edwin H. Land, chairman, president, and research director of Polaroid Corporation, won the 1974 Perkin Medal. The award, made by the American Section of the Society of Chemical Industry, is the highest given in the United States for applied chemistry.

Land, a scientist and inventor of the Polaroid Land camera and the new Polaroid instant color camera, has spent 30 years in developmental work that included synthesis of new dyes and related chemicals and structuring of a 17-layer, self-processing film.

Born in Bridgeport, Conn., Land attended Harvard University, but left to produce polarizing sheets of plastics. This led to the first practical polarizers, with widely varied applications ranging from sunglasses to three-dimensional color motion pictures. Land holds more than 150 patents on plastics and on photographic devices. He also perfected a technique for observing living cells in natural color.

Priestley Medal. Paul J. Flory, chemistry professor at Stanford University, won the 1974 Priestley Medal, highest award given by the American Chemical Society. A physical chemist, Flory is noted for his pioneering research on large repetitive molecules called polymers.

Flory studied at Manchester College in Indiana and Ohio State University. He worked as a research chemist for DuPont, Standard Oil Company of New Jersey, and Goodyear Tire & Rubber Company and as executive director of research at the Mellon Institute in Pittsburgh. He served as professor of chemistry at Cornell University from 1948 to 1956.

Physics. Awards recognizing major work in physics included:

Nobel Prize. Three physicists shared the 1973 Nobel prize in physics for their discoveries concerning the tunneling effects of electrons in solids.

Ivar Giaever of the General Electric (GE) Research and Development Center, Schenectady, N.Y., and Leo Esaki of International Business Machines Company, Yorktown Heights, N.Y., shared half of the $122,000 prize. Brian D. Josephson of Cambridge, England, received the other half (see ELECTRONICS, Close-Up).

Giaever, 44, a native of Norway, was honored for his discovery of tunneling in superconductors. Born in Bergen, he studied engineering at the Norwegian

Institute of Technology. He joined GE in 1955, working first in Canada. He earned a Ph.D. in physics from Rensselaer Polytechnic Institute in Troy, N.Y., and he later studied at the University of Cambridge in England.

Esaki, 48, who was born in Japan, was honored for his discovery of tunneling in semiconductors, which led to invention of the Esaki tunnel diode. He studied at the University of Tokyo and headed an advanced development group for the Sony Corporation. Esaki came to the United States in 1959.

Josephson received the award for predictions of tunneling that he made as a 22-year-old student at Cambridge. A native of Cardiff, Wales, Josephson earned bachelor's, master's, and Ph.D. degrees at Cambridge and spent a year as a research assistant at the University of Illinois.

Buckley Prize. Michael Tinkham of Harvard received the Oliver E. Buckley Price for solid-state physics, given by the American Institute of Physics. He was honored "for his experimental investigations of the electromagnetic properties of superconductors."

Tinkham, a native of Ripon, Wis., studied at Ripon College, M.I.T., Oxford University in England, and the University of Paris in France. He was a research assistant at M.I.T. and taught at the University of California, Berkeley.

Geosciences. Awards for important work in the geosciences included:

Day Medal. David T. Griggs, professor of geophysics at the University of California, Los Angeles, won the 1974 Arthur L. Day Medal, presented by the Geological Society of America (GSA). He was honored for research on earthquakes, convection beneath the earth's crust, and the evolution of the plates that make up the earth's crust.

Penrose Medal. M. King Hubbert received the 1974 Penrose Medal from the GSA. He was honored for his original contributions, particularly his work on the physics of underground fluids.

Hubbert attended Texas country schools and later studied at the University of Chicago. He worked 20 years for the Shell Oil and Shell Development companies in Houston. He is now research geophysicist with the U.S. Geological Survey and professor emeritus of geology and geophysics at Stanford University.

Life
Sciences

Konrad Lorenz

John F. J. Cade

Biology. Among the awards presented in biology were the following:

Franklin Medal. Theodosius G. Dobzhansky, professor of genetics at the University of California, Davis, won the 1973 Franklin Medal, the highest honor given by the Franklin Institute of Philadelphia. The award was given for Dobzhansky's "intellectual leadership in advancing our experimental and theoretical knowledge of genetics. . . ."

Dobzhansky came to the United States from Russia in 1927. He is noted for his book, *Genetics and the Origin of the Species* (1937), and for his experimental work adding to the knowledge of chromosome structure, the arrangement of genes in the chromosomes, and the inheritances of all living creatures. He has taught at the University of Leningrad, Rockefeller and Columbia universities, California Institute of Technology, and the Polytechnique Institute in Kiev.

Horwitz Prize. Research biologists Renato Dulbecco, Harry Eagle, and Theodore Puck shared the Louisa Gross Horwitz Prize given in 1973 by Columbia University for their outstanding contributions to tissue culture research. They will share the $25,000 honorarium.

Dulbecco, 59, is assistant director of research at the Imperial Cancer Research Fund Laboratories in London. He devised new ways to study normal cell life after cells are exposed to viruses. Eagle, a professor at the Albert Einstein College of Medicine in New York City, developed a media in which mammalian cells could grow. This permitted study of cell growth and development. Puck, a professor of biophysics and genetics at the University of Colorado, contributed to the study of the genetics of mammalian cells.

Lilly Award. Joseph R. Kates, chairman of the Department of Microbiology, State University of New York, Stony Brook, received the 1974 Eli Lilly and Company Award in Microbiology and Immunology.

The award, a medal and $1,000, was for outstanding research. Kates's research has had great influence, particularly in studies of the molecular biology of gene expression in animal viruses and nucleated cells.

U.S. Steel Foundation Award. David Baltimore, American Cancer Society professor of microbiology at the Massachusetts Institute of Technology, received the 1973 U.S. Steel Foundation Award in molecular biology. The award includes an honorarium of $5,000.

Baltimore was honored "as a distinguished leader in virus research, who by his discoveries on the reproduction and enzymology of RNA viruses has greatly advanced the science of molecular biology." His most important scientific contribution was the discovery of reverse transcriptase in 1970, which led to advances in studying the relationship between viruses and cancer.

Medicine. Major awards in medical sciences included the following:

Nobel Prize. Three zoologists shared the 1973 Nobel prize in physiology and medicine for their pioneering work in ethology, the comparative study of behavior. They are Karl von Frisch, 87, former director of the Zoological Institute of the University of Munich; Konrad Lorenz, 70, of the Institute for Behavior Research in Gruenau, Austria; and Nikolaas Tinbergen, 67, of the University of Oxford in England.

Von Frisch is best known for his discovery that bees direct hive mates to a new source of honey by performing a dance. He concluded that such dances are innate patterns, not learned behavior.

Lorenz discovered that animals inherit certain instincts, but that other kinds of behavior are imprinted, or learned early in life. He applied these theories to man in such books as *King Solomon's Ring* (1949) and *On Aggression* (1963).

Tinbergen, a post-doctoral student under Lorenz, studied the movements that some animals use to communicate with members of the same species. He studied the stickleback fish and such birds as the herring gull. Tinbergen is the second Nobelist in his family. His brother won the economics prize in 1969.

Gairdner Awards. Six medical scientists were honored in 1973 by the Gairdner Foundation of Toronto, Canada, for outstanding research.

Dr. Roscoe Brady of the National Institute of Neurological Diseases and Strokes, Bethesda, Md., received $10,000 for work on the enzymology of complex lipids (fats and oils) and the management of lipid storage diseases.

Drs. Kimishige and Teruko Ishizaka, husband-and-wife research team at Johns Hopkins School of Medicine in Bal-

Theodosius Dobzhansky was awarded the Franklin Medal in 1973 for his outstanding contributions to the field of genetics.

Life Sciences

Continued

timore, received $5,000 each. They were honored for identifying and characterizing the new immunoglobulin class IgE, which has aided understanding of allergic mechanisms.

Dr. Harold Johns, head of the physics division of the Ontario Cancer Institute in Toronto, received a $10,000 award for developing cobalt radiation therapy and for his contributions to education and research in clinical physics and biophysics.

Dr. Denis Burkitt, of the Medical Research Council in London, received a $10,000 award for his recognition, clinical description, and epidemiological study of an unusual form of cancer tumor called Burkitt's lymphoma.

Dr. John Charnley, director of the Center for Hip Surgery near Wigan, England, received a $10,000 award for developing a practical, low-friction artificial hip joint.

Kittay Award. Dr. John F. J. Cade, an Australian psychiatrist, and Dr. Mogens Schou, a Danish physician, were awarded the $25,000 Kittay International Award for psychiatry in 1974. They were hon-

ored for their psychopharmacological work with lithium, which led to the control and prevention of manic psychosis. The Kittay Award is given annually for outstanding work in the field of mental health.

Cade, 62, is psychiatrist superintendent and dean of the Clinical School in Melbourne. He discovered the specific effect of lithium while working on the causes of manic depressive psychosis. Lithium salts had not been used in medicine for many years because of their toxic effects. However, Cade found that injections of lithium citrate protected guinea pigs from developing convulsions, and he concluded that the drug might be useful in treating manic excitement in human beings. Further tests proved it to be very effective.

Yet, Cade's work might have gone unnoticed had it not been for the research of Schou, head of the Psychopharmacology Research Unit, Arhus University Psychiatric Institute, in Denmark. Schou and his collaborators proved the drug's value in treating manic psychosis and in preventing its recurrence.

Space Sciences

Aerospace. The highest awards granted in the aerospace sciences included:

Collier Trophy. The three Skylab crews and William C. Schneider, director of the National Aeronautics and Space Administration (NASA) Skylab program, received the 1973 Collier Trophy. They were honored for proving that man can live and work effectively in space.

The astronauts honored were: Charles Conrad, Jr., Joseph P. Kerwin, and Paul J. Weitz, Skylab 1; Alan L. Bean, Owen K. Garriott, and Jack R. Lousma, Skylab 2; Gerald P. Carr, Edward G. Gibson, and William R. Pogue, Skylab 3. Altogether they made 2,400 revolutions around the earth, returned over 40,000 photographs of the earth, compiled 175,000 feet of earth resources data on tape, over 200,-000 frames of solar data, and performed over 800 man-hours of medical tests.

Goddard Award. Three men shared the 1974 Goddard Award. They are Paul D. Castenholz of Rockwell International; Richard C. Mulready of the Pratt & Whitney Division, United Aircraft Corporation; and John L. Sloop, retired, National Aeronautics and Space Administration.

The three were honored "for their significant contributions to the development of practical Lox-hydrogen rocket engines which have played an essential role in the nation's space program and in the advancement of space technology." The award, given by the American Institute of Aeronautics and Astronautics (AIAA), includes gold medals and $10,000.

Guggenheim International Astronautics Award. Max A. Faget, director of engineering and development at the Johnson Space Center near Houston, was awarded the Daniel and Florence Guggenheim International Astronautics Award in 1973. He was honored by the International Academy of Astronautics for playing a major role in developing "the basic ideas and original designs concepts" that have been part of all U.S. manned spacecraft.

Hill Space Transportation Award. Kurt H. Debus, director of NASA's John F. Kennedy Space Center in Florida since 1963, received the AIAA's 1973 Hill Space Transportation Award. He was honored for "pioneering the scientific, engineering, and organizational techniques" used in preparing and launching manned and unmanned U.S. space missions. The award includes $5,000.

Astronomy. Important contributions in astronomy were honored with the following awards:

Bruce Medal. Sir Martin Ryle, 56, director of the Mullard Radio Astronomy Observatory at the University of Cambridge in England, received the 1974 Catherine Wolfe Bruce Medal. The gold medal is presented by the Astronomical Society of the Pacific.

Ryle was honored "for the outstanding role he has played in developing radio astronomy as an important branch of modern astronomy." The society cited his research contributions to radio source counts, his studies of the structure of galaxies, and his primary role in the development of innovative astronomical instrumentation.

He has most recently been involved in radio astrometry, the study of the positions of objects in the sky. Ryle is the ninth Bruce Medal recipient from Great Britain, but only the second honored for work in radio astronomy.

Draper Medal. Lyman Spitzer, Jr., professor of astronomy and director of the observatory at Princeton University, received the 1973 Henry Draper Medal, which includes a $1,000 award, for his notable investigations in astronomical physics.

Spitzer's early studies of the chemical composition and interactions of interstellar matter established the basis for much of the present work on processes leading to star formation. Spitzer was also among the first to suggest magnetic containment as a means of achieving controlled nuclear fusion, and was a leading force in establishing Princeton's Plasma Physics Laboratory.

Michelson Medal. S. Jocelyn Bell Burnell of The University, Southampton, England, and Antony Hewish of the University of Cambridge in England received the Michelson Medal in 1973. The Franklin Institute award to the British scientists was for their outstanding work in the discovery, identification, and continued study of pulsars.

Hewish was largely responsible for the concept, method of observation, and design of a new radio telescope, and led the team that put the telescope into operation. Burnell showed, through independent study, that the strange pulsing signals came from the sky and were not earth static.

Richard C. Mulready

Kurt H. Debus

General Awards

Science and Man. Awards for outstanding contributions to science and mankind included the following:

Founders Medal. J. Erik Jonsson, mayor of Dallas from 1964 to 1971 and honorary chairman of the board of Texas Instruments, Incorporated, won the 1974 Founders Medal. The award is given by the National Academy of Engineering (NAE) for contributions to engineering and society.

Jonsson was cited for using engineering knowledge to "improve the quality of life through pioneering efforts in the manufacture of high-technology products, and innovative use of technology in solving the basic problems of cities." Jonsson received primary credit for a Greater Dallas redevelopment plan, which included redesigning and rebuilding the central business district and a transit system that separates vehicular and pedestrian traffic.

National Medal of Science. The U.S. government's highest award for outstanding contributions in science, mathematics, and engineering was presented to 11 Americans in 1973. They are:

Daniel I. Arnon, University of California, Berkeley, for research in plant nutrition and the mechanism by which green plants utilize light.

Carl Djerassi, Stanford University, for the application of steroid hormones to medicinal chemistry and population control. SEE CARL DJERASSI.

Harold E. Edgerton, Massachusetts Institute of Technology, for pioneering in stroboscopic photography and inventions of instruments that are used to explore the ocean depths.

William M. Ewing, University of Texas Medical Branch at Galveston, for improving geological and geophysical methods to study the ocean floor.

Arie Jan Haagen-Smit, California Institute of Technology, for unique discoveries of the chemical nature of smog and for smog abatement efforts.

Vladimir Haensel, Universal Oil Products Company, Des Plaines, Ill., for research in the catalytic reforming of hydrocarbons.

Frederick Seitz, Rockefeller University, for pioneering in the modern quantum theory of the solid state of matter.

Earl W. Sutherland, Jr., University of Miami, for research which increased the understanding of the mechanisms that control and regulate the processes of life at the cellular level. See DEATHS OF NOTABLE SCIENTISTS.

John W. Tukey, Bell Laboratories, Murray Hill, N.J., and Princeton University, for studies in mathematical and theoretical statistics.

Richard T. Whitcomb, National Aeronautics and Space Administration, Langley Research Center, Hampton, Va., for his discoveries and inventions in aerodynamics.

Robert R. Wilson, National Accelerator Laboratory, Batavia, Ill., for ingenuity in designing experiments to explore the fundamental particles of matter and in designing and building machines to produce the particles, culminating in the world's most powerful particle accelerator.

Oersted Medal. Melba Newell Phillips, visiting professor of physics at the State University of New York, Stony Brook, received the Oersted Medal in 1974. The medal is the highest honor awarded by the American Association of Physics Teachers (AAPT). She was cited for her contributions to physics education.

Phillips co-authored two textbooks, one on electricity at the graduate level and the other on physical science at the introductory level. In addition, she has influenced the teaching of science in elementary and secondary grades through her own courses for prospective teachers.

Phillips completed her undergraduate studies at Oakland City College in Indiana in 1926, then taught in high school and college. She completed her doctoral work at the University of California at Berkeley in 1933 with a specialty in atomic theory. Subsequently, she worked with such leading theorists as Robert Oppenheimer and Edward Condon.

She has taught at Brooklyn College, Connecticut College, and the universities of California, Chicago, Minnesota, and Washington.

Zworykin Award. Ivar Giaever, a physicist at the General Electric Research and Development Center, Schenectady, N.Y., won the 1974 Vladimir K. Zworykin Award. He was honored by the NAE for "his original contributions to the fields of electronic tunneling, superconductivity, and *in situ* protein detection." He also shared the 1973 Nobel prize in physics for this work. SEE ELECTRONICS, CLOSE-UP.

[Joseph P. Spohn]

Melba N. Phillips

Ivar Giaever

Major Awards and Prizes

Award winners treated more fully in the first portion of this section are indicated by an asterisk (*)

Adolph Lomb Medal (physics): James Forsyth

American Chemical Society Award in Enzyme Chemistry: Michael J. Chamberlin

American Physical Society High-Polymer Physics Prize: Frank A. Bovey

Bonner Prize (nuclear physics): Denys H. Wilkinson

*Bruce Medal (astronomy): Sir Martin Ryle

*Buckley Solid-state Physics Prize: Michael Tinkham

Carski Foundation Award (teaching): Frank E. Swatek

*Collier Trophy (astronautics): William C. Schneider, Charles Conrad, Jr., Joseph P. Kerwin, Paul J. Weitz, Alan L. Bean, Owen K. Garriott, Jack R. Lousma, Gerald P. Carr, Edward G. Gibson, William R. Pogue

Comet Medal (astronomy): John E. Bortle

*Cope Award (chemistry): Donald J. Cram

Cresson Medal: Allan R. Sandage, John Paul Stapp

Davisson-Germer Prize (optics): Norman Ramsey

*Day Medal (geology): David T. Griggs

Debye Award (physical chemistry): Walter H. Stockmayer

Dickson Prize: Elias J. Corey

*Founders Medal (engineering): J. Erik Jonsson

*Franklin Medal (genetics): Theodosius G. Dobzhansky

*Gairdner Awards (medicine): Dr. Roscoe Brady, Dr. Kimishige Ishizaka, Dr. Teruko Ishizaka, Dr. Harold Johns, Dr. Denis Burkitt, Dr. John Charnley

Garvan Medal (chemistry): Joyce J. Kaufman

Gibbs Brothers Medal (marine engineering): Phillip Eisenberg

*Goddard Award (aerospace): Paul D. Castenholz, Richard Mulready, John Sloop

*Guggenheim Award (aerospace): Max A. Faget

Haley Astronautics Award: John Young, Thomas Mattingly II, Charles Duke, Jr.

Heineman Prize (mathematical physics): Subrahmanyan Chandrasekhar

*Hill Space Transportation Award (astronautics): Kurt H. Debus

*Horwitz Prize (biology): Renato Dulbecco, Harry Eagle, Theodore Puck

Industrial Research Institute Medal (chemistry): Robert W. Cairns

Ives Medal (optics): Rudolph Kingslake

*Kittay Award (psychiatry): Dr. John Cade, Dr. Mogens Schou

Langmuir Prize (chemical physics): Harry G. Drickamer

Lasker Awards (medical research): William B. Kouwenhoven, Paul M. Zoll

Leo Szilard Award (physics): David R. Inglis

Lilly Award (diabetes): Arthur H. Rubenstein

*Lilly Award (microbiology): Joseph R. Kates

Meggers Award (spectroscopy): Curtis J. Humphreys

*Michelson Medal (astronomy): S. Jocelyn Bell Burnell, Antony Hewish

NAS Award for Environmental Quality: G. Evelyn Hutchinson

*National Medal of Science: Daniel I. Arnon, Carl Djerassi, Harold E. Edgerton, William M. Ewing, Arie Jan Haagen-Smit, Vladimir Haensel, Frederick Seitz, Earl W. Sutherland, Jr., John W. Tukey, Richard T. Whitcomb, Robert Rathbun Wilson

*Nobel Prize: chemistry, Ernst O. Fischer and Geoffrey Wilkinson; physics, Ivar Giaever, Leo Esaki, and Brian D. Josephson; physiology and medicine, Karl von Frisch, Konrad Lorenz, and Nikolaas Tinbergen

*Oersted Medal (teaching): Melba Newell Phillips

Oppenheimer Memorial Prize (physics): Edwin E. Salpeter

Pendray Award (aerospace): Frederick Ordway

*Penrose Medal (geology): M. King Hubbert

*Perkin Medal (chemistry): Edwin H. Land

*Priestley Medal (chemistry): Paul J. Flory

Reed Award (aerospace): Willis Hawkins

Richardson Medal (physics): Roderic M. Scott

Trumpler Award (astronomy): D.N. Schramm

*U.S. Steel Foundation Award (molecular biology): David Baltimore

Viking Fund Medal (anthropology): John Grahame Douglas Clark

Waksman Award (microbiology): Renato Dulbecco

Warner Prize (astronomy): Dmitri M. Mihalas

*Zworykin Award (engineering): Ivar Giaever

Deaths of Notable Scientists

Notable scientists who died between June 1, 1973, and June 1, 1974, include those listed below. An asterisk (*) indicates that a biography of the person appears in *The World Book Encyclopedia.*

Abbot, Charles G. (1872-Dec. 17, 1973), astronomer, pioneered in studies of the sun, and its uses as an energy source. He was chief executive of the Smithsonian Institution from 1928 to 1944.

Anokhin, Pyotr K. (1898-March 7, 1974), Russian brain specialist, was a pupil of physiologist Ivan P. Pavlov. He enlarged on Pavlov's principle of the conditioned reflex, declaring that an "intention" must come between the stimulus and the action.

Bates, Marston (1906-April 3, 1974), cultural biologist and professor of zoology at the University of Michigan, was noted for research on mosquitoes and malaria and yellow fever, two diseases they spread.

Bose, Satyendra Nath (1894-Feb. 4, 1974), Indian theoretical physicist, helped Albert Einstein and others develop quantum mechanics in the mid-1920s.

Carmichael, Leonard (1898-Sept. 16, 1973), psychologist, helped to develop the electroencephalograph and, in 1935, became the first to measure brain waves. He was president of Tufts College from 1938 to 1952, secretary of the Smithsonian Institution from 1953 to 1964, and organized recruitment of U.S. scientists for World War II research work.

Chow, Bacon (1909-Sept. 27, 1973), a biochemist, helped to isolate the first pure antibody while working in China in 1936.

*__Condon, Edward U.__ (1902-March 26, 1974), made great contributions to theoretical physics. He played a leading role in U.S. atomic-bomb and radar programs during World War II and in the creation of the Atomic Energy Commission after World War II.

Diehl, Harold S. (1891-June 27, 1973), former director of research and medical affairs for the American Cancer Society, contended that there was a close relationship between cigarette smoking and lung cancer.

Dunn, Leslie C. (1893-March 19, 1974), a geneticist, was noted for his research into heredity and evolution. Since his retirement from the Columbia University faculty in 1962, he had worked as a research associate at the university's Nevis Biological Laboratories.

Eckart, Carl H. (1902-Oct. 23, 1973), physicist and oceanographer, in 1926 united two rival theories of quantum mechanics. In 1946, he founded the Marine Physical Laboratory of the Scripps Institution of Oceanography.

Einstein, Hans A. (1904-July 26, 1973), son of the theoretical physicist, Albert Einstein, was professor emeritus of civil engineering at the University of California, Berkeley.

Ewing, W. Maurice (1906-May 4, 1974), geophysicist, perfected underwater communications techniques and pioneered the use of seismic waves to explore the ocean floor.

Feinberg, Samuel M. (1895-July 10, 1973), Russian-born physician, was noted for his research on allergy mechanisms and the relief of allergies.

Fryxell, Roald (1934-May 18, 1974), Washington State University anthropologist, in 1968 discovered the oldest documented human remains found in the Pacific Northwest. He found the bones of Marmes man, who lived between 11,500 and 13,000 years ago, on a ranch in southeast Washington.

Gast, Paul F. (1916-May 27, 1974), senior physicist at Argonne National Laboratory, helped to develop the atomic bomb. He worked on the design of nuclear reactors for the DuPont Company at the Hanford (Wash.) Works in 1943 and 1944, and was chief of the physics section at the Hanford Works for the General Electric Company from 1946 to 1956.

Gerard, Ralph W. (1900-Feb. 17, 1974), physiologist, produced evidence that faulty body chemistry causes schizophrenia. His work on the electrical impulse of nerve cells also formed a basis for research in learning and memory.

Godley, Paul F. (?-Oct. 20, 1973), a radio pioneer, conducted successful short-wave radio tests between the United States and Scotland in 1921. These led to transatlantic radio telegraph and telephone communications.

Harvey, Roger A. (1910-July 17, 1973), cancer specialist, was the first to film the circulation of cancer cells in the blood stream. He also pioneered in use of the betatron for cancer treatment.

Hess, Walter R. (1881-Aug. 22, 1973), Swiss physiologist, won the Nobel Prize for physiology and medicine in 1949 for discovering how certain parts of the brain control body organs.

Edward U. Condon

Walter R. Hess

Gerard P. Kuiper

Deaths of Notable Scientists

Continued

Earl W. Sutherland, Jr.

Selman A. Waksman

Karl Ziegler

Jorpes, J. Erik (1894-July 10, 1973), Swedish biochemist, identified the structure of heparin, a substance now used in therapy for clots caused by thrombophlebitis and heart and lung conditions.

Krusen, Frank H. (1898-Sept. 15, 1973), expert on physical medicine and rehabilitation, started the physical medicine departments at the Mayo Clinic and Temple University. He also headed the Sister Kenny Foundation.

Kuiper, Gerard P. (1905-Dec. 23, 1973), Dutch-born astronomer, directed the Ranger lunar photographic missions that helped set Apollo landing sites on the moon. He also discovered carbon monoxide in Mars's atmosphere and the satellites of the planets Uranus and Neptune.

Lauritsen, Thomas (1915-Oct. 15, 1973), Danish-born nuclear physicist, showed through his research on the nuclei of atoms how stars generate energy and how the universe evolved.

MacDowell, Edwin C. (1887-Nov. 7, 1973), medical researcher, was noted for Carnegie Institution studies of leukemia in mice, size inheritance in rabbits, and the influence of alcohol on prenatal mortality.

Meyer, Karl F. (1884-April 27, 1974), Swiss-born viral scientist, discovered two of the viruses that cause encephalitis and did work on plague and other diseases.

Nord, Friedrich F. (1889-July 18, 1973), Fordham University biochemist, established the concept of cryobiology, or low-temperature biology, and isolated lignin, which, with cellulose, forms the main part of woody tissues in plants.

Raginsky, Bernard B. (1902-April 28, 1974), Russian-born Canadian physician, developed sensory hypnoplasty, a technique combining the use of modeling clay and hypnosis, for use in psychotherapy.

Romer, Alfred S. (1894-Nov. 12, 1973), authority on evolution, directed the Harvard Museum of Comparative Zoology from 1946 to 1961.

Rousselot, Louis M. (1902-March 28, 1974), surgeon, was an authority on hepatorenal and pancreatic diseases. He also served as the assistant secretary of defense for health and environment from 1967 to 1970 and as a special assistant at the National Institutes of Health from 1970 to 1973.

Rubey, William W. (1898-April 12, 1974), geologist, received the National Medal of Science in 1965 for his contributions to the discovery and definition of basic geological principles.

Sutherland, Earl W., Jr. (1915-March 9, 1974), professor of biochemistry at the University of Miami, won the Nobel prize for physiology and medicine in 1971 for his discoveries of the ways hormones act. He discovered cyclic AMP, a chemical that influences the action of hormones on body processes.

Taylor, Sir Hugh (1890-April 17, 1974), British-born dean of Princeton University's Graduate School, aided development of the atomic bomb by discovering the most effective catalyst for producing heavy water.

Taylor, T. Ivan (1909-July 26, 1973), research chemist, worked during World War II on the research control group of the Manhattan project to develop the atomic bomb.

Tikhonravov, Mikhail (?-March 4, 1974), Russian pioneer in rocketry, helped to develop the first Russian liquid-fuel rocket.

*Virtanen, Artturi (1895-Nov. 10, 1973), Finnish biochemist, received the Nobel prize for chemistry in 1945 for his work on the preservation of fodder crops.

Vishniac, Wolf V. (1922-Dec. 10, 1973), German-born microbiologist, was a specialist in the biology of space operations. He helped plan and carry out quarantine procedures used for returning astronauts.

*Waksman, Selman A. (1888-Aug. 16, 1974), Russian-born microbiologist, won the Nobel prize in physiology and medicine in 1952 for the discovery of the antibiotic streptomycin.

Watson-Watt, Sir Robert (1892-Dec. 5, 1973), British engineer and scientist, developed the first radar system in the late 1930's.

*White, Paul Dudley (1886-Oct. 31, 1973), personal physician to President Dwight D. Eisenhower, was a noted authority on blood and heart diseases.

Ziegler, Karl (1898-Aug. 12, 1973), German chemist, won the Nobel prize in chemistry in 1963 for producing organometallic compounds, work which led to improved plastics products.

Zwicky, Fritz (1898-Feb. 8, 1974), Bulgarian-born astronomer and inventor, taught at the California Institute of Technology, worked at Hale Observatories, and was a leading authority on jet propulsion.

[Joseph P. Spohn]

Nuclear Power: How Great Is the Risk?

A nuclear engineer and a nuclear physicist examine the perils and promises of energy from the atom

During the winter of 1973-1974, while the United States was trying to cope with an energy crisis, a long-brewing controversy over the safety of generating electricity with nuclear reactors came to a head. The Atomic Energy Commission (AEC) and the nuclear manufacturers have been maintaining that the reactors are safe and reliable; that the risk of an accident that will injure people and property is negligible. The critics of nuclear power are equally sure that the risks presently are unacceptably high. They feel that nuclear power should be limited until the safety problems are resolved. If this cannot be accomplished, nuclear power should be eliminated.

Both sides argue convincingly, leaving the public confused and concerned. For this reason, the editors of *Science Year* asked two leading authorities, who hold opposing views, to discuss the facts of nuclear safety as they see them: Norman C. Rasmussen, professor of nuclear engineering at Massachusetts Institute of Technology (M.I.T.); and Henry W. Kendall, professor of high-energy physics, also at M.I.T.

Science Year: Dr. Rasmussen, in May, 1972, the AEC asked you to head a group of technical experts to investigate the probability and consequences of a major accident in operating nuclear reactors. Why did the AEC feel that this study was necessary?

Rasmussen: To update a study made in 1957 on the theoretical consequences of a major nuclear-reactor accident. During the 1960s, the Aerospace Industry and the Department of Defense developed a number of techniques to analyze systems and, based on the data on failure rates that had been collected, predict the reliability of a new system. With these techniques we can now reasonably estimate the probability of various kinds of reactor accidents, and also make a realistic estimate of the consequences.

The 1957 study delineated the consequences of the worst kind of release of radioactivity under the worst weather conditions. It estimated several thousand fatalities and billions of dollars worth of property damage. The new study was made to give a more complete picture. We now think we can say, if the core of a reactor melts, for example, what is the most *likely* consequence.

SY: Dr. Kendall, you are a member of a group called the Union of Concerned Scientists (UCS), which has taken a stand on the nuclear safety controversy. Why was this group started and what does it hope to accomplish?

Kendall: The UCS was organized in 1969. It contains scientists, engineers, technologists, and lawyers from the Cambridge, Mass., area who have been concerned with the wide variety of problems related to technology and advanced industrialization techniques. We want to identify and bring to public attention the deleterious side effects and damage that frequently seem to accompany technology in widespread use.

SY: When did UCS become involved with nuclear safety?

K: In 1971, when we learned about tests on certain aspects of emergency systems that had unexpectedly failed.

SY: Could you briefly explain what those tests were?

K: They were a sequence of tests carried out at the AEC's National Reactor Testing Station in Idaho Falls, Idaho. They made a miniature reactor, less than a foot in diameter, with fuel elements that were electrically heated to simulate the fuel in a reactor.

They simulated a pipe rupture in the reactor water-cooling system, and then applied emergency water from the emergency system. The emergency system failed to deliver any water to this model; it was ejected out of the break, along with the primary water. In addition, computer predictions of the test results failed to predict satisfactorily what actually occurred in the tests. We got hold of the test results and documents on other aspects of reactor safety. It then became clear to me that there was quite likely a very serious safety problem in the nuclear reactor program.

SY: What did you do about this?

K: We immediately wrote a technical report that laid out our views of the implications of these test failures and began to summarize certain aspects of the weaknesses in the emergency systems. As our report neared completion in June, the AEC published a new set of safety criteria in which they made substantial changes in certain temperatures associated with accidents. But in our view the new criteria did not adequately take care of the uncertainties that the test results raised.

SY: Before we go on with the safety problems of nuclear reactors, we ought to first briefly examine the anatomy of a reactor. In other words, what is a nuclear reactor, and how does it work?

Henry W. Kendall,
Professor of Physics,
Massachusetts
Institute of Technology:
Critic.

R: A nuclear reactor generates steam to turn a turbine, which turns a generator to produce electricity. It is similar to oil- and coal-fired plants, where fire boils water and produces steam. In the nuclear plant, the fuel is a uranium-dioxide which provides a self-sustaining chain reaction and generates heat by the fission process.

In this process, neutrons are absorbed in the uranium, which splits some of the uranium atoms in half; in so doing, the uranium atoms give up more neutrons which have very high energy. To get these readily absorbed back in uranium again, we need to reduce the energy of the neutrons that come out and we do that by letting them scatter off the nuclei of atoms like hydrogen. In water reactors, this scattering process, called moderation, is accomplished by water which, of course, contains a lot of hydrogen. The neutrons bounce off the hydrogen nuclei in the water, slow down, and are then reabsorbed in the uranium.

The uranium-dioxide is in the form of ceramic pellets that are stacked in rods and sealed in a skin, or cladding, of a zirconium alloy. The rods are ½ to ¾ inch in diameter and 12 feet long. They are assembled in a uniform array in a cylinder, 12 feet in diameter and about 12 feet high, which is full of water. The fission process is controlled by moving rods containing boron in or out of the core; this "poisons" the neutrons and achieves whatever level of heat generation you want. All of this equipment is sealed inside a pressurized vessel.

Henry C. Rasmussen,
Professor of Nuclear
Engineering,
Massachusetts
Institute of Technology:
Proponent.

As the water is pumped past the uranium-containing rods, it picks up the heat, and takes it to a turbine. In the boiling-water reactor (BWR), it boils as it passes the rods and the steam goes directly to the turbine. In the pressurized-water reactor (PWR), the heat from the hot water is transferred to a steam generator which provides steam for the turbine.

SY: We hear about the dangers of the "radioactivity" in nuclear reactors. What is this?

R: Radioactivity is any material—solid or gas—that spontaneously radiates energy. As the reactor operates, a large amount of these materials accumulate in the fuel. These are the by-products of the fission process. It is very important to keep them sealed up and out of contact with the environment.

K: It cannot be emphasized too strongly how important it is to keep these materials, some of the most toxic known, totally confined. Some of them, in amounts the size of a grain of pollen, can cause lung cancer. A typical nuclear reactor may contain over a ton of radioactive material.

SY: How is the radioactivity kept under control?

R: First, the ceramic pellets very effectively trap everything but some gaseous products, such as krypton and xenon. The cladding prevents the leak of the gases. The water is at high pressure—2,000 psi—which requires a very strong, tight system. Finally, surrounding the whole plant is an airtight containment system which can catch any radioactivity that gets by the first three barriers in case there is an accident.

SY: What is this containment made of, and how big is it?

R: It can be made either of steel or reinforced concrete. A PWR is typically 150 to 200 feet in diameter and 150 feet high. The BWR is somewhat smaller.

SY: With all that protection, what problems can we have?

R: The only real risk from these reactors is accidents which might inadvertently release a significant fraction of the radioactivity from the core. Now, what could do that? If we lose the water, by boiling it away, or through a burst pipe, for example, the fuel might overheat and melt; in so doing, it would destroy the ceramic barrier, the cladding barrier, and even the containment. And so we want to ensure that the core does not melt.

However, when the water is removed, the chain reaction stops—it shuts itself off.

SY: Then what is the problem?

R: So much radioactivity has been created that after shut-down, heat is generated at about 7 per cent of the total that was being generated when the chain reaction was underway. Now that heat rate decays rather quickly. It's down to less than 1 per cent in 24 hours and to less than 1/10 of 1 per cent in a few weeks.

SY: The first few hours are very critical then?

R: Very critical, because a large reactor operates at 3,000 megawatts thermal, and 7 per cent of that is 210 megawatts—enough heat, if left uncooled, to melt the fuel.

SY: What happens then?

R: Once you melt the core you release significant quantities of radioactive gases and particles into the containment. However, sprays are automatically turned on to wash the radioactivity out of the containment air to trap it on the floor. Even if those systems fail, as long as the containment stays intact, a significant amount of this radioactivity will settle on the floor and "plate" out on the walls.

K: But if the heat is not removed within a minute or two, the application of cooling water will aggravate the accident.

SY: How is that?

K: When the core temperature climbs above 2,000 degrees or so, the zirconium cladding will react increasingly vigorously with water and release heat. The material starts to burn in the oxygen which it liberates from the water. It also liberates hydrogen which can be an explosion hazard and add additional gas to the containment, raising the pressure beyond what it was designed to withstand. AEC accident analysis does not contemplate the liberation of very much hydrogen.

SY: How do gases and particulates get out?

K: Presumably when a pipe ruptures inside the containment, which is designed to retain radioactivity. But, in the event of an accident, the containment might rupture from production of gases or from a chemical explosion caused by hydrogen.

SY: Obviously, then, the big problem is the escape of the gases.

R: Right. The worst accident you can postulate is one where the containment ruptures and the gases are released to the atmosphere. But what happens then depends strongly on the nature of the release. Was it an explosion that blew the radioactivity up into the air, providing a lot of quick mixing? Was it a cold release that seeped out and moved along the ground? What was the magnitude of the release? Because if the release was as large as the worst you can postulate, the radioactive gases contain enough heat to heat the air and cause it to rise rapidly.

SY: Even if you had a temperature inversion?

R: It can rise up through that, yes. It will disperse much more rapidly than the conservative estimate of how it would disperse without this heat in it.

SY: What about the molten material itself?

R: If not cooled, it might melt right through the concrete floor and into the ground beneath. Now, that is an accident that critics often cite as a terrible tragedy. But the ground is a very good ion exchange medium and it traps radioactivity very effectively. In fact, it provides a filter, so that almost no radioactivity would be released to the environment, but rather would be trapped in the ground beneath the reactor. In the soil it moves at very slow velocities, a few feet per year.

K: But then we're back to gases again, which would escape from the breeching of the structure. Once the bottom of the building was breeched, then you could expect that gases would seep up through the earth around the plant and be free to be borne by the wind.

R: Yes, but a large fraction of the most hazardous isotopes would be trapped by the soil.

SY: What about the ground water?

K: There are some 200 radioactive materials generated in the nuclear fuel and some of them are extremely hazardous. There are 500 to 700 pounds of plutonium, for example, described by its discoverer Glenn Seaborg, as "fiendishly toxic." As this and other material leaches into the ground it would have to contaminate the water.

R: Ground water seeps through the soil and tends to dissolve this material, but the material tends to be recaptured by the next soil particles it passes by. It is not as though someone dumped poison in the water supply. The soil will keep it sealed there for a long time.

SY: There is also a safety hazard from the molten mass?

K: No question about it. Now, the AEC has reversed itself on how serious this matter is. They carried out two studies—the one in 1957 that estimated the thousands of casualties and billions of dollars of property damage, and an updated study in 1964-1965 that concluded that a major accident could incapacitate an area the size of Pennsylvania. One of the most important points in the later report was that increased reactor sizes simply made the size and scale of a maximum accident much worse than the 1957 report found.

But in 1973, the AEC carried out a study which claims that an accident could not approach the scale which the two previous studies concluded was possible. It has widely publicized this conclusion, particularly since January, 1974. But they have so far failed to release any of the supporting information that backs up their claims, so no outside scientific group such as UCS can subject these claims to any kind of an analysis.

SY: What is the central theme of this conclusion?

R: In the unlikely event of a core melt, the most likely consequence is rather modest compared to what many critics have claimed.

SY: What is most likely to happen then?

R: Should a core melt, we believe it most likely that the systems designed to reduce the release of radioactivity would be quite effective in reducing the consequences. To get very large consequences, there must be a melt-down, a very rapid containment failure, a failure of the fission product removal systems — all combined with the worst possible set of weather conditions, with the wind blowing over a very high population sector. The large accident often discussed is the combination of a very long chain of unlikely events.

We have emergency safety features that are designed to cope with what we call our "Design Basis Accident." First, we build the reactor so it won't have an accident. Second, we monitor the operation and automatically shut down the reactor if it starts to have an accident. Finally, if we have an accident despite this, there are emergency safety features to deal with it.

SY: In a sense you have three levels of protection?

R: That is right. And the third level — the emergency safety features — includes the emergency core cooling system (ECCS) to deal with the loss of coolant accident, the containment system to deal with any radioactive releases, and the fission product removal systems — the "wash down" — to remove any radioactive release.

K: The nuclear proponents tend to emphasize the positive features of these systems and do not adequately consider the circumstances which would stop these systems from performing their functions. They have a high level of confidence in design, superior quality assurance, rigorous operator training, and so forth. But we simply don't agree that these claims are substantiated by actual experience. First of all, we know that the AEC is concerned about the operation of the shutdown and control system. The weakness in this has been identified by the British, who have carried out a study of American reactors because they considered buying some. Moreover, prudence requires more than just consideration of the consequences of the "most likely" accident. The maximum consequences are just too catastrophic not to take into consideration.

The British also identified another flaw in the safety assurances — that the pressure vessels will never rupture. The emergency systems are not designed to cope with pressure vessel failure. What happens to the safety protection then?

SY: You mean that the ECCS wouldn't work?

K: That is correct. They are not designed to cope with such an event. On top of that, the containment buildings which surround the

Reactor head of Connecticut Yankee nuclear power station, Haddam Neck, Conn.

reactors are not designed to withstand the effects of pressure vessel ruptures. In other words, the building will split.

R: This is true for massive pressure vessel rupture, but not for small cracks and leaks. There has never been such a massive failure in over three-quarters of a million vessel years of service during the past 20 years.

SY: Why don't the emergency systems include dealing with a pressure vessel rupture?

K: I have an interesting story in this regard. The AEC said that the probability of rupture was sufficiently low so that they need not provide protection against it. But the real reason why they don't provide protection against it came out in a remarkably candid statement a little over a year ago by Peter Morris of the AEC's Division of Regulatory Operations: "Within the AEC, it has been the policy that design should not be required to provide protection against pressure vessel failure. So the question of whether or not such an event was credible did not arise. The reason was very simple: No design was available for a building which could withstand the consequences of pressure vessel failure, so it was decided to accept the risk."

SY: Let's go back to the ECCS. How is it designed to operate?

R: Let's suppose a pipe broke. Sensors note a high amount of steam, a high pressure in the containment, a high humidity in the containment, and a loss of pressure in the system. This automatically turns on a set of pumps which begin to pump water from an independent water supply into the reactor core.

SY: This water just floods the whole compartment?

R: It floods the pressure vessel, not the whole containment building.

SY: Much of the recent controversies are over the assurance of whether or not this system would work.

R: The controversy is not so much over the reliability of this system but over whether the water pumped in there would actually be enough to cool the core. In our calculations, we can estimate the worst condition that might exist at various points and make sure that we can cope with it. So the amount and speed of water flow needed are determined by conservative estimates of how fast it can remove heat. A number of experts, in the beginning of the ECCS hearings, voiced concern over certain assumptions used in that calculation. As a result, the AEC reviewed the information and they made some changes in their recommendations to accommodate what they thought were the issues raised. They have now issued a new set of acceptance criteria. The same experts have recently testified that they now feel these calculation methods are satisfactory.

K: These flooding rates were initially expected to be 8 to 10 inches a second. This fell to 5 to 4 to 3 and now, for some reactor types, the expected flooding rates are in the range from 0.9 to 1.25 inches per second. Calculations show that the level of uncontrollability is at flooding rates of about 0.7 inches per second. Thus, the performance of these emergency systems is marginal at best, and there are certain accidents for which these emergency systems simply will not work.

SY: Can you give an example of a change in criteria as a result of the most recent AEC study?

R: The maximum temperature permitted in the fuel has been lowered from 2300° to 2200° F. In addition, there were changes made in the calculation procedures.

SY: This is during a loss-of-cooling accident?

R: Right. Fuel normally operates with a surface temperature of 600 to 700°F. The cladding will oxidize at about 2700 or 2800°. In their original criteria, the AEC had said that the temperature may never exceed 2300°. After the new evidence was in, they lowered that to 2200°. If too much of the cladding oxidizes it could become brittle and break up. And so the AEC ruled that no more than 17 per cent of the wall thickness may be oxidized from the time you go up to the high temperature until it is cooled down again.

SY: Does that mean that you have to pump in more water?

R: That means that your analysis has to show that if the temperature exceeds 2200°, you either improve the ECCS to get more water in, or you lower the reactor power a little.

SY: What about the problem of the transport and storage of nuclear waste?

R: We think that the ultimate disposal is likely to be underground, probably in salt beds. Meanwhile, the AEC is using what they call interim storage—from 20 to 40 years—while they study alternatives for ultimate storage. The alternatives range from firing it into the sun to burying it in salt mines and other geological formations. It might also be exposed to neutrons and converted into something that is not so dangerous.

K: Some of these alternatives are frightening. You can shoot it into the sun if you can afford the rocket launch failures. No knowledgeable person believes we can achieve a sufficiently low failure rate. Think about a single inadvertent re-entry of a rocket loaded with radioactive waste materials.

SY: What are we doing with waste right now?

R: Separated from the fuel, the waste is a highly radioactive liquid that we store in tanks for a year or so to let some of the radioactivity decay away. Within 5 years it must be converted into an insoluble solid form—glasslike rods—and sealed into stainless steel cans. These will be stored in an aboveground facility where they can be retrieved at a later date, either for some practical use or for ultimate disposal.

SY: Are there sites around the country where this is being done?

R: The AEC does not have its aboveground storage sites built yet because at the moment we are not processing any waste. None of the fuel coming out of reactors today is being processed and won't be for another year or so, so the problem doesn't really exist now. There are, of course, large quantities of radioactivity from our weapons program being stored.

SY: But where is the used fuel itself?

R: It's being kept in storage underwater in pools until the processing plants are built.

K: A very serious problem exists now. There are some 80 million gallons of waste, mainly stored in the underground tanks in Hanford, Wash. Most of it is from the nuclear weapons program. If not cooled continuously, these tanks would boil and release their radioactive contents by themselves because of the heat still being generated. The tanks, which were alleged to be satisfactory for many hundreds of years, are corroding and leaking very large quantities — more than 500,000 gallons to date — of radioactive materials into the ground. There has been a large gap between promises of how things will work and the performance.

The radioactive materials have to be kept from the environment for immensely long times — more than 100,000 years. And the AEC announced in the late 1960s that it had a satisfactory solution to the disposal of the materials — a salt mine in Kansas. It turned out that the whole proposal was technically unsound and the resulting controversy caused the AEC to withdraw it. In the face of this, the AEC has now retreated to a position which it had earlier publicly abandoned — to put the materials in temporary storage.

People with high technical competence are not as optimistic as the AEC or the nuclear industry of having the stability of society that's needed to guard even temporary storage for tens or hundreds of years, or of the ultimate possibilities of avoiding an accident in the permanent storage. Consider storing these materials in geological formations, and think what happens if you have a major ice age, erosion of continental masses of hundreds of feet, or changes in the level of the sea, all of which can occur during the immensely long periods in which the materials remain toxic.

Let me add one more thing: These materials are being handed on to future generations who won't get any benefit out of them. We get the transient benefit of electric power and then hand this material on to people whom we will never know, who will simply be asked to guard it without any choice on their part.

R: The argument about future generations always bothers me because it implies that nuclear power is unique in this respect. I think we should all recognize that man's existence has always generated some changes in our environment that future generations inherit. For example, we are rapidly depleting coal, oil, and gas reserves to generate energy. We have irrevocably changed many of our rivers into a series of lakes. We have destroyed large buffalo herds to provide farmland to feed our growing population. Now, we have a proposal that would dig up mountains in Colorado to recover oil shale.

The use of nuclear power does mean that some radioactive waste will be left for future generations, but it also means that more coal, oil, and gas will also be left for them. These fossil fuels are a key raw material for making fertilizer. With the current world food crisis, it seems to me that the fossil fuel may be much more valuable in the future for food production than for energy production. Thus, I believe that nuclear waste, handled properly, is a far better thing to leave future generations than no oil or coal.

Steam generator of Dresden nuclear power station, Morris, Ill.

SY: Would it be physically possible for a group of people to take over a nuclear plant and threaten to blow it up?

K: It certainly is possible.

SY: Wouldn't somebody in that group have to know a lot about how a reactor worked?

K: They would have to know something about how it worked, certainly. But that kind of knowledge is not that restricted. Late last year the Director of Regulation for the AEC conceded that a band of what he described as highly trained, sophisticated terrorists could conceivably take over a nuclear power plant in such a way as to destroy it and to kill thousands, or, in his words, "perhaps even millions of people."

The development of an accident to the point where it melts through takes a number of hours, and there is certainly adequate time for terrorists to carry out the initiation of an uncontrollable accident and then escape. The guard systems on most nuclear reactors are simply inadequate to stop a determined armed band.

R: From what I know of a nuclear plant, I think it would be very difficult for one person, or a few people, to cause damage with serious public consequences. Not only must they destroy all the right systems in the plant, they must do it under a set of conditions where the weather and population distribution must be "right."

SY: There has been talk, particularly with the development of plutonium for breeder reactors, about the security of nuclear fuel.

R: In the normal fuel cycle of today's water reactors, there's very little material available which could be made into explosives. At the end of the fuel's life, the reactor does contain some plutonium which is separated. The volumes today are modest, but by the middle 1980s, those volumes will be large and very strict rules and methods for dealing with them will have to be developed.

K: People outside the AEC, scientists skilled in weapons work, regard this as a very serious problem. Recently, Theodore Taylor, a nuclear weapons designer, formerly of the Los Alamos Scientific Laboratory, announced the results of a study that he and others have carried out. It can be summarized by saying that the AEC's safeguards mechanisms are inadequate.

SY: But the material used in reactors is not weapons grade material, is it?

K: It is in the high-temperature, gas-cooled reactors.

SY: What fuel do these reactors use?

K: They use 90 per cent enriched uranium 235, which is weapons grade. But in any reactor fuel that contains plutonium—particularly the unirradiated fuel which is safe to handle because it doesn't have any radioactive fission products in it—it would be very easy to separate out the plutonium. And when you obtain the plutonium either as a metal or as an oxide, you can make a weapon out of either form with relative ease.

SY: What about natural disasters—earthquakes, floods, tornadoes. Are there some built-in safety features?

R: Yes. For example, every reactor must be built to withstand the largest earthquake geologists feel is plausible for that geologic region.

SY: What do you do to make a reactor survive an earthquake?

R: You build it strong enough to withstand the forces put on it by the shaking ground. You must make sure that the pipes don't get twisted and broken, so you have restraints, or snubbers, that clamp everything down so that it can't move and jiggle. And you make the pipes strong enough to take the loads impressed on them by the earthquake forces.

K: As in many of these things, there is a substantial gap between the wish and the fulfillment. The 1972 earthquake, in the San Fernando Valley, north of Los Angeles, was found to have three to five times stronger ground forces than predictions indicated it should. The nearby San Onofre reactor's design protection was substantially below the level required to protect it against an earthquake of that intensity.

Another major problem has shown up in that the snubbing systems have been failing at an unexpectedly high rate.

SY: In tests?

K: No, in operating reactors. Quite a large number of snubbers have been found to be defective. It appears from studies that the present class of reactors is, in fact, not earthquake-proof against the kinds of earthquakes that they can reasonably expect in California.

R: It is interesting to note that the nearby San Onofre reactor operated through the earthquake with no adverse effects.

SY: What has been the most critical accident to date in commercial reactors?

R: There has never been what I call a serious radioactive release. There have been small explosions due to hydrogen admitted to the stack. There have been equipment failures—one valve failure led to

Core rod master
control panel,
Dresden nuclear power
station, Morris, Ill.

the scalding of two workers. The one serious kind of accident that occurs sometimes is the opening of relief valves on the BWR, which releases steam to the containment. In one case, it jammed open and released the pressure in the system. It didn't uncover the core and it didn't come close to melting the fuel, but it was an event you would like not to have happened.

K: The performance of the emergency systems—as predicted by computers—has degraded continuously over the last 10 years. And this has arisen because of the recent identification of damaging physical phenomena which were simply not considered carefully enough, or even identified, when the big reactors that we now have were designed. In light of present knowledge, there are important design deficiencies in operating reactors.

On top of that, AEC and nuclear-industry claims that the devices are built to "surpassing" technical quality standards are simply false. I should add that during the three years that the UCS has been involved, we have had literally hundreds of very damaging documents leaked to us from within the AEC, identifying some very serious matters. In January, 1974, we were leaked a particularly damaging, and secret, AEC task force report concerning the probabilities of accidents and accidents that have occurred. That document said that the reactor program was besieged "by safety problems." It called attention to 850 abnormal occurrences which were reported to the AEC during a 17-month period.

SY: What does that mean in terms of safety?

K: Let me give you a couple of examples. In one case, a reactor's pressure vessel was overpressured by more than twice the maximum allowed in the specifications when pumps were left running inadvertently while the reactor operator went to answer the telephone. In another circumstance, radioactivity was identified in the drinking-water fountains in the reactor plant. A radioactive waste storage tank had been inadvertently connected to the potable water system.

SY: These are all human errors.

K: Yes, and as the AEC knows, they can cause or seriously aggravate an accident. Let's look at an example of a design flaw. An intervener group in Chicago got an anonymous letter about the Kewaunee nuclear reactor which was nearing completion in Wisconsin, outside the Chicago area. It said that they should look at the placement of the steam lines which come outside of the containment building and carry steam to the turbines where electricity is generated. Following this tip, the interveners looked at the steam lines and discovered that they passed right through the so-called auxiliary building which contained all the central controls and switch gear for all of the emergency shut-down and emergency systems equipment on the reactor. If there had been a rupture of those steam lines within that building, all of the emergency systems would have been disabled. In addition, the steam lines also passed next to the control room where a rupture would have subjected all the control room and the operators to 300° steam, killing the operators and risking the orderly shut-down of the plant.

R: We have discovered several plants where a break could compromise some safety actions by letting steam into central areas. These things have been repaired or are being repaired in all of the plants. Most of these occurrences were very minor in nature. The overall safety record of about 200 reactor years of operating experience, with no major radioactive release and no injury to the public, reflects that the defense-in-depth philosophy in reactor safety is effective.

SY: Do you feel that it is inevitable that we are going to have nuclear energy in one way or another? And if you do agree to that, what do you think we ought to do?

K: Well, it is hard to know what is inevitable in this society. We have something in excess of 42 operable reactors—and they don't operate very well. The operation of the reactors at Indian Point, north of New York City, has been the major contributing factor in bringing Consolidated Edison, the people who own that reactor, to the point of bankruptcy, literally. The same with the Vermont Yankee plant and the Vermont Power Company. The deliverability of power over the whole reactor program has been far short of expectation; it has been running around 50 per cent of the theoretically available power. In December, 1973, a third of the nuclear reactors were completely off-line—many of them for safety related defects.

R: I have to say that the record of on-line availability in nuclear plants is not what I would think it should be. It's more like 70 per cent, however, which turns out to be exactly the same percentage for new large fossil-fuel plants. Actually, I think nuclear plants are a little better, but we're so safety conscious that we don't do some of the things with a reactor that we might do with a coal-fired plant. For example, you might run without a reserve pump in a coal-fired plant, but you wouldn't in a nuclear reactor plant because of the safety implications.

Look, let's be honest. There's risk in operating nuclear plants. You can't accumulate that much radioactivity without risk. Then, why should we take these risks? Well, it gives us another supply of energy independent of our fossil fuels, energy that creates essentially no air pollution. It gives us a way of getting cheaper electricity. You must weigh these things against a small risk—small compared to other risks to which we all are exposed. It seems to me that you come out with an overwhelming case that nuclear energy is in society's best interest. Just a reduction in health problems from no air pollution must far outweigh the chance that maybe, once in a long time, we'll have an accident that releases some radioactivity. Any estimates of the effects of the fossil-fuel plant air pollution on public health show a sizable number of people whose health is seriously affected.

SY: Do the critics want a moratorium?

K: Moratoriums come in different colors. Some parts of the country are already quite heavily dependent on nuclear power, particularly in the Chicago area and New England. But nationally the figure is only 5 per cent. As a consequence, we recommend that operable reactors be allowed to continue operation, but under stringent controls—speed limits—that would improve the present narrow or nonexistent safety margins. Until the safety problems and waste storage difficulties are clearly resolved we would like to see a total halt to new reactor construction.

It is clear that the country grossly wastes energy. For example, improved housing construction can incorporate insulation at an economic level which would save from 40 to 50 per cent of the energy used in home heating, air conditioning, and hot water.

Beyond that, you have a really pathetic lack of attention to alternative energy sources, which many people believe could make a substantial contribution to the energy picture in this country. It is particularly common for nuclear proponents to say that solar energy is not going to pan out and has no place in the energy field. Yet, people who have looked at this seriously—the National Science Foundation-National Aeronautics and Space Administration Joint Study of Solar Power—have identified it as a great potential benefit.

SY: Let's talk about risks versus benefits. If people could really understand the risk of nuclear power, do you think most of them would accept it to get the benefits it offers?

R: Yes, if they really perceived it, I think they would accept it. There are lots of rare events that we can postulate. If you ask what is the worst thing that can happen in the chemical or petroleum industries—fires or explosions—in every case, if I am at all clever, I can predict horrendous accidents which combine such an unlikely set of circumstances that the public normally doesn't concern themselves with. And I judge nuclear energy to be at the same level, except it's not perceived of that way because of the way it has been presented. We are victims of our own safety record because we have never had a bad accident. If we had had a few, without serious consequences, the nuclear reactor hazard would be looked at like a fire or some other accident with which we are familiar. These are things people have experienced, and they accept them as part of life.

K: The point is, I don't think people need nuclear energy. If you look at the energy needs in the light of what is unnecessary—that is, what you can save by conservation, what you can save by the design of machines which use energy more efficiently—then it becomes clear that nuclear energy is not absolutely necessary. The results from the recent Ford Foundation Energy Policy Study appear to bear out these conclusions.

It seems to me that a prudent society would diminish the role of nuclear power, consistent with the society's rock-bottom needs for energy, and that it would devote the effort and money needed to develop alternative sources of energy.

R: Although I would strongly support an all-out effort toward energy conservation, I do not believe our complex technical society can operate without some further increase in energy, particularly electricity. The only viable means available today to obtain this electricity is from nuclear or fossil fuels. I believe for the immediate future we will have to exploit both these resources to meet our needs.

Index

This index covers the contents of the 1973, 1974, and 1975 editions of *Science Year,* The World Book Science Annual.

Each index entry is followed by the edition year in *italics* and the page numbers:

Superconductors, *75*-341, *73*-355

This means that information about Superconductors begins on the page indicated for each of the editions.

An index entry that is the title of an article appearing in *Science Year* is printed in boldface italic letters: ***Archaeology.*** An entry that is not an article title, but a subject discussed in an article of some other title, is printed: **Behaviorism.**

The various "See" and "See also" cross references in the index are to other entries within the index. Clue words or phrases are used when the entry needs further definition or when two or more references to the same subject appear in *Science Year.* These make it easy to locate the material on the page.

Photosynthesis: cell evolution, *73*-108; nitrogen fixation, *75*-237. See also **Plant.**

The indication*"il."* means that the reference is to an illustration only, as:

Peanut shells, *il., 75*-236

Index

A

Index

Index

Index

Index

Index

Index

Index

Index

Index

Index

Index

Index

Index

Index

Index

Index

Index

Acknowledgments

The publishers of *Science Year* gratefully acknowledge the courtesy of the following artists, photographers, publishers, institutions, agencies, and corporations for the illustrations in this volume. Credits should be read from left to right, top to bottom, on their respective pages. All entries marked with an asterisk (*) denote illustrations created exclusively for *Science Year*. All maps were created by the *World Book* Cartographic Staff.

Cover

NASA; Jet Propulsion Laboratory; Jet Propulsion Laboratory; Jet Propulsion Laboratory

Special Reports

10	John Huehnergarth*; William R. Curtsinger, Rapho Guillumette; Ivan Massar, Black Star*; Joseph A. Erhardt*; George Roth*; NASA; Edward S. Ross
12	Jackson-Zender*
14	NASA
15	*Stern* from Black Star; NASA; Bettmann Archive
16-17	Bettmann Archive
18	Jackson-Zender*
19	Department of Astronomy, University of Michigan; Hale Observatories; Hale Observatories
20	Jackson-Zender*
21	NASA
22-23	Jackson-Zender*
24	NASA
26-27	Joseph A. Erhardt*
29	U.S. War Department, General Staff; Brown Brothers; Bettmann Archive
31	*Natural History* Magazine
33	Jackson-Zender*; Wyeth Laboratories, Inc.
34-38	Jackson-Zender*
40-41	Joseph A. Erhardt*
42	Jackson-Zender*; Medical Illustration Department, Veterans Administration Hospital
43	Robert O. Becker, M.D., Veterans Administration Hospital; Jackson-Zender*
44	Jackson-Zender*; Robert O. Becker, M.D., Veterans Administration Hospital; Robert O. Becker, M.D., Veterans Administration Hospital; Robert O. Becker, M.D., Veterans Administration Hospital
47	Robert O. Becker, M.D., Veterans Administration Hospital; Jackson-Zender*; Robert O. Becker, M.D., Veterans Administration Hospital; Robert O. Becker, M.D., Veterans Administration Hospital
48	Jackson-Zender*; Robert O. Becker, M.D., Veterans Administration Hospital; Robert O. Becker, M.D., Veterans Administration Hospital
50	Jackson-Zender*; Stephen Smith, M.D., University of Kentucky; Stephen Smith, M.D., University of Kentucky; Stephen Smith, M.D., University of Kentucky
53	Jackson-Zender*; Robert O. Becker, M.D., Veterans Administration Hospital
54	Robert O. Becker, M.D., Veterans Administration Hospital
56-57	Dick Kramer*
58	Norton Rock*
59	Illustration from *Dissertatio de Arthritio* by Willem ten Rhyne, London, 1683. The John Crerar Library, Chicago. Illustration from *Ancient Therapeutic Arts* by Heinemann Medical Books, Ltd., London; Dick Kramer*
61-66	Dick Kramer*
68-78	George Roth*
81-83	John Huehnergarth*
85	Product Illustration, Inc.*
88-89	John Huehnergarth*
91	Product Illustration, Inc.*
94-95	William R. Curtsinger, Rapho Guillumette
97	Franz Lazi
98	Kendrick Frazier, *Science News*; Björn Bölstad from Peter Arnold
98-99	William R. Curtsinger, Rapho Guillumette
100	Franz Lazi
101	William R. Curtsinger, Rapho Guillumette
102	Kendrick Frazier, *Science News*; Bruce Parker, Virginia Polytechnic Institute and State University; Franz Lazi
103	Roy E. Cameron, Darwin Research Institute
105	Franz Lazi; Kendrick Frazier
106	William R. Curtsinger, Rapho Guillumette
108-109	George Roth*
110	American Cancer Society; American Cancer Society; D. K. Miller, The Salk Institute
111	George Roth*
112	"The Rapid Intermixing of Cell Surface Antigens After Formation of Mouse-Human Heterocaryons" by L. D. Frye and M. Edidin, © 1970 *Journal of Cell Science*
113	Garth Nicolson, The Salk Institute
114-115	George Roth*
116	Garth Nicolson, The Salk Institute
116-117	George Roth*
120-121	NASA
122	General Electric Company
123-124	NASA
125	Chester T. Wezernak, Environmental Research Institute of Michigan
126-127	Itek Corporation
128-141	NASA
143	U.S. Naval Research Laboratory
145-149	NASA
150	Cornell University
151-152	Product Illustration, Inc.*
153	NASA
154	Carl Sagan and Joseph Veverka, Cornell University; Product Illustration, Inc.*
155	Jet Propulsion Laboratory
156	NASA; Jet Propulsion Laboratory
158	Jet Propulsion Laboratory
161	Hale Observatories
171-172	Ivan Massar, Black Star*
173	C. Richard Taylor, Harvard University
174-175	Ivan Massar, Black Star*
176-177	Product Illustration, Inc.*
178-179	Milton Hildebrand, University of California, Riverside; C. Richard Taylor, Harvard University; Ivan Massar, Black Star*
181	Ivan Massar, Black Star*
182	Product Illustration, Inc.*
184-185	Doug Wilson, Black Star
186-190	Ed Hoppe, Alfa Studios*
192-193	Edward S. Ross
195	G. B. Staal, Zoecon Corporation
196	Donald Weidhass, USDA, Agricultural Research Service, Florida
198	Karl Knaack, T.F.H. Publications; Max E. Badgley, E. F. Legner, University of California, Riverside
199	Max E. Badgley, E. F. Legner, University of California, Riverside
200	Edward G. Platzer, University of California, Riverside
201	James J. Petersen, USDA, Agricultural Research Service, Louisiana
202	Max E. Badgley, Irwin M. Hall, University of California, Riverside; Max E. Badgley, Irwin M. Hall, University of California, Riverside; James J. Petersen,

Typography

Display–Univers
Monsen Typographers, Inc., Chicago
Text–Baskerville Linofilm
Total Typography, Inc., Chicago
Text–Baskerville Linofilm
Black Dot Computer Typesetting Corporation
Monsen Typographers, Inc., Chicago

Offset Positives

Jahn & Ollier Engraving Co., Chicago
Process Color Plate Company, Chicago

Printing

Kingsport Press, Inc., Kingsport, Tenn.

Binding

Kingsport Press, Inc., Kingsport, Tenn.

Paper

Text
Childcraft Text, Web Offset (basis 60 pound)
Mead, Escanaba, Mich.

Cover Material

Flax Lexotone
White Offset Blubak
Holliston Mills, Inc., Kingsport, Tenn.